# space
# sciences

# space
# sciences

VOLUME **4**
**Our Future in Space**

**Pat Dasch, Editor in Chief**

MACMILLAN
REFERENCE
USA™

THOMSON
GALE

New York • Detroit • San Diego • San Francisco • Cleveland • New Haven, Conn. • Waterville, Maine • London • Munich

Macmillan Reference USA          Gale Group
300 Park Avenue South           27500 Drake Rd.
New York, NY 10010              Farmington Hills, MI 48331-3535

**Library of Congress Cataloging-in-Publication Data**
Space sciences / Pat Dasch, editor in chief.
  p. cm.
Includes bibliographical references and indexes.
ISBN 0-02-865546-X (set : alk. paper)
 1. Space sciences. I. Dasch, Pat.
  QB500 .S63 2002
  500.5—dc21

        2002001707

Volume 1: ISBN 0-02-865547-8
Volume 2: ISBN 0-02-865548-6
Volume 3: ISBN 0-02-865549-4
Volume 4: ISBN 0-02-865550-8

Printed in the United States of America
1  2  3  4  5  6  7  8  9  10

# Preface

Astronomers have studied the heavens for more than two millennia, but in the twentieth century, humankind ventured off planet Earth into the dark vacuum void of space, forever changing our perspective of our home planet and on our relationship to the universe in which we reside.

Our explorations of space—the final frontier in our niche in this solar system—first with satellites, then robotic probes, and finally with humans, have given rise to an extensive space industry that has a major influence on the economy and on our lives. In 1998, U.S. space exports (launch services, satellites, space-based communications services, and the like) totaled $64 billion. As we entered the new millennium, space exports were the second largest dollar earner after agriculture. The aerospace industry directly employs some 860,000 Americans, with many more involved in subcontracting companies and academic research.

## Beginnings

The Chinese are credited with developing the rudiments of rocketry—they launched rockets as missiles against invading Mongols in 1232. In the nineteenth century William Congrieve developed a rocket in Britain based on designs conceived in India in the eighteenth century. Congrieve extended the range of the Indian rockets, adapting them specifically for use by armies. Congrieve's rockets were used in 1806 in the Napoleonic Wars.

## The Birth of Modern Space Exploration

The basis of modern spaceflight and exploration came with the writings of Konstantin Tsiolkovsky (1857–1935), a Russian mathematics teacher. He described multi-stage rockets, winged craft like the space shuttle developed in the 1970s, space stations like Mir and the International Space Station, and interplanetary missions of discovery.

During the same period, space travel captured the imagination of fiction writers. Jules Verne wrote several novels with spaceflight themes. His book, *From the Earth to the Moon* (1865), describes manned flight to the Moon, including a launch site in Florida and a spaceship named Columbia—the name chosen for the Apollo 11 spaceship that made the first lunar landing in July 1969 and the first space shuttle, which flew in April 1981. In the twentieth century, Arthur C. Clarke predicted the role of communications satellites and extended our vision of human space exploration while television series such as *Star Trek* and *Dr. Who* challenged the imagination and embedded the idea of space travel in our culture.

The first successful test of the V-2 rocket developed by Wernher von Braun and his team at Peenemünde, Germany, in October 1942 has been described as the "birth of the Space Age." After World War II some of the Peenemünde team under von Braun came to the United States, where they worked at the White Sands Missile Range in New Mexico, while others went to Russia. This sowed the seeds of the space race of the 1960s. Each team worked to develop advanced rockets, with Russia developing the R-7, while a series of rockets with names like Thor, Redstone, and Titan were produced in the United States.

When the Russians lofted Sputnik, the first artificial satellite, on October 4, 1957, the race was on. The flights of Yuri Gagarin, Alan Shepard, and John Glenn followed, culminating in the race for the Moon and the Apollo Program of the 1960s and early 1970s.

## The Emergence of a Space Industry

The enormous national commitment to the Apollo Program marked a new phase in our space endeavors. The need for innovation and technological advance stimulated the academic and engineering communities and led to the growth of a vast network of contract supporters of the aerospace initiative and the birth of a vibrant space industry. At the same time, planetary science emerged as a new geological specialization.

Following the Apollo Program, the U.S. space agency's mission remained poorly defined through the end of the twentieth century, grasping at major programs such as development of the space shuttle and the International Space Station, in part, some argue, to provide jobs for the very large workforce spawned by the Apollo Program. The 1980s saw the beginnings of what would become a robust commercial space industry, largely independent of government programs, providing communications and information technology via space-based satellites. During the 1990s many thought that commercialization was the way of the future for space ventures. Commercially coordinated robotic planetary exploration missions were conceived with suggestions that NASA purchase the data, and Dennis Tito, the first paying space tourist in 2001, raised hopes of access to space for all.

The terrorist attacks on the United States on September 11, 2001 and the U.S. recession led to a re-evaluation of the entrepreneurial optimism of the 1990s. Many private commercial space ventures were placed on hold or went out of business. Commentators suggested that the true dawning of the commercial space age would be delayed by up to a decade. But, at the same time, the U.S. space agency emerged with a more clearly defined mandate than it had had since the Apollo Program, with a role of driving technological innovation—with an early emphasis on reducing the cost of getting to orbit—and leading world class space-related scientific projects. And military orders, to fill the needs of the new world order, compensated to a point for the downturn in the commercial space communications sector.

It is against this background of an industry in a state of flux, a discipline on the cusp of a new age of innovation, that this encyclopedia has been prepared.

## Organization of the Material

The 341 entries in *Space Sciences* have been organized in four volumes, focusing on the business of space exploration, planetary science and astronomy, human space exploration, and the outlook for the future exploration of space. Each entry has been newly commissioned for this work. Our contributors are drawn from academia, industry, government, professional space institutes and associations, and nonprofit organizations. Many of the contributors are world authorities on their subject, providing up-to-the-minute information in a straightforward style accessible to high school students and university undergraduates.

One of the outstanding advantages of books on space is the wonderful imagery of exploration and achievement. These volumes are richly illustrated, and sidebars provide capsules of additional information on topics of particular interest. Entries are followed by a list of related entries, as well as a reading list for students seeking more information.

## Acknowledgements

I wish to thank the team at Macmillan Reference USA and the Gale Group for their vision and leadership in bringing this work to fruition. In particular, thanks to Hélène Potter, Cindy Clendenon, and Gloria Lam. My thanks to Associate Editors Nadine Barlow, Leonard David, and Frank Sietzen, whose expertise, commitment, and patience have made *Space Sciences* possible. My thanks also go to my husband, Julius, for his encouragement and support. My love affair with space began in the 1970s when I worked alongside geologists using space imagery to plan volcanological field work in remote areas of South America, and took root when, in the 1980s, I became involved in systematic analysis of the more than 3,000 photographs of Earth that astronauts bring back at the end of every shuttle mission. The beauty of planet Earth, as seen from space, and the wealth of information contained in those images, convinced me that space is a very real part of life on Earth, and that I wanted to be a part of the exploration of space and to share the wonder of it with the public. I hope that *Space Sciences* conveys the excitement, achievements, and potential of space exploration to a new generation of students.

*Pat Dasch*
Editor in Chief

# For Your Reference

The following section provides information that is applicable to a number of articles in this reference work. Included in the following pages is a chart providing comparative solar system planet data, as well as measurement, abbreviation, and conversion tables.

## SOLAR SYSTEM PLANET DATA

| | Mercury | Venus[2] | Earth | Mars | Jupiter | Saturn | Uranus | Neptune | Pluto |
|---|---|---|---|---|---|---|---|---|---|
| Mean distance from the Sun (AU): [1] | 0.387 | 0.723 | 1 | 1.524 | 5.202 | 9.555 | 19.218 | 30.109 | 39.439 |
| Siderial period of orbit (years): | 0.24 | 0.62 | 1 | 1.88 | 11.86 | 29.46 | 84.01 | 164.79 | 247.68 |
| Mean orbital velocity (km/sec): | 47.89 | 35.04 | 29.79 | 24.14 | 13.06 | 9.64 | 6.81 | 5.43 | 4.74 |
| Orbital essentricity: | 0.206 | 0.007 | 0.017 | 0.093 | 0.048 | 0.056 | 0.047 | 0.009 | 0.246 |
| Inclination to ecliptic (degrees): | 7.00 | 3.40 | 0 | 1.85 | 1.30 | 2.49 | 0.77 | 1.77 | 17.17 |
| Equatorial radius (km): | 2439 | 6052 | 6378 | 3397 | 71492 | 60268 | 25559 | 24764 | 1140 |
| Polar radius (km): | same | same | 6357 | 3380 | 66854 | 54360 | 24973 | 24340 | same |
| Mass of planet (Earth = 1):[3] | 0.06 | 0.82 | 1 | 0.11 | 317.89 | 95.18 | 14.54 | 17.15 | 0.002 |
| Mean density (gm/cm [3]): | 5.44 | 5.25 | 5.52 | 3.94 | 1.33 | 0.69 | 1.27 | 1.64 | 2.0 |
| Body rotation period (hours): | 1408 | 5832.R | 23.93 | 24.62 | 9.92 | 10.66 | 17.24 | 16.11 | 153.3 |
| Tilt of equator to orbit (degrees): | 0 | 2.12 | 23.45 | 23.98 | 3.08 | 26.73 | 97.92 | 28.8 | 96 |

[1]AU indicates one astronomical unit, defined as the mean distance between Earth and the Sun ($\sim 1.495 \times 10^8$ km).
[2]R indicates planet rotation is retrograde (i.e., opposite to the planet's orbit).
[3]Earth's mass is approximately $5.976 \times 10^{26}$ grams.

## SI BASE AND SUPPLEMENTARY UNIT NAMES AND SYMBOLS

| Physical Quality | Name | Symbol |
|---|---|---|
| Length | meter | m |
| Mass | kilogram | kg |
| Time | second | s |
| Electric current | ampere | A |
| Thermodynamic temperature | kelvin | K |
| Amount of substance | mole | mol |
| Luminous intensity | candela | cd |
| Plane angle | radian | rad |
| Solid angle | steradian | sr |

### Temperature

Scientists commonly use the Celsius system. Although not recommended for scientific and technical use, earth scientists also use the familiar Fahrenheit temperature scale (°F). $1°F = 1.8°C$ or K. The triple point of $H_2O$, where gas, liquid, and solid water coexist, is 32°F.

- To change from Fahrenheit (F) to Celsius (C):
$°C = (°F-32)/(1.8)$
- To change from Celsius (C) to Fahrenheit (F):
$°F = (°C \times 1.8) + 32$
- To change from Celsius (C) to Kelvin (K):
$K = °C + 273.15$
- To change from Fahrenheit (F) to Kelvin (K):
$K = (°F-32)/(1.8) + 273.15$

## UNITS DERIVED FROM SI, WITH SPECIAL NAMES AND SYMBOLS

| Derived Quantity | Name of SI Unit | Symbol for SI Unit | Expression in Terms of SI Base Units |
|---|---|---|---|
| Frequency | hertz | Hz | $s^{-1}$ |
| Force | newton | N | $m\ kg\ s^{-2}$ |
| Pressure, stress | Pascal | Pa | $N\ m^{-2} = m^{-1}\ kg\ s^{-2}$ |
| Energy, work, heat | Joule | J | $N\ m = m^2\ kg\ s^{-2}$ |
| Power, radiant flux | watt | W | $J\ s^{-1} = m^2\ kg\ s^{-3}$ |
| Electric charge | coulomb | C | $A\ s$ |
| Electric potential, electromotive force | volt | V | $J\ C^{-1} = m^{-2}\ kg\ s^{-3}\ A^{-1}$ |
| Electric resistance | ohm | — | $V\ A^{-1} = m^2\ kg\ s^{-3}\ A^{-2}$ |
| Celsius temperature | degree Celsius | C | K |
| Luminous flux | lumen | lm | $cd\ sr$ |
| Illuminance | lux | lx | $cd\ sr\ m^{-2}$ |

## UNITS USED WITH SI, WITH NAME, SYMBOL, AND VALUES IN SI UNITS

The following units, not part of the SI, will continue to be used in appropriate contexts (e.g., angtsrom):

| Physical Quantity | Name of Unit | Symbol for Unit | Value in SI Units |
|---|---|---|---|
| Time | minute | min | 60 s |
| | hour | h | 3,600 s |
| | day | d | 86,400 s |
| Plane angle | degree | ° | $(\pi/180)$ rad |
| | minute | ' | $(\pi/10,800)$ rad |
| | second | " | $(\pi/648,000)$ rad |
| Length | angstrom | Å | $10^{-10}$ m |
| Volume | liter | l, L | $1\ dm^3 = 10^{-3}\ m^3$ |
| Mass | ton | t | $1\ mg = 10^3\ kg$ |
| | unified atomic mass unit | $u\ (=m_a(^{12}C)/12)$ | $\approx 1.66054 \times 10^{-27}$ kg |
| Pressure | bar | bar | $10^5\ Pa = 10^5\ N\ m^{-2}$ |
| Energy | electronvolt | $eV\ (= e \times V)$ | $\approx 1.60218 \times 10^{-19}$ J |

## CONVERSIONS FOR STANDARD, DERIVED, AND CUSTOMARY MEASUREMENTS

### Length

| | |
|---|---|
| 1 angstrom (Å) | 0.1 nanometer (exactly) |
| | 0.000000004 inch |
| 1 centimeter (cm) | 0.3937 inches |
| 1 foot (ft) | 0.3048 meter (exactly) |
| 1 inch (in) | 2.54 centimeters (exactly) |
| 1 kilometer (km) | 0.621 mile |
| 1 meter (m) | 39.37 inches |
| | 1.094 yards |
| 1 mile (mi) | 5,280 feet (exactly) |
| | 1.609 kilometers |
| 1 astronomical unit (AU) | $1.495979 \times 10^{13}$ cm |
| 1 parsec (pc) | 206,264.806 AU |
| | $3.085678 \times 10^{18}$ cm |
| | 3.261633 light-years |
| 1 light-year | $9.460530 \times 10^{17}$ cm |

### Area

| | |
|---|---|
| 1 acre | 43,560 square feet (exactly) |
| | 0.405 hectare |
| 1 hectare | 2.471 acres |
| 1 square centimeter (cm²) | 0.155 square inch |
| 1 square foot (ft²) | 929.030 square centimeters |
| 1 square inch (in²) | 6.4516 square centimeters (exactly) |
| 1 square kilometer (km²) | 247.104 acres |
| | 0.386 square mile |
| 1 square meter (m²) | 1.196 square yards |
| | 10.764 square feet |
| 1 square mile (mi²) | 258.999 hectares |

## MEASUREMENTS AND ABBREVIATIONS

### Volume

| | |
|---|---|
| 1 barrel (bbl)*, liquid | 31 to 42 gallons |
| 1 cubic centimeter (cm³) | 0.061 cubic inch |
| 1 cubic foot (ft³) | 7.481 gallons |
| | 28.316 cubic decimeters |
| 1 cubic inch (in³) | 0.554 fluid ounce |
| 1 dram, fluid (or liquid) | 1/8 fluid ounce (exactly) |
| | 0.226 cubic inch |
| | 3.697 milliliters |
| 1 gallon (gal) (U.S.) | 231 cubic inches (exactly) |
| | 3.785 liters |
| | 128 U.S. fluid ounces (exactly) |
| 1 gallon (gal) (British Imperial) | 277.42 cubic inches |
| | 1.201 U.S. gallons |
| | 4.546 liters |
| 1 liter | 1 cubic decimeter (exactly) |
| | 1.057 liquid quarts |
| | 0.908 dry quart |
| | 61.025 cubic inches |
| 1 ounce, fluid (or liquid) | 1.805 cubic inches |
| | 29.573 milliliters |
| 1 ounce, fluid (fl oz) (British) | 0.961 U.S. fluid ounce |
| | 1.734 cubic inches |
| | 28.412 milliliters |
| 1 quart (qt), dry (U.S.) | 67.201 cubic inches |
| | 1.101 liters |
| 1 quart (qt), liquid (U.S.) | 57.75 cubic inches (exactly) |
| | 0.946 liter |

### Units of mass

| | |
|---|---|
| 1 carat (ct) | 200 milligrams (exactly) |
| | 3.086 grains |
| 1 grain | 64.79891 milligrams (exactly) |
| 1 gram (g) | 15.432 grains |
| | 0.035 ounce |
| 1 kilogram (kg) | 2.205 pounds |
| 1 microgram (μg) | 0.000001 gram (exactly) |
| 1 milligram (mg) | 0.015 grain |
| 1 ounce (oz) | 437.5 grains (exactly) |
| | 28.350 grams |
| 1 pound (lb) | 7,000 grains (exactly) |
| | 453.59237 grams (exactly) |
| 1 ton, gross or long | 2,240 pounds (exactly) |
| | 1.12 net tons (exactly) |
| | 1.016 metric tons |
| 1 ton, metric (t) | 2,204.623 pounds |
| | 0.984 gross ton |
| | 1.102 net tons |
| 1 ton, net or short | 2,000 pounds (exactly) |
| | 0.893 gross ton |
| | 0.907 metric ton |

### Pressure

| | |
|---|---|
| 1 kilogram/square centimeter (kg/cm²) | 0.96784 atmosphere (atm) |
| | 14.2233 pounds/square inch (lb/in²) |
| | 0.98067 bar |
| 1 bar | 0.98692 atmosphere (atm) |
| | 1.02 kilograms/square centimeter (kg/cm²) |

* There are a variety of "barrels" established by law or usage. For example, U.S. federal taxes on fermented liquors are based on a barrel of 31 gallons (141 liters); many state laws fix the "barrel for liquids" as 31½ gallons (119.2 liters); one state fixes a 36-gallon (160.5 liters) barrel for cistern measurment; federal law recognizes a 40-gallon (178 liters) barrel for "proof spirts"; by custom, 42 gallons (159 liters) comprise a barrel of crude oil or petroleum products for statistical purposes, and this equivalent is recognized "for liquids" by four states.

# Milestones in Space History

| | |
|---|---|
| **c. 850** | The Chinese invent a form of gunpowder for rocket propulsion. |
| **1242** | Englishman Roger Bacon develops gunpowder. |
| **1379** | Rockets are used as weapons in the Siege of Chioggia, Italy. |
| **1804** | William Congrieve develops ship-fired rockets. |
| **1903** | Konstantin Tsiolkovsky publishes *Research into Interplanetary Science by Means of Rocket Power*, a treatise on space travel. |
| **1909** | Robert H. Goddard develops designs for liquid-fueled rockets. |
| **1917** | Smithsonian Institute issues grant to Goddard for rocket research. |
| **1918** | Goddard publishes the monograph *Method of Attaining Extreme Altitudes*. |
| **1921** | Soviet Union establishes a state laboratory for solid rocket research. |
| **1922** | Hermann Oberth publishes *Die Rakete zu den Planetenräumen*, a work on rocket travel through space. |
| **1923** | Tsiolkovsky publishes work postulating multi-staged rockets. |
| **1924** | Walter Hohmann publishes work on rocket flight and orbital motion. |
| **1927** | The German Society for Space Travel holds its first meeting. |
| | Max Valier proposes rocket-powered aircraft adapted from Junkers G23. |
| **1928** | Oberth designs liquid rocket for the film *Woman in the Moon*. |
| **1929** | Goddard launches rocket carrying barometer. |
| **1930** | Soviet rocket designer Valentin Glusko designs U.S.S.R. liquid rocket engine. |

| | |
|---|---|
| **1931** | Eugene Sänger test fires liquid rocket engines in Vienna. |
| **1932** | German Rocket Society fires first rocket in test flight. |
| **1933** | Goddard receives grant from Guggenheim Foundation for rocket studies. |
| **1934** | Wernher von Braun, member of the German Rocket Society, test fires water-cooled rocket. |
| **1935** | Goddard fires advanced liquid rocket that reaches 700 miles per hour. |
| **1936** | Glushko publishes work on liquid rocket engines. |
| **1937** | The Rocket Research Project of the California Institute of Technology begins research program on rocket designs. |
| **1938** | von Braun's rocket researchers open center at Pennemünde. |
| **1939** | Sänger and Irene Brendt refine rocket designs and propose advanced winged suborbital bomber. |
| **1940** | Goddard develops centrifugal pumps for rocket engines. |
| **1941** | Germans test rocket-powered interceptor aircraft Me 163. |
| **1942** | V-2 rocket fired from Pennemünde enters space during ballistic flight. |
| **1943** | First operational V-2 launch. |
| **1944** | V-2 rocket launched to strike London. |
| **1945** | Arthur C. Clarke proposes geostationary satellites. |
| **1946** | Soviet Union tests version of German V-2 rocket. |
| **1947** | United States test fires Corporal missile from White Sands, New Mexico. |
| | X-1 research rocket aircraft flies past the speed of sound. |
| **1948** | United States reveals development plan for Earth satellite adapted from RAND. |
| **1949** | Chinese rocket scientist Hsueh-Sen proposes hypersonic aircraft. |
| **1950** | United States fires Viking 4 rocket to record 106 miles from USS Norton Sound. |
| **1951** | Bell Aircraft Corporation proposes winged suborbital rocket-plane. |
| **1952** | Wernher von Braun proposes wheeled Earth-orbiting space station. |
| **1953** | U.S. Navy D-558II sets world altitude record of 15 miles above Earth. |
| **1954** | Soviet Union begins design of RD-107, RD-108 ballistic missile engines. |
| **1955** | Soviet Union launches dogs aboard research rocket on suborbital flight. |

**1956**          United States announces plan to launch Earth satellite as part of Geophysical Year program.

**1957**          U.S. Army Ballistic Missile Agency is formed.

Soviet Union test fires R-7 ballistic missile.

Soviet Union launches the world's first Earth satellite, Sputnik-1, aboard R-7.

United States launches 3-stage Jupiter C on test flight.

United States attempts Vanguard 1 satellite launch; rocket explodes.

**1958**          United States orbits Explorer-1 Earth satellite aboard Jupiter-C rocket.

United States establishes the National Aeronautics and Space Administration (NASA) as civilian space research organization.

NASA establishes Project Mercury manned space project.

United States orbits Atlas rocket with Project Score.

**1959**          Soviet Union sends Luna 1 towards Moon; misses by 3100 miles.

NASA announces the selection of seven astronauts for Earth space missions.

Soviet Union launches Luna 2, which strikes the Moon.

**1960**          United States launches Echo satellite balloon.

United States launches Discoverer 14 into orbit, capsule caught in midair.

Soviet Union launches two dogs into Earth orbit.

Mercury-Redstone rocket test fired in suborbital flight test.

**1961**          Soviet Union tests Vostok capsule in Earth orbit with dummy passenger.

Soviet Union launches Yuri Gagarin aboard Vostok-1; he becomes the first human in space.

United States launches Alan B. Shepard on suborbital flight.

United States proposes goal of landing humans on the Moon before 1970.

Soviet Union launches Gherman Titov into Earth orbital flight for one day.

United States launches Virgil I. "Gus" Grissom on suborbital flight.

United States launches first Saturn 1 rocket in suborbital test.

| 1962 | United States launches John H. Glenn into 3-orbit flight. |
| | United States launches Ranger to impact Moon; craft fails. |
| | First United States/United Kingdom international satellite launch; Ariel 1 enters orbit. |
| | X-15 research aircraft sets new altitude record of 246,700 feet. |
| | United States launches Scott Carpenter into 3-orbit flight. |
| | United States orbits Telstar 1 communications satellite. |
| | Soviet Union launches Vostok 3 and 4 into Earth orbital flight. |
| | United States launches Mariner II toward Venus flyby. |
| | United States launches Walter Schirra into 6-orbit flight. |
| | Soviet Union launches Mars 1 flight; craft fails. |
| 1963 | United States launches Gordon Cooper into 22-orbit flight. |
| | Soviet Union launches Vostok 5 into 119-hour orbital flight. |
| | United States test fires advanced solid rockets for Titan 3C. |
| | First Apollo Project test in Little Joe II launch. |
| | Soviet Union orbits Vostok 6, which carries Valentina Tereshkova, the first woman into space. |
| | Soviet Union tests advanced version of R-7 called Soyuz launcher. |
| 1964 | United States conducts first Saturn 1 launch with live second stage; enters orbit. |
| | U.S. Ranger 6 mission launched towards Moon; craft fails. |
| | Soviet Union launches Zond 1 to Venus; craft fails. |
| | United States launches Ranger 7 on successful Moon impact. |
| | United States launches Syncom 3 communications satellite. |
| | Soviet Union launches Voshkod 1 carrying three cosmonauts. |
| | United States launches Mariner 4 on Martian flyby mission. |
| 1965 | Soviet Union launches Voshkod 2; first space walk. |
| | United States launches Gemini 3 on 3-orbit piloted test flight. |
| | United States launches Early Bird 1 communications satellite. |
| | United States launches Gemini 4 on 4-day flight; first U.S. space walk. |

United States launches Gemini 5 on 8-day flight.

United States launches Titan 3C on maiden flight.

Europe launches Asterix 1 satellite into orbit.

United States Gemini 6/7 conduct first space rendezvous.

**1966**    Soviet Union launches Luna 9, which soft lands on Moon.

United States Gemini 8 conducts first space docking; flight aborted.

United States launches Surveyor 1 to Moon soft landing.

United States tests Atlas Centaur advanced launch vehicle.

Gemini 9 flight encounters space walk troubles.

Gemini 10 flight conducts double rendezvous.

United States launches Lunar Orbiter 1 to orbit Moon.

Gemini 11 tests advanced space walks.

United States launches Saturn IB on unpiloted test flight.

Soviet Union tests advanced Proton launch vehicle.

United States launches Gemini 12 to conclude two-man missions.

**1967**    Apollo 1 astronauts killed in launch pad fire.

Soviet Soyuz 1 flight fails; cosmonaut killed.

Britain launches Ariel 3 communications satellite.

United States conducts test flight of M2F2 lifting body research craft.

United States sends Surveyor 3 to dig lunar soils.

Soviet Union orbits anti-satellite system.

United States conducts first flight of Saturn V rocket (Apollo 4).

**1968**    Yuri Gagarin killed in plane crash.

Soviet Union docks Cosmos 212 and 213 automatically in orbit.

United States conducts Apollo 6 Saturn V test flight; partial success.

Nuclear rocket engine tested in Nevada.

United States launches Apollo 7 in three-person orbital test flight.

Soviet Union launches Soyuz 3 on three-day piloted flight.

United States sends Apollo 8 into lunar orbit; first human flight to Moon.

**1969**    Soviet Union launches Soyuz 4 and 5 into orbit; craft dock.

Largest tactical communications satellite launched.

United States flies Apollo 9 on test of lunar landing craft in Earth orbit.

United States flies Apollo 10 to Moon in dress rehearsal of landing attempt.

United States cancels military space station program.

United States flies Apollo 11 to first landing on the Moon.

United States cancels production of Saturn V in budget cut.

Soviet lunar rocket N-1 fails in launch explosion.

United States sends Mariner 6 on Mars flyby.

United States flies Apollo 12 on second lunar landing mission.

Soviet Union flies Soyuz 6 and 7 missions.

United States launches Skynet military satellites for Britain.

**1970**    China orbits first satellite.

Japan orbits domestic satellite.

United States Apollo 13 mission suffers explosion; crew returns safely.

Soviet Union launches Venera 7 for landing on Venus.

United States launches military early warning satellite.

Soviet Union launches Luna 17 to Moon.

United States announces modifications to Apollo spacecraft.

**1971**    United States flies Apollo 14 to Moon landing.

Soviet Union launches Salyut 1 space station into orbit.

First crew to Salyut station, Soyuz 11, perishes.

Soviet Union launches Mars 3 to make landing on the red planet.

United States flies Apollo 15 to Moon with roving vehicle aboard.

**1972**    United States and the Soviet Union sign space cooperation agreement.

United States launches Pioneer 10 to Jupiter flyby.

Soviet Union launches Venera 8 to soft land on Venus.

United States launches Apollo 16 to moon.

India and Soviet Union sign agreement for launch of Indian satellite.

United States initiates space shuttle project.

United States flies Apollo 17, last lunar landing mission.

| | |
|---|---|
| **1973** | United States launches Skylab space station. |
| | United States launches first crew to Skylab station. |
| | Soviet Union launches Soyuz 12 mission. |
| | United States launches second crew to Skylab space station. |
| **1974** | United States launches ATS research satellite. |
| | Soviet Union launches Salyut 3 on unpiloted test flight. |
| | Soviet Union launches Soyuz 12, 13, and 14 flights. |
| | Soviet Union launches Salyut 4 space station. |
| **1975** | Soviet Union launches Soyuz 17 to dock with Salyut 4 station. |
| | Soviet Union launches Venera 9 to soft land on Venus. |
| | United States and Soviet Union conduct Apollo-Soyuz Test Project joint flight. |
| | China orbits large military satellite. |
| | United States sends Viking 1 and 2 towards landing on Martian surface. |
| | Soviet Union launches unpiloted Soyuz 20. |
| **1976** | Soviet Union launches Salyut 5 space station. |
| | First space shuttle rolls out; Enterprise prototype. |
| | Soviet Union docks Soyuz 21 to station. |
| | China begins tests of advanced ballistic missile. |
| **1977** | Soyuz 24 docks with station. |
| | United States conducts atmospheric test flights of shuttle Enterprise. |
| | United States launches Voyager 1 and 2 on deep space missions. |
| | Soviet Union launches Salyut 6 space station. |
| | Soviet Soyuz 25 fails to dock with station. |
| | Soyuz 26 is launched and docks with station. |
| **1978** | Soyuz 27 is launched and docks with Salyut 6 station. |
| | Soyuz 28 docks with Soyuz 27/Salyut complex. |
| | United States launches Pioneer/Venus 1 mission. |
| | Soyuz 29 docks with station. |
| | Soviet Union launches Progress unpiloted tankers to station. |
| | Soyuz 30 docks with station. |
| | United States launches Pioneer/Venus 2. |
| | Soyuz 31 docks with station. |

| | |
|---|---|
| **1979** | Soyuz 32 docks with Salyut station. |
| | Voyager 1 flies past Jupiter. |
| | Soyuz 33 fails to dock with station. |
| | Voyager 2 flies past Jupiter. |
| **1980** | First Ariane rocket launches from French Guiana; fails. |
| | Soviet Union begins new Soyuz T piloted missions. |
| | STS-1 first shuttle mission moves to launching pad. |
| **1981** | Soviet Union orbits advanced Salyut stations. |
| | STS-1 launched on first space shuttle mission. |
| | United States launches STS-2 on second shuttle flight; mission curtailed. |
| **1982** | United States launches STS-5 first operational shuttle flight. |
| **1983** | United States launches Challenger, second orbital shuttle, on STS-6. |
| | United States launches Sally Ride, the first American woman in space, on STS-7. |
| | United States launches Guion Bluford, the first African-American astronaut, on STS-8. |
| | United States launches first Spacelab mission aboard STS-9. |
| **1984** | Soviet Union tests advanced orbital station designs. |
| | Shuttle Discovery makes first flights. |
| | United States proposes permanent space station as goal. |
| **1985** | Space shuttle Atlantis enters service. |
| | United States announces policy for commercial rocket sales. |
| | United States flies U.S. Senator aboard space shuttle Challenger. |
| **1986** | Soviet Union launches and occupies advanced Mir space station. |
| | Challenger—on its tenth mission, STS-51-L—is destroyed in a launching accident. |
| | United States restricts payloads on future shuttle missions. |
| | United States orders replacement shuttle for Challenger. |
| **1987** | Soviet Union flies advanced Soyuz T-2 designs. |
| | United States' Delta, Atlas, and Titan rockets grounded in launch failures. |
| | Soviet Union launches Energyia advanced heavy lift rocket. |

**1988**     Soviet Union orbits unpiloted shuttle Buran.

United States launches space shuttle Discovery on STS-26 flight.

United States launches STS-27 military shuttle flight.

**1989**     United States launches STS-29 flight.

United States launches Magellan probe from shuttle.

**1990**     Shuttle fleet grounded for hydrogen leaks.

United States launches Hubble Space Telescope.

**1992**     Replacement shuttle Endeavour enters service.

United States probe Mars Observer fails.

**1993**     United States and Russia announce space station partnership.

**1994**     United States shuttles begin visits to Russian space station Mir.

**1995**     Europe launches first Ariane 5 advanced booster; flight fails.

**1996**     United States announces X-33 project to replace shuttles.

**1997**     Mars Pathfinder lands on Mars.

**1998**     First elements of International Space Station launched.

**1999**     First Ocean space launch of Zenit rocket in Sea Launch program.

**2000**     Twin United States Mars missions fail.

**2001**     United States cancels shuttle replacements X-33 and X-34 because of space cutbacks.

United States orbits Mars Odyssey probe around Mars.

**2002**     First launches of United States advanced Delta IV and Atlas V commercial rockets.

*Frank Sietzen, Jr.*

# Human Achievements in Space

*The road to space has been neither steady nor easy, but the journey has cast humans into a new role in history. Here are some of the milestones and achievements.*

**Oct. 4, 1957** The Soviet Union launches the first artificial satellite, a 184-pound spacecraft named Sputnik.

**Nov. 3, 1957** The Soviets continue pushing the space frontier with the launch of a dog named Laika into orbit aboard Sputnik 2. The dog lives for seven days, an indication that perhaps people may also be able to survive in space.

**Jan. 31, 1958** The United States launches Explorer 1, the first U.S. satellite, and discovers that Earth is surrounded by radiation belts. James Van Allen, who instrumented the satellite, is credited with the discovery.

**Apr. 12, 1961** Yuri Gagarin becomes the first person in space. He is launched by the Soviet Union aboard a Vostok rocket for a two-hour orbital flight around the planet.

**May 5, 1961** Astronaut Alan Shepard becomes the first American in space. Shepard demonstrates that individuals can control a vehicle during weightlessness and high gravitational forces. During his 15-minute suborbital flight, Shepard reaches speeds of 5,100 mph.

**May 24, 1961** Stung by the series of Soviet firsts in space, President John F. Kennedy announces a bold plan to land men on the Moon and bring them safely back to Earth before the end of the decade.

**Feb. 20, 1962** John Glenn becomes the first American in orbit. He flies around the planet for nearly five hours in his Mercury capsule, Friendship 7.

**June 16, 1963** The Soviets launch the first woman, Valentina Tereshkova, into space. She circles Earth in her Vostok spacecraft for three days.

**Nov. 28, 1964** NASA launches Mariner 4 spacecraft for a flyby of Mars.

**Mar. 18, 1965** Cosmonaut Alexei Leonov performs the world's first space walk outside his Voskhod 2 spacecraft. The outing lasts 10 minutes.

**Mar. 23, 1965** Astronauts Virgil I. "Gus" Grissom and John Young blast off on the first Gemini mission and demonstrate for the first time how to maneuver from one orbit to another.

**June 3, 1965** Astronaut Edward White becomes the first American to walk in space during a 21-minute outing outside his Gemini spacecraft.

**Mar. 16, 1966** Gemini astronauts Neil Armstrong and David Scott dock their spacecraft with an unmanned target vehicle to complete the first joining of two spacecraft in orbit. A stuck thruster forces an early end to the experiment, and the crew makes America's first emergency landing from space.

**Jan. 27, 1967** The Apollo 1 crew is killed when a fire breaks out in their command module during a prelaunch test. The fatalities devastate the American space community, but a subsequent spacecraft redesign helps the United States achieve its goal of sending men to the Moon.

**Apr. 24, 1967** Tragedy also strikes the Soviet space program, with the death of cosmonaut Vladimir Komarov. His new Soyuz spacecraft gets tangled with parachute lines during re-entry and crashes to Earth.

**Dec. 21, 1968** Apollo 8, the first manned mission to the Moon, blasts off from Cape Canaveral, Florida. Frank Borman, Jim Lovell and Bill Anders orbit the Moon ten times, coming to within 70 miles of the lunar surface.

**July 20, 1969** Humans walk on another world for the first time when astronauts Neil Armstrong and Edwin "Buzz" Aldrin climb out of their spaceship and set foot on the Moon.

**Apr. 13, 1970** The Apollo 13 mission to the Moon is aborted when an oxygen tank explosion cripples the spacecraft. NASA's most serious inflight emergency ends four days later when the astronauts, ill and freezing, splash down in the Pacific Ocean.

**June 6, 1971** Cosmonauts blast off for the first mission in the world's first space station, the Soviet Union's Salyut 1. The crew spends twenty-two days aboard the outpost. During re-entry, however, a faulty valve leaks air from the Soyuz capsule, and the crew is killed.

**Jan. 5, 1972** President Nixon announces plans to build "an entirely new type of space transportation system," pumping life into NASA's dream to build a reusable, multi-purpose space shuttle.

**Dec. 7, 1972** The seventh and final mission to the Moon is launched, as public interest and political support for the Apollo program dims.

**May 14, 1973** NASA launches the first U.S. space station, Skylab 1, into orbit. Three crews live on the station between May 1973 and February 1974. NASA hopes to have the shuttle flying in time to reboost and resupply Skylab, but the outpost falls from orbit on July 11, 1979.

**July 17, 1975**    In a momentary break from Cold War tensions, the United States and Soviet Union conduct the first linking of American and Russian spaceships in orbit. The Apollo-Soyuz mission is a harbinger of the cooperative space programs that develop between the world's two space powers twenty years later.

**Apr. 12, 1981**    Space shuttle Columbia blasts off with a two-man crew for the first test-flight of NASA's new reusable spaceship. After two days in orbit, the shuttle lands at Edwards Air Force Base in California.

**June 18, 1983**    For the first time, a space shuttle crew includes a woman. Astronaut Sally Ride becomes America's first woman in orbit.

**Oct. 30, 1983**    NASA's increasingly diverse astronaut corps includes an African-American for the first time. Guion Bluford, an aerospace engineer, is one of the five crewmen assigned to the STS-8 mission.

**Nov. 28, 1983**    NASA flies its first Spacelab mission and its first European astronaut, Ulf Merbold.

**Feb. 7, 1984**    Shuttle astronauts Bruce McCandless and Robert Stewart take the first untethered space walks, using a jet backpack to fly up to 320 feet from the orbiter.

**Apr. 9–11, 1984**    First retrieval and repair of an orbital satellite.

**Jan. 28, 1986**    Space shuttle Challenger explodes 73 seconds after launch, killing its seven-member crew. Aboard the shuttle was Teacher-in-Space finalist Christa McAuliffe, who was to conduct lessons from orbit. NASA grounds the shuttle fleet for two and a half years.

**Feb. 20. 1986**    The Soviets launch the core module of their new space station, Mir, into orbit. Mir is the first outpost designed as a module system to be expanded in orbit. Expected lifetime of the station is five years.

**May 15, 1987**    Soviets launch a new heavy-lift booster from the Baikonur Cosmodrome in Kazakhstan.

**Oct. 1, 1987**    Mir cosmonaut Yuri Romanenko breaks the record for the longest space mission, surpassing the 236-day flight by Salyut cosmonauts set in 1984.

**Sept. 29, 1988**    NASA launches the space shuttle Discovery on the first crewed U.S. mission since the 1986 Challenger explosion. The shuttle carries a replacement communications satellite for the one lost onboard Challenger.

**May 4, 1989**    Astronauts dispatch a planetary probe from the shuttle for the first time. The Magellan radar mapper is bound for Venus.

**Nov. 15, 1989**    The Soviets launch their space shuttle Buran, which means snowstorm, on its debut flight. There is no crew onboard, and unlike the U.S. shuttle, no engines to help place it into orbit. Lofted into orbit by twin Energia heavy-lift boosters, Buran circles Earth twice and lands. Buran never flies again.

**Apr. 24, 1990**    NASA launches the long-awaited Hubble Space Telescope, the cornerstone of the agency's "Great Observatory" program, aboard space shuttle Discovery. Shortly after placing the telescope in orbit, astronomers discover that the telescope's prime mirror is misshapen.

**Dec. 2, 1993**    Space shuttle Endeavour takes off for one of NASA's most critical shuttle missions: repairing the Hubble Space Telescope. During an unprecedented five space walks, astronauts install corrective optics. The mission is a complete success.

**Feb. 3, 1994**    A Russian cosmonaut, Sergei Krikalev, flies aboard a U.S. spaceship for the first time.

**Mar. 16, 1995**    NASA astronaut Norman Thagard begins a three and a half month mission on Mir—the first American to train and fly on a Russian spaceship. He is the first of seven Americans to live on Mir.

**Mar. 22, 1995**    Cosmonaut Valeri Polyakov sets a new space endurance record of 437 days, 18 hours.

**June 29, 1995**    Space shuttle Atlantis docks for the first time at the Russian space station Mir.

**Mar. 24, 1996**    Shannon Lucid begins her stay aboard space aboard Mir, which lasts 188 days—a U.S. record for spaceflight endurance at that time.

**Feb. 24, 1997**    An oxygen canister on Mir bursts into flames, cutting off the route to the station's emergency escape vehicles. Six crewmembers are onboard, including U.S. astronaut Jerry Linenger.

**June 27, 1997**    During a practice of a new docking technique, Mir commander Vasily Tsibliyev loses control of an unpiloted cargo ship and it plows into the station. The Spektr module is punctured, The crew hurriedly seals off the compartment to save the ship.

**Oct. 29, 1998**    Senator John Glenn, one of the original Mercury astronauts, returns to space aboard the shuttle.

**Nov. 20, 1998**    A Russian Proton rocket hurls the first piece of the International Space Station into orbit.

**Aug. 27, 1999**    Cosmonauts Viktor Afanasyev, Sergei Avdeyev, and Jean-Pierre Haignere leave Mir. The station is unoccupied for the first time in almost a decade.

**Oct. 31, 2000**   The first joint American-Russian crew is launched to the International Space Station. Commander Bill Shepherd requests the radio call sign "Alpha" for the station and the name sticks.

**Mar. 23, 2001**   The Mir space station drops out of orbit and burns up in Earth's atmosphere.

**Apr. 28, 2001**   Russia launches the world's first space tourist for a week-long stay at the International Space Station. NASA objects to the flight, but is powerless to stop it.

*Irene Brown*

# Contributors

Richard G. Adair
*Allochthon Enterprises*
Reno, Nevada

Constance M. Adams
*Lockheed Martin Space Operations
Company*
Houston, Texas

Joseph K. Alexander
*Space Studies Board of the National
Research Council*
Washington, D.C.

Judith H. Allton
*Apollo Historian*
Houston, Texas

Ulises R. Alvarado
*Instrumentation Technology
Associates, Inc.*
Exton, Pennsylvania

Susan Ames
*University of Bonn*
Bonn, Germany

Jayne Aubele
*New Mexico Museum of Natural
History and Science*
Albuquerque, New Mexico

Michael Babich
*University of Illinois*
Rockford, Illinois

Nadine G. Barlow
*Northern Arizona University*
Flagstaff, Arizona

William E. Barrett
*GIO Space*
Sydney, Australia

Jill Bechtold
*University of Arizona*
Tucson, Arizona

James Bell
*Cornell University*
Ithaca, New York

Gregory R. Bennett
*Bigelow Aerospace Co.*
Las Vegas, Nevada

James W. Benson
*SpaceDev*
Poway, California

Joseph T. Bielitzki
*Arlington, Virginia*

William Bottke
*Southwest Research Institute*
Boulder, Colorado

Chad Boutin
*Chicago, Illinois*

Irene Brown
*Melbourne, Florida*

Lance B. Bush
*NASA Headquarters*
Washington, D.C.

Vickie Elaine Caffey
*Milano, Texas*

Sherri Chasin Calvo
*Clarksville, Maryland*

Len Campaigne
*IBM Global Services*
Colorado Springs, Colorado

Humberto Campins
*University of Arizona*
Tucson, Arizona

John M. Cassanto
*Instrumentation Technology
Associates, Inc.*
Exton, Pennsylvania

Michael R. Cerney
*Space Age Publishing Company*
Kailua–Kona, Hawaii

Charles M. Chafer
*Celestic Inc.*
Houston, Texas

Clark R. Chapman
*Southwest Research Institute*
Boulder, Colorado

David Charbonneau
*California Institute of Technology*
Pasadena, California

Carissa Bryce Christensen
*The Tauri Group, LLC*
Alexandria, Virginia

Anita L. Cochran
*University of Texas*
Austin, Texas

Larry S. Crumpler
*New Mexico Museum of Natural
History and Science*
Albuquerque, New Mexico

Neil Dahlstrom
*Space Business Archives*
Alexandria, Virginia

Thomas Damon
*Pikes Peak Community College*
Colorado Springs, Colorado

E. Julius Dasch
*NASA Headquarters*
Washington, D.C.

Pat Dasch
*RCS International*
Washington, D.C.

Leonard David
*SPACE.com*
Boulder, Colorado

Dwayne A. Day
*Space Policy Institute*
Washington, D.C.

Peter J. Delfyett
*University of Central Florida*
Orlando, Florida

Lawrence J. DeLucas
*University of Alabama at
Birmingham*
Birmingham, Alabama

David Desrocher
*The Aerospace Corporation*
Colorado Springs, Colorado

Neelkanth G. Dhere
*Florida Solar Energy Center*
Cocoa, Florida

Peter H. Diamandis
*Zero-Gravity Corporation*
Santa Monica, California

John R. Dickel
*University of Illinois*
Urbana, Illinois

Taylor Dinerman
*SpaceEquity.com*
New York, New York

Dave Dooling
*Infinity Technology Inc.*
Huntsville, Alabama

Michael B. Duke
*Colorado School of Mines*
Golden, Colorado

Douglas Duncan
*University of Chicago*
Chicago, Illinois

Frederick C. Durant III
*Raleigh, North Carolina*

Steve Durst
*Space Age Publishing Company*
Kailua–Kona, Hawaii

Peter Eckart
*Technische Universität München*
Munich, Germany

Stephen J. Edberg
*Jet Propulsion Laboratory*
Pasadena, California

Meridel Ellis
*Orlando, Florida*

Bruce G. Elmegreen
*IBM T.J. Watson Research Center*
Yorktown Heights, New York

Debra Meloy Elmegreen
*Vassar College*
Poughkeepsie, New York

Kimberly Ann Ennico
*NASA Ames Research Center*
Moffett Field, California

R. Bryan Erb
*Sunsat Energy Council*
Friendswood, Texas

Jack D. Farmer
*Arizona State University*
Tempe, Arizona

Adi R. Ferrara
*Bellevue, Washington*

Margaret G. Finarelli
*International Space University*
Washington, D.C.

Rick Fleeter
*AeroAstro, Inc.*
Herndon, Virginia

Theodore T. Foley II
*NASA Johnson Space Center*
Houston, Texas

Jeff Foust
*Rockville, Maryland*

Wendy L. Freedman
*Carnegie Observatories*
Pasadena, California

Michael Fulda
*Fairmont State College*
Fairmont, West Virginia

Lori Garver
*DFI International*
Washington, D.C.

Sarah Gibson
*National Center for Atmospheric
Research*
Boulder, Colorado

John F. Graham
*American Military University*
Manassas, Virginia

Bernard Haisch
*Palo Alto, California*

Robert L. Haltermann
*Space Transportation Association*
Alexandria, Virginia

Heidi B. Hammel
*Space Sciences Institute*
Boulder, Colorado

Alan Harris
*Jet Propulsion Laboratory*
Pasadena, California

Albert A. Harrison
*University of California, Davis*
Davis, California

Mary Kay Hemenway
*University of Texas*
Austin, Texas

Henry R. Hertzfeld
*Space Policy Institute*
Washington, D.C.

Adrian J. Hooke
*Jet Propulsion Laboratory*
Pasadena, California

Brian Hoyle
*BDH Science Communications*
Bedford, Nova Scotia

Robert P. Hoyt
*Tethers Unlimited, Inc.*
Seattle, Washington

Edward Hujsak
*Mina-Helwig Company*
La Jolla, California

Nadine M. Jacobson
*Takoma Park, Maryland*

Kevin Jardine
*Spectrum Astro, Inc.*
Gilbert, Arizona

Terry C. Johnson
*Kansas State University*
Manhattan, Kansa

Brad Jolliff
*Washington University*
St. Louis, Missouri

Thomas D. Jones
*The Space Agency*
Houston, Texas

Mark E. Kahn
*National Air and Space Museum*
Washington, D.C.

Marshall H. Kaplan
*Launchspace, Inc.*
Rockville, Maryland

Michael S. Kelley
*NASA Johnson Space Center*
Houston, Texas

Michael S. Kelly
*Kelly Space & Technology*
San Bernardino, California

Lisa Klink
*Cement City, Michigan*

Peter Kokh
*Lunar Reclamation Society, Inc.*
Milwaukee, Wisconsin

Randy L. Korotev
*Washington University*
St. Louis, Missouri

Roger E. Koss
*Ormond Beach, Florida*

Lillian D. Kozloski
*James Monroe Museum and
Memorial Library*
Fredericksburg, Virginia

Saunders B. Kramer
*Montgomery Village, Maryland*

John F. Kross
*Ad Astra Magazine*
Lincoln University, PA

Timothy B. Kyger
*Universal Space Lines*
Alexandria, Virginia

Geoffrey A. Landis
*NASA John Glenn Research Center*
Cleveland, Ohio

Roger D. Launius
*NASA History Office*
Washington, D.C.

Jennifer Lemanski
*Orlando, Florida*

Andrew J. LePage
*Visidyne, Inc.*
Burlington, Masschusetts

Debra Facktor Lepore
*Kistler Aerospace Corporation*
Kirkland, Washington

David H. Levy
*Jarnac Observatory, Inc.*
Vail, Arizona

John S. Lewis
*University of Arizona*
Tucson, Arizona

David L. Lihani
*Pierson and Burnett, L.L.P.*
Washington, D.C.

Arthur H. Litka
*Seminole Community College*
Sanford, Florida

Bill Livingstone
*GlobalOptions, Inc.*
Washington, D.C.

John M. Logsdon
*Space Policy Institute*
Washington, D.C.

Rosaly M. C. Lopes
*Jet Propulsion Laboratory*
Pasadena, California

Mark L. Lupisella
*NASA Goddard Space Flight Center*
Greenbelt, Maryland

Jeff Manber
*Space Business Archives*
Alexandria, Virginia

John C. Mankins
*NASA Headquarters*
Washington, D.C.

Robert L. Marcialis
*University of Arizona*
Tucson, Arizona

Margarita M. Marinova
*Massachusetts Institute of Technology*
Cambridge, Massachusetts

John T. Mariska
*Naval Research Laboratory*
Washington, D.C.

Shinji Matsumoto
*Shimizu Corporation*
Tokyo, Japan

Julie L. McDowell
*Baltimore, Maryland*

Christopher P. McKay
*NASA Ames Research Center*
Moffett Field, California

David A. Medek
*Palo Verde Nuclear Generating Station*
Wintersburg, Arizona

Karen J. Meech
*University of Hawaii*
Honolulu, Hawaii

Wendell Mendell
*NASA Johnson Space Center*
Houston, Texas

Douglas M. Messier
*SpaceJobs.com*
Arlington, Virginia

Mark Miesch
*National Center for Atmospheric Research*
Boulder, Colorado

Frank R. Mignone
*University of Central Florida*
Orlando, Florida

Ron Miller
*King George, Virginia*

Julie A. Moberly
*Microgravity News*
Hampton, Virginia

Jefferson Morris
*Aerospace Daily*
Washington, D.C.

Clayton Mowry
*Arianespace, Inc.*
Washington, D.C.

Peter Norvig
*NASA Ames Research Center*
Moffett Field, California

Tim Palucka
*Pittsburgh, Pennsylvania*

Jay Pasachoff
*Williams College*
Williamstown, Massachusetts

Chris A. Peterson
*University of Hawaii*
Honolulu, Hawaii

A. G. Davis Philip
*ISO & Union College*
Schenectady, New York

Deborah Pober
*Montgomery County, Maryland*

Barbara Poppe
*NOAA Space Environment Center*
Boulder, Colorado

David S. F. Portree
*Flagstaff, Arizona*

Jane Poynter
*Paragon Space Development Corporation*
Tucson, Arizona

Cynthia S. Price
*Celestic Inc.*
Houston, Texas

Nick Proach
*Nick Proach Models*
Sechelt, British Columbia, Canada

Margaret S. Race
*SETI Institute*
Mountain View, California

Sudhakar Rajulu
*NASA/NSBRI–Baylor College of Medicine*
Houston, Texas

Clinton L. Rappole
*University of Houston*
Houston, Texas

Martin Ratcliffe
*International Planetarium Society*
Wichita, Kansas

Pat Rawlings
*Science Applications International Corporation*
Houston, Texas

Elliot Richmond
*Education Consultants*
Austin, Texas

Carlos J. Rosas-Anderson
*Kissimmee, Florida*

John D. Rummel
*NASA Headquarters*
Washington, D.C.

Graham Ryder
*Lunar and Planetary Institute*
Houston, Texas

Salvatore Salamone
*New York, New York*

Craig Samuels
*University of Central Florida*
Orlando, Florida

Eagle Sarmont
*AffordableSpaceFlight.com*
Stockton, California

Joel L. Schiff
*Meteorite! Magazine and Auckland University*
Takapuna-Auckland, New Zealand

Mark A. Schneegurt
*Wichita State University*
Wichita, Kansas

David G. Schrunk
*Quality of Laws Institute*
Poway, California

Alison Cridland Schutt
*National Space Society*
Washington, D.C.

Derek L. Schutt
*Carnegie Institution of Washington*
Washington, D.C.

Seth Shostak
*SETI Institute*
Mountain View, California

Frank Sietzen, Jr.
*Space Transportation Association*
Alexandria, Virginia

Samuel Silverstein
*Space News for SPACE.com*
Springfield, Virginia

Michael A. Sims
*NASA Ames Research Center*
Moffett Field, California

Phil Smith
*Futron Corporation*
Bethesda, Maryland

Amy Paige Snyder
*Federal Aviation Administration*
Washington, D.C.

Mark J. Sonter
*Asteroid Enterprises Pty Ltd*
Hawthorne Dene, South Australia

Barbara Sprungman
*Space Data Resources & Information*
Boulder, Colorado

S. Alan Stern
*Southwest Research Institute*
Boulder, Colorado

Robert G. Strom
*University of Arizona*
Tucson, Arizona

Angela Swafford
*Miami Beach, Florida*

Amy Swint
*Houston, Texas*

Leslie K. Tamppari
*Pasadena, California*

Jeffrey R. Theall
*NASA Johnson Space Center*
Houston, Texas

Frederick E. Thomas
*Orlando, Florida*

Robert Trevino
*NASA Johnson Space Center*
Houston, Texas

Roeland P. van der Marel
*Space Telescope Science Institute*
Baltimore, Maryland

Anthony L. Velocci, Jr.
*Aviation Week & Space Technology*
New York, New York

Joan Vernikos
*Thirdage LLC*
Alexandria, Virginia

Ray Villard
*Space Telescope Science
Institute*
Baltimore, Maryland

Matt Visser
*Washington University*
St. Louis, Missouri

Linda D. Voss
*Arlington, Virginia*

Charles D. Walker
*Annandale, Virginia*

Timothy R. Webster
*Science Applications International
Corporation*
Torrance, California

Jean-Marie (J.-M.) Wersinger
*Auburn University*
Auburn, Alabama

Joshua N. Winn
*Harvard–Smithsonian Center for
Astrophysics*
Cambridge, Massachusetts

Grace Wolf-Chase
*Adler Planetarium & Astronomy
Museum and the University of
Chicago*
Chicago, Illinois

Sidney C. Wolff
*National Optical Astronomy
Observatory*
Tucson, Arizona

Cynthia Y. Young
*University of Central Florida*
Orlando, Florida

# Table of Contents

## VOLUME 3: HUMANS IN SPACE

# Antimatter Propulsion

Imagine an energy source that is more powerful than nuclear **fission** or even nuclear **fusion**. Antimatter-matter reactions could offer an amount of energy that is not comparable to today's energy sources. When particles of matter and particles of antimatter collide, large amounts of energy are produced as a by-product. Because matter can neither be created nor destroyed, it is turned into tremendous amounts of energy.

Antimatter is the exact opposite of normal matter. Whereas a proton is a positively-charged particle, its antimatter counterpart, called an antiproton, is negatively charged. The antimatter counterpart to the negatively-charged electron is the positron, which is positively charged. All of the sub-atomic particles' charges are reversed, forming antiatoms. These antiatoms were first theorized in 1928 by Paul A. M. Dirac, a British physicist. In 1932 the first antimatter particle was created in a laboratory experiment by Carl Anderson, who is credited with coining the word "positron." Speculation continued throughout the 1950s, but because of the complexity of creating these particles, astrophysicists were unable to produce antimatter atoms until the late 1990s.

Antimatter particles are difficult to produce because of their very nature. When a particle or atom of antimatter comes into contact with a particle or atom of normal matter, both are annihilated and energy is released. The synthesized antiatoms have lasted only 40 billionths of a second before their annihilation. The particles were accelerated at close to the speed of light. Antihydrogen is the simplest antimatter atom to produce, yet, that feat took decades of research and billions of dollars. Even the European Organization for Nuclear Research (CERN), the laboratory in which the experiment was performed, admitted that this method of creating antimatter is far too expensive and difficult to be subject to mass production. Instead, cheaper and faster methods must be developed to make antimatter more than a dream of the future.

Developing antimatter is worth the effort because the energy created by sustainable matter-antimatter reactions would be so powerful that many people believe that faster-than-light travel, or "warp speed," could be achieved. Other possible uses include powering long-term spaceflight for humans and probes.

The main hope for antimatter is that one day this energy source could be used as a fuel. Hydrogen would be annihilated with anti-hydrogen, and

**fission** act of splitting a heavy atomic nucleus into two lighter ones, releasing tremendous energy

**fusion** releasing nuclear energy by combining lighter elements such as hydrogen into heavier elements

Flights to the Moon could employ detachable crew modules atop nuclear thermal transfer vehicles.

**rocket** vehicle or device especially designed to travel through space, propelled by one or more engines

the energy would be funneled into a magnetic nozzle of a **rocket**. Such energy would propel the ship or probe at tremendous speeds compared to today's methods of propulsion. One of the problems with this model is that much of the energy is given off as neutrally charged particles that cannot be harnessed. To make use of the majority of the energy produced, these particles would have to be captured.

The amount of thrust produced by the space shuttle's boosters is equal to the energy released from 71 milligrams of antimatter. The benefits of antimatter propulsion will be worth the effort when this energy can be used to explore the universe in a way that has only been dreamed of so far. SEE ALSO FASTER-THAN-LIGHT TRAVEL (VOLUME 4); INTERSTELLAR TRAVEL (VOLUME 4); NUCLEAR PROPULSION (VOLUME 4); ROCKETS (VOLUME 3).

*Craig Samuels*

**Bibliography**

Barnett, Michael R., Henry Muehry, Helen R. Quinn, and Gordon Aubrecht. *The Charm of Strange Quarks: Mysteries and Revolutions of Particle Physics.* New York: AIP Press, 2000.

**Internet Resources**

"Antimatter Clouds and Fountain Discovered in the Milky Way." NASA Headquarters. <http://www.hq.nasa.gov/pub/pao/pressrel/1997/97-083.txt>.

"A Smattering of Antimatter." *Scientific American.* <http://www.sciam.com/0496 issue/0496scicit05.html>.

"What is Antimatter?" *Scientific American.* <http://www.sciam.com/askexpert/physics/ physics56/>.

"What's the Matter with Antimatter?" *Science@NASA.* <http://www.spacescience .com/headlines/y2000/ast29may_1m.htm>.

# Asteroid Mining

Future large-scale space operations, including space hotels, solar power satellites, and orbital factories, will require volatiles such as water, methane, ammonia, and carbon dioxide.✳ These materials can be used to produce propellant, metal for facility construction (such as nickel-iron alloy), semiconductors for manufacturing **photovoltaic** power systems (such as silicon, arsenic, and germanium), and simple mass for **ballast** and **shielding**. The cost to transport these commodities from Earth today is $10,000 per kilogram. In the future, the extraction of these materials from easy-access asteroids will become a competitive option.

All of these resources are present in asteroids. About 10 percent of the near-Earth asteroids (NEAs) are more accessible than the Moon, requiring a velocity increase (delta-v) from **low Earth orbit** of less than 6 kilometers per second (km/s; 3.75 miles per second) for rendezvous, with a return departure delta-v of 1 km/s or less. A few are extremely accessible, only marginally more demanding to reach than a launch or a satellite to **geostationary orbit**.

The return of asteroidal materials using propellant derived from the target asteroid will enable potentially unlimited mass availability in low Earth orbit. That will break the logistical bottleneck and cost constraints of launching from Earth. Asteroid-sourced raw materials will enable and catalyze the development of an Earth-Moon space economy and humankind's expansion into the solar system.

The growing recognition of the "impact threat" to Earth has prompted several successful NEA search programs, with approximately 1,800 NEAs now identified (as of April 2002), up from about 30 NEAs twenty years ago. Some 400 are classified as potentially hazardous asteroids (PHAs) that come to within 7.5 million kilometers (4.7 million miles) of Earth orbit on occasion. New potential mining targets are found every month.

Based on meteorite studies, astronomers recognize that NEAs have diverse compositions, including silicate, carbonaceous and hydrocarbon-bearing, metallic, and ice-bearing materials. Some may be loose rubble piles held together only by self-gravity.

Insights from comet modeling, studies of orbital dynamics, and observation of comet-asteroid transition objects indicate that 30 to 40 percent of NEAs may be extinct or dormant comets.

There has recently been major work on modeling of the development on comets of a crust or **regolith** of dust, fragmented rock, and **bitumen** that has been prompted by the Giotto spacecraft's observations of Halley's comet in 1986 and other comets. This insulating "mantle," if allowed to

✳ **Volatiles easily pass into the vapor stage when heated.**

**photovoltaic** pertaining to the direct generation of electricity from electromagnetic radiation (light)

**ballast** heavy substance used to increase the stability of a vehicle

**shielding** providing protection for humans and electronic equipment from cosmic rays, energetic particles from the Sun, and other radioactive materials

**low Earth orbit** an orbit between 300 and 800 kilometers above Earth's surface

**geostationary orbit** a specific altitude of an equatorial orbit where the time required to circle the planet matches the time it takes the planet to rotate on its axis

## THE IMPACT OF NICKEL-IRON PRODUCTION

A by-product of asteroidal nickel-iron production will be the increased availability of platinum group metals for export to Earth for use as catalysts in an expanding fuel-cell energy economy. These metals include platinum, palladium, and rhodium.

In this rendering of a mining operation on an asteroid traveling near Earth, the unit on the asteroid is doing the actual mining, while power and other necessities are supplied by an orbital construction platform in conjunction with the surrounding solar arrays.

**regolith** upper few meters of a body's surface, composed of inorganic matter, such as unconsolidated rocks and fine soil

**bitumen** a thick, almost solid form of hydrocarbons, often mixed with other minerals

**cometary outgassing** vaporization of the frozen gases that form a comet nucleus as the comet approaches the Sun and warms

grow to completion, eliminates **cometary outgassing**, and the object then takes on the appearance of an inactive asteroid. These **cryptocometary** bodies, if in near-Earth orbits, will stabilize with a deep-core temperature of about $-50°C$. The deep core would probably be depleted of CO and $CO_2$ and highly porous but would retain water ice in crystalline form and in combination with silicates as well as bituminous hydrocarbons. This ice could be extracted by drilling and circulation of hot fluid or by mining with subsequent heat processing.

Photographs of the asteroids Gaspra, Ida and Dactyl, Mathilde, Braille, and Eros by various space probes and radar images of Castalia, Toutatis, 1998 KY26, Kleopatra, 1999 JM8, and Geographos reveal a varied, bizarre, and poorly understood collection of objects. Many images show evidence of a thick loose regolith or gravel/sand/silt layer that could be collected easily by scooping or shoveling. Eros shows slump sheets in the sides of craters where fresh material has been uncovered, a lack of small craters, an abundance of boulders, and pooled dust deposits in the bases of craters.

Eros and Mathilde have improbably low densities, suggesting that they have large internal voids or are highly porous; Mathilde has craters so large that their generating impacts should have split it asunder. Both Toutatis and Castalia appear to be contact binaries: twin asteroids in contact with each other. Eros and Geographos are improbably elongated, shaped like sweet potatoes. Kleopatra is a 140-kilometer-long (87.5 miles) dog-bone shape. 1998 KY26 is tiny and spins so fast that any loose material on its surface must be flung off into space, implying that it must be a monolithic solid object under tension.

## Mining Concepts

The choice of mining and processing methods is driven by what and how much is desired, difficulty of separation, duration of mining season, and propulsion demands in returning the product to the nominated orbit. Minimization of project cost and technical risk, together with maximization of returns in a short timeframe, will be major factors in project planning.

If the required product is water, which can be used as the propellant for the return journey, underground rather than surface mining will be required because of the dryness of the asteroid surface. Some sort of **tunnelborer** will be needed, or a large-diameter auger-type drill. If the product is nickel-iron metal sand, surface regolith collection by scraping or shoveling is indicated. Surface reclaim is threatened by problems of containment and anchoring. **In situ** volatilization (melting and vaporizing ice at the bottom of a drill hole for extraction as steam) has been proposed for mining **comet matrix material** but is subject to fluid loss and blowouts.

The processing methods depend on the desired product. If it is water and other volatiles, a heating and condensation process is essential. If it is nickel-iron sand, then density, magnetic, or electrostatic separation will be used to produce a concentrate from the collected regolith. Terrestrial centrifugal grinding mills and **density-separation jigs** can be adapted for this work.

Initial asteroid mining operations will probably be carried out by small, low-cost, robotic, remotely controlled or autonomous integrated miner-processors designed to return a few hundred to a few thousand tons of product per mission, with propulsion systems using asteroid-derived material for propellant.

## Conclusion

The knowledge and technologies required to develop the resources of asteroids and enable the industrialization and colonization of the inner solar system will provide humankind with the ability to protect society and Earth from threats of asteroid and comet impacts. SEE ALSO ASTEROIDS (VOLUME 2); CLOSE ENCOUNTERS (VOLUME 2); GETTING TO SPACE CHEAPLY (VOLUME 1); HOTELS (VOLUME 4); IMPACTS (VOLUME 4); SOLAR POWER SYSTEMS (VOLUME 4); SPACE RESOURCES (VOLUME 4).

*Mark J. Sonter*

Asteroids contain many of the major elements that provide the basis for life and industry on Earth.

**cryptocometary** asteroids that contain a high percentage of carbon compounds mixed with frozen gases

**tunnelborer** a mining machine designed to dig a tunnel using rotating cutting disks

**in situ** in the natural or original location

**comet matrix material** the substances that form the nucleus of a comet; dust grains embedded in frozen methane, ammonia, carbon dioxide, and water

### WHAT IS THE DELTA-V?

The measure of the energy needed to transfer from one orbit to another, or the difficulty of carrying out a space mission, is the delta-v: the velocity change, or boost, needed to achieve the required new trajectory. The delta-v necessary to achieve low Earth orbit is 8 km/s (5 miles/sec); to go from low Earth orbit to Earth-escape velocity (achieve an orbit around the Sun, free of the Earth's gravity) requires an extra 3.2 km/s (2 miles/sec). The delta-v to achieve geostationary orbit from low Earth orbit is 3.6 km/s (2.25 miles). The most accessible asteroids have a delta-v as low as 4 km/s (2.5 miles/sec).

**density-separation jigs** a form of gravity separation of materials with different densities that uses a pulsating fluid

**Bibliography**

Binzel, Richard P., et al., eds. *Asteroids III.* Tucson: University of Arizona Press, in press.

Gehrels, T., ed. *Hazards Due to Asteroids and Comets.* Tucson: University of Arizona Press, 1994.

Lewis, John S. *Mining the Sky.* Reading, MA: Helix/Addison Wesley, 1996.

Lewis, John S., Mildred Shapley Matthews, and Mary L. Guerrieri, eds. *Resources of Near-Earth Space.* Tucson: University of Arizona Press, 1993.

# Astrobiology

Astrobiology is a new interdisciplinary science that studies the origin, evolution, distribution, and destiny of life in the cosmos. Other terms that have been used to describe the search for life beyond Earth include exobiology, exopaleontology, and bioastronomy. Astrobiology is a broadly based, interdisciplinary science that embraces the fields of biology and microbiology, microbial ecology, molecular biology and biochemistry, geology and paleontology, space and gravitational biology, planetology, and astronomy, among others.

The development of astrobiology as a discipline began in the early 1990s with the recognition of a growing synergy between various sciences in seeking answers to the question of extraterrestrial life. The National Aeronautics and Space Administration (NASA) promoted the development of astrobiology by funding a research institute (the NASA Astrobiology Institute, or NAI), which consists of interdisciplinary teams of scientists from fifteen separate institutions in the United States, including both government laboratories and universities. Important scientific discoveries have changed the way scientists think about the origin, evolution, and persistence of life on Earth. These discoveries have helped fuel the growth of astrobiology by defining the broad conceptual framework and scope of the field and by opening up new possibilities for the existence of extraterrestrial life.

## Earth's Microbial Biosphere

**biosphere** the interaction of living organisms on a global scale

Since the late 1980s, advances in genetics and molecular biology have radically altered scientists' view of the **biosphere** and the contribution of microbial life to planetary biodiversity. The opportunity to compare gene sequences from a wide variety of living organisms and environments has shown that living organisms cluster into one of three biological domains: the Archaea, Bacteria, or Eukarya. Each of these domains is made up of dozens of biological kingdoms, the vast majority of which are microbial. Species inferred to be the most primitive forms so far discovered are all found at high temperatures (greater than 80°C [176°F]) where they use simple forms of chemical energy. However, knowledge of Earth's biodiversity is still very much a work in progress. While biologists have sampled a wide range of environments, it is estimated that only a small fraction, perhaps 1 to 2 percent of the total biodiversity present, has so far been captured. Still, the three-domain structure has remained stable. New organisms are being discovered each year, adding diversity to each domain, but many discoveries still lie ahead.

These advances in biology have led to a growing awareness that Earth is overwhelmingly dominated by microscopic life and that these simple forms have dominated nearly the entire history of the biosphere. Indeed, advances in paleontology have now pushed back the record of microbial life to within half a billion years of the time scientists believe Earth first became inhabitable. This suggests that once the conditions necessary for life's origin were in place, it arose very quickly. Exactly how quickly is not yet known, but in geologic terms, it was a much shorter period than previously thought. This view significantly improves the possibility that life may have originated on other planets such as Mars, where liquid water may have been present at the surface for only a few hundred million years, early in the planet's history.

## The Evolution of Complex Life

Studies of the fossil record have revealed that complex, multicellular forms of life (plants and animals) did not appear on Earth until about 600 million years ago, which is recent in geological history. Animals are multicellular consumers that require oxygen for their metabolism. Scientists believe that their late addition to the biosphere was triggered by the buildup of oxygen in the oceans and atmosphere to a threshold of about 10 percent of the present atmospheric level. ✶ It is clear that the high level of oxygen found in the atmosphere today could have been generated only through photosynthesis, a biological process that captures sunlight and uses the energy to convert carbon dioxide and water to organic matter and oxygen. Clearly, oxygen-evolving photosynthesis has had a profound effect on the biosphere. If oxygen was required for the appearance of complex animal life, then a detailed understanding of photosynthetic processes and their evolution is crucial to create a proper context for evaluating the cosmological potential for life to evolve to the level of sentient beings and advanced technologies elsewhere in the cosmos. This research also provides a context for the SETI program (Search for Extraterrestrial Intelligence), which is currently exploring the heavens for advanced civilizations elsewhere in the galaxy by monitoring radio waves.

## Basic Requirements for Life

The most basic requirement of living systems is liquid water, the universal medium that organisms use to carry out the chemical reactions of metabolism. Water is a unique dipolar compound (positively charged on one side and negatively charged on the other) with special solvent properties that allow it to act as a universal medium of transport and exchange in chemical reactions. In addition, the physical properties of water allow it to remain liquid over a very broad range of temperatures, thus enhancing its availability to living systems. In exploring for life elsewhere in the cosmos, the recognition of the importance of liquid water as a requirement for life is reflected in NASA's basic exploration strategy, which seeks to "follow the water."

But to exist, living systems also require sources of nutrients and energy. The common biogenic elements (carbon, hydrogen, nitrogen, oxygen, phosphorus, and sulfur), which comprise the basic building blocks of life, appear to be widely distributed in the universe. These elements are forged in the

NASA's Controlled Ecology Life Support System studies self-contained systems for applications related to future space colony environments. These sealed flasks contain shrimp, algae, and other microorganisms capable of generating their own water, oxygen, and food.

✶ Oxygen currently makes up 21 percent of Earth's atmosphere.

Mouse-ear cress plants were part of the Plant Growth Investigations in the Microgravity 1 experiment aboard the space shuttle Columbia.

**nuclear fusion** the combining of low-mass atoms to create heavier ones; the heavier atom's mass is slightly less than the sum of the mass of its constituents, with the remaining mass converted to energy

**supernova** an explosion ending the life of a massive star; caused by core collapse or the sudden onset of nuclear fusion

**hydrothermal** relating to high temperature water

**desiccation** the process of drying up

interiors of stars through **nuclear fusion** reactions, and through normal processes they produce elements with masses up to that of iron—56. The heavier metallic elements, some of which living systems also require, are formed only in very massive stars during **supernova** explosions. A key question of astrobiology concerns the distribution of massive stars in galaxies, which in turn may control the distribution of heavy elements essential for life.

By applying new methods of molecular biology and genetics over a broad range of environmental extremes, scientists' knowledge of the environmental limits of life on Earth (and the ways that organisms obtain nutrients and energy) has expanded dramatically. This area of inquiry comprises a relatively new area of biology known as extremophile (extreme-loving) research. This research has revealed that microbial species thrive in environments with broad extremes of temperature, ranging from deep-sea, **hydrothermal** vents (about 114°C [237°F]) to Siberian permafrost (−15°C [5°F]). (Above about 130°C [266°F], complex organic molecules become unstable and begin to break down. This temperature may comprise an absolute upper limit for life based on the limitations of carbon chemistry.) In addition, microorganisms occupy nearly the entire pH range from about 1.4 (extremely acid) to about 13.5 (extremely alkaline). Microbial life also occupies an equally broad salinity range from freshwater to saturated brines (containing about 300 percent dissolved solids) where salt (NaCl) precipitates. Finally, organisms also survive at very low water availability by creating **desiccation**-resistant structures that can survive for prolonged inclement periods.

## Alternative Energy Sources

Within the basic constraint of liquid water, barriers to life appear to be few. However, it is important to understand that the level of productivity possible for living systems is strictly constrained by the quality of the energy sources they are able to exploit. On Earth, more than 99 percent of the energy powering the biosphere is derived from photosynthesis. This is not surprising given that, per unit area of Earth's surface, energy from the Sun is several hundred times more abundant than the thermal and chemical energy sources derived from *within* Earth. Clearly, there is a great advantage (energetically speaking) in exploiting solar energy. But the potential importance of chemical sources was also made clear in 1977 when American oceanographers Jack Corliss and Robert Ballard piloted the deep submersible, *Alvin*, to hydrothermal springs on the seafloor located more than 2.4 kilometers (1.5 miles) deep. At this depth, no sunlight exists for photosynthesis, and yet complex ecosystems were found there in which the organisms (including large, multicelled animals) derived their energy entirely from chemical sources provided by the hot fluids. This discovery shocked biologists, as they realized that even though photosynthesis provides much more energy, simple forms of chemical energy are still capable of supporting complex ecosystems. Since 1977, many other examples of deep-sea vent ecosystems have been found in virtually every ocean basin on Earth.

## A Deep Subsurface Biosphere

As methods of exploration and observation have improved, life's environmental limits have continued to expand. In 1993 American biochemist Thomas Gold suggested that single-celled forms of life survive and grow in the deep subsurface of Earth, residing within tiny pore spaces and fractures in **indurated rocks**. In fact, volumetrically, such subsurface life forms could comprise more than half of Earth's biomass. Microscopic life is also thought to exist in a deep subglacial lake called Vostoc, which lies more than 3 kilometers (1.9 miles) beneath the ice cap of Antarctica. While many subsurface microbes appear to depend on photosynthetically derived organic matter that washes down from the surface, some species can make their own organic molecules from inorganic sources. Called lithoautotrophs (which literally means "self-feeding on rocks"), these organisms use the byproducts of simple weathering processes in which carbon dioxide dissolved in groundwater reacts with rocks to yield hydrogen. Hydrogen in turn is exploited for available energy. These organisms hold special importance for astrobiology because their existence allows the possibility that subsurface life can exist completely independently of surface (photosynthetic) production. Such lifestyles hold important implications for Mars and Europa (one of Jupiter's largest moons), where deep subsurface habitats are postulated to exist.

Studies of **extremophiles** have revealed that terrestrial life occupies virtually every imaginable habitat where liquid water, chemical nutrients, and simple forms of energy coexist. This observation has dramatically expanded the range of habitats available to life as well as the potential for life elsewhere in the solar system or beyond.

## Exploring for a Martian Biosphere

Liquid water is unstable in surface environments on Mars today, thus imposing a formidable barrier to the development and survival of Martian life. Nevertheless, models suggest that a global groundwater system could exist on Mars today at a depth of several kilometers below the surface. Indeed,

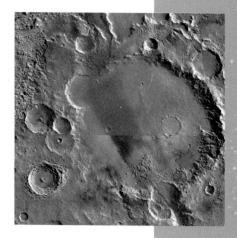

Several impact craters on Mars show evidence of having held lakes at some time in the past. This image of Gusev crater shows the rim of the crater cut by a channel that likely deposited water in the floor of the crater.

## HOW VIABLE ARE MICROBES UNDER HARSH CONDITIONS?

In addition to an astounding range of ecological adaptations, many microbial species have been shown to survive in a state of stasis under inclement conditions for prolonged periods of time. In even the driest deserts on Earth, some species survive by living inside porous rocks where they find a safe haven from ultraviolet radiation, springing to life only occasionally, when water needed for growth becomes available. An even more interesting example is bacteria that have been germinated from spores preserved in Dominican amber dated at more than 30 million years old. Given this propensity for prolonged survival, the potential for microorganisms to survive under extreme conditions, for example on Mars, has been greatly enhanced.

Clouds and sunlight glint over the Indian Ocean, as seen from the space shuttle Discovery. Liquid water is the basic requirement for life, and Earth's abundant supply supports millions of organisms.

**indurated rocks** rocks that have been hardened by natural processes

**extremophiles** microorganisms surviving in extreme environments such as high salinity or near boiling water

**biosignatures** the unique traces left in the geological record by living organisms

the Viking orbiters revealed many ancient channel features on Mars that formed when groundwater escaped and flooded onto the surface. But could groundwater still exist there today? In 2001 planetary scientists Michael Malin and Kenneth Edgett, using a high resolution camera onboard the Mars Global Surveyor mission, detected more than 140 sites on Mars where water appears to have seeped out of the subsurface, carving small channels in the surface. Under current conditions, average crustal temperatures on Mars are well below the freezing point of freshwater almost everywhere on the surface. Such surface springs of liquid water, however, could be sustained by warm, saline brines (salt lowers the freezing point of water) derived from deep hydrothermal sources. If this hypothesis is proven, the presence of liquid water—even hot, salty water—will substantially enhance the biological potential of Mars.

On Earth, scientists have found fossil **biosignatures** in sedimentary rocks going as far back as there are sedimentary sequences to sample. By studying the processes that govern the preservation of fossil biosignatures in similar environments on Earth, scientists are continuing to refine their understanding of the factors that govern fossil preservation. This provides a basis for the strategic selection of sites on Mars to explore with future landed missions and for sample returns. Due to the lack of plate tectonic recycling and extensive aqueous weathering on Mars, rocks preserved in the heavily cratered, ancient highlands appear to extend back to the earliest history of the planet. The rocks of these old crustal regions could be much better preserved on Mars than they are on Earth. In fact, a meteorite of

---

**SEARCHING FOR LIFE ON MARS**

Although present surface conditions on Mars appear unfavorable for life, orbital images of Mars show numerous water-carved channels and possible paleolake basins where water may have once ponded. Geological relationships suggest that during the early history of the planet, liquid water was widespread over the surface. Some scientists have even suggested that during this time a large ocean existed on the northern plains of Mars. Indications are that liquid water disappeared from the surface of Mars about 3 billion years ago, perhaps as a result of gradual losses of the atmosphere by crustal weathering processes (which sequester $CO_2$ in rocks and soils) and losses to space. If surface life developed on Mars during an early Earth-like period, it quite likely left behind a fossil record. As on Earth, this record should be preserved in ancient, water-formed sedimentary rocks.

Given the complexity and scale of the problem, one cannot expect to land just anywhere on Mars and find evidence of past or present life. The astrobiology community has recommended a phased approach in which global reconnaissance is combined with preliminary surface missions to target the best sites for detailed surface investigations and sample return. The basic goal is to locate sites where there is evidence of past or present water activity and geologic environments that were favorable for the capture and preservation of fossil biosignatures.

In exploring for extant life-forms, there is an interest in finding habitable zones of liquid water in the shallow subsurface that can be accessed by drilling from robotic platforms. This may prove challenging given that models for a groundwater system on Mars suggest that if present, it should be located at a depth of several kilometers, requiring deep drilling technologies that are currently undeveloped. It may actually be simpler to discover a record of ancient life by targeting water-formed sedimentary deposits laid down by ancient hydrothermal systems or in paleolake basins. A key step in implementing this approach is to better understand the mineralogy of the Martian surface. The Thermal Emission Spectrometer instrument began mapping from Mars orbit in 1999 and in 2000 discovered coarse-grained ("specular") hematite deposits at Sinus Meridiani. Hematite is a form of iron-oxide, which in a coarse-grained form strongly suggests the past activity of water. This site has been targeted for possible landed missions in the future.

---

Martian origin (ALH 84001), which has been dated at about 4.56 billion years, shows very little evidence of aqueous weathering.

## Searching for Life in the Outer Solar System

The discovery that life can survive in deep subsurface environments on Earth, where no sunlight exists, has dramatically reshaped the ways scientists think about the potential for subsurface life on other planets. In the outer reaches of the solar system, energy from sunlight is inadequate to maintain the temperatures required for liquid water at the surface, much

## LIFE IN A MARTIAN METEORITE?

In 1996 a team of scientists proposed a very intriguing hypothesis regarding the possible biological origin of about a half-dozen features observed in a Martian meteorite, ALH 84001. In part, the hypothesis involved tiny grains of the naturally magnetic mineral magnetite, which is commonly found in basalt (a high-temperature volcanic rock that makes up oceanic crust). While most magnetite on Earth is inorganic, some bacteria have discovered ways to make minute grains of geochemically pure, low-temperature magnetite, which they organize into chains within their cells to use as a kind of directional compass. This enables cells to better control their movement in the environment and to track favorable environmental conditions. Some of the magnetites found in the Martian meteorite bear a strong resemblance to the magnetites formed by terrestrial bacteria. But is the population of magnetites in the meteorite a reliable indicator of life? Scientists are still debating this question.

**fault** a fracture in rock in the upper crust of a planet along which there has been movement

**infrared** portion of the electromagnetic spectrum with waves slightly longer than visible light

**extrasolar planets** planets orbiting stars other than the Sun

less for photosynthesis. However, where internal heat sources exist, liquid water could in principle be present in the subsurface.

Three of the larger satellites of Jupiter (Io, Europa, and Ganymede) appear to possess actively heated interiors that are maintained by gravitational tidal forces. These forces continually distort the shapes of these moons, creating internal friction that is capable of melting rock. In one of Jupiter's satellites, Io, the internal heating is manifested as widespread, active volcanic activity at the surface. On Europa, however, interior heating is manifested in a complexly fractured and largely uncratered (constantly renewed) outer shell of water ice. In many places, blocks of crust have drifted apart and liquid water or warm ice has welled up from below and frozen out in between, forming long, narrow ridges in the spaces between. Over time, some ridge segments have shifted laterally, offsetting older ridge segments along **faults**. Other more localized areas appear to have melted over broad regions and blocks of ice have foundered, tilted, and become refrozen. At an even finer scale, there are smaller, mounded features that are thought to have formed as ice "volcanoes" erupted water or warm ice erupted water from the subsurface.

While the concept of a Europan ocean is still controversial, measurements of the magnetic field of the moon obtained during the Galileo mission have strengthened the case. In order to account for the induced magnetism measured by Galileo, it is likely that a salty ocean exists beneath the water ice crust. (Similar arguments have also been made for two other large satellites of Jupiter, Ganymede and Callisto.) The idea of an ocean of brine beneath the icy crust is consistent with **infrared** spectral data from orbit, which suggest that magnesium and/or sodium sulfate salts are present in surface ices.

In assessing the potential for life on Europa, the presence of liquid water is regarded as crucial, both as a medium for biochemical processes and as a source for the chemical energy necessary to sustain life. There does not appear to be enough solar energy at the surface of Europa to support life. However, in 2001 planetary scientist Chris Chyba proposed a model that predicts that chemical energy sources for supporting life may exist from radiation processing of Europa's surface ice, in combination with the decay of radioactive potassium. Together, these processes could decompose water to hydrogen and oxygen (with the hydrogen escaping to space) and the chemical disequilibrium created potentially exploited for energy by organisms.

## Habitable Environments Beyond the Solar System

The discovery of planets orbiting other Sun-like stars in the galaxy is a key scientific discovery that has played a central role in the astrobiological revolution. The original discoveries, made in the mid-1990s, have continued. By the early twenty-first century, **extrasolar planets** have been found orbiting almost seventy solar-mass stars in the nearby region of the galaxy. Six of these discoveries are of planetary systems with two or more planets. Present discovery methods are based on the detection of a slight shift or "wobble" in the position of the star that results from the gravitational pull of an orbiting planet(s). With existing technologies, this method allows for the detection of planets that are Jupiter-sized or larger. Some of the extrasolar planets detected occupy orbits within the habitable zone where liquid water could exist. Gas giants (such as Jupiter and Saturn) are planets that lack a solid surface, but they could contain interior zones of liquid water, or might have large (undetectable) satellites with solid surfaces and liquid water. These discoveries have revealed planets around other stars to be commonplace in the Milky Way, thus widening the possibilities for life elsewhere in the cosmos. SEE ALSO EXTRASOLAR PLANETS (VOLUME 2); JUPITER (VOLUME 2); MARS (VOLUME 2); MARS MISSIONS (VOLUME 4); PLANETARY PROTECTION (VOLUME 4); SCIENTIFIC RESEARCH (VOLUME 4); SETI (VOLUME 2); TERRAFORMING (VOLUME 4).

*Jack D. Farmer*

**Bibliography**

Chang, Sherwood. "The Planetary Setting of Prebiotic Evolution." In *Early Life on Earth*, ed. S. Bengston. New York: Columbia University Press, 1994.

Chyba, C., and K. Hand. "Life without Photosynthesis." *Science* 292 (2001): 2,026–2,027.

Fredrickson, J. K., and T. C. Onstott. "Microbes Deep Inside the Earth." *Scientific American* 275, no. 4 (1996):42–47.

Klein, H. P. "The Search for Life on Mars: What We Learned from Viking." *Journal of Geophysical Research* 103 (1998):28,463–28,466.

Lemonick, Michael D. *Other Worlds: The Search for Life in the Universe*. New York: Simon & Schuster, 1998.

Pappalardo, R. T., J. W. Head, and R. Greeley. "The Hidden Ocean of Europa." *Scientific American* (October 1999):34–43.

---

**EXPLORING EUROPA**

The next Europa mission, planned for launch sometime after 2009, is expected to carry high-resolution spectrometers to map the surface and determine the mineralogical and organic composition of the surface ice. In addition, radar sounding will be used to probe the subsurface from orbit in search of zones of liquid water. This will allow a more thorough test of the hypothesis of a subsurface ocean and help identify the best sites for surface exploration. If a subsurface ocean is in fact found, the next step could be to send robotic landers to search for biosignatures preserved in the ice. Eventually we may be able to deploy small "cryobots" that would melt their way through the ice, deploying minisubmarines to explore for signs of life or organic chemistry.

---

# Biotechnology

Biotechnology research in space is predicated on understanding and exploiting the effects of the unique **microgravity** environment on chemical and biological systems. The results of these experiments could point the way not only to commercial enterprises in space but also to new research directions for laboratories on Earth. Protein crystallization and cell biology are two areas in which microgravity research is particularly promising.

## Protein Crystallization

Researchers are interested in determining the structure of proteins because the twists and folds of these complex molecules provide clues to their specific functions and how they have evolved over time. However, for scientists to study their structures, the molecules must be "held in place" through crystallization. Large, good-quality crystals are valued by structural biologists, but some organic molecules are easier to crystallize than others are. In some cases the resolution of important biological questions awaits the ability to produce adequate crystals for structural analysis.

For more than fifteen years it has been known that with other conditions being equal, protein crystals grown in a microgravity environment are

**microgravity** the condition experienced in freefall as a spacecraft orbits Earth or another body; commonly called weightlessness; only very small forces are perceived in freefall, on the order of one-millionth the force of gravity on Earth's surface

NASA-sponsored bioreactor research has been instrumental in helping scientists better understand normal and cancerous tissue development.

larger than those grown on Earth. However, the impact of this realization has been limited because of the irregular, short-term nature of space shuttle flights and the lack of a permanent laboratory with adequate vibration control.

Facilities aboard the International Space Station (ISS) may be able to address this need. Even if there is only an incremental increase in quality when crystals are produced in orbiting rather than Earth laboratories, that increase may make the difference in terms of being able to determine the structure of some proteins, providing new knowledge of biological mechanisms. An X-ray **crystallography** facility planned for the ISS would provide robotic equipment not only for growing the crystals but also for initial testing. Only the most promising specimens would be stored in the station's limited freezer space to be brought back to Earth aboard a shuttle.

**crystallography** the study of the internal structure of crystals

## Cell Biology

Cell biology is another area in which space-based research may produce valuable findings. In this case the key attribute of the microgravity environment is the ability to grow three-dimensional **cell cultures** that more closely mimic the way the cells would behave in the organism.

When cells are grown, or "cultured," for experiments on Earth, gravity encourages them to spread out in two-dimensional sheets. For most tissues this is not a particularly realistic configuration. As a result, the interactions between the cells and the biological processes within them are different from what would be seen in nature. At a molecular level this is seen as differences in gene expression, the degree to which a particular gene is "turned on" to make a protein that serves a specific function in the organism.

In a microgravity environment it is easier to get the cells to adopt the same three-dimensional form that they have during normal growth and development. This means that the gene expression pattern in the cultured cells is more like the pattern that occurs in nature. In addition, it suggests the possibility of culturing not only realistic three-dimensional tissues but entire organs that could have both research and clinical applications.

Because of the potential importance of this work, scientists have attempted to duplicate the microgravity environment on Earth. They have done this by placing tissue cultures in rotating vessels called bioreactors where the **centrifuge** effect cancels out the force of gravity.

Some success has been experienced with small cultures when the rotating vessel technique has been used. However, as the cultures grow larger, the vessel must be spun faster and faster to balance out their weight and keep them in suspension. At that point rotational effects such as shear forces damage the cells and cause their behavior to diverge from what is seen in the organism. This is a problem that could be solved if the experiments were done in space.

## Technology and Politics

However, in considering the potential for biotechnology in space, it is important to understand the technological and political context. Researchers are making rapid progress in both protein crystallization and three-dimensional tissue culture in laboratories on Earth, generally at significantly lower cost than that associated with space programs. Any perception that coveted research funds are being diverted to space-based programs without adequate justification causes resentment of such programs within the scientific community.

In addition, the difficulties of funding a large, expensive space station over the many years of planning and construction have resulted in numerous changes to the ISS's design, facilities, and staffing. Refrigerator and freezer space, for example, has been reduced, creating a potential problem for biology research. Exacerbating the problem is uncertainty in the schedule on which shuttles will be available to transport specimens. Another change of major concern to scientists contemplating participation in the program is a possible reduction in crew size, at least initially, from the planned complement of ten to a "skeleton crew" of only three.

**cell culture** a means of growing mammalian (including human) cells in the research laboratory under defined experimental conditions

**centrifuge** a device that uses centrifugal force to separate substances of different density

The reduced crew size drastically limits the ability of astronauts to assist with the research, meaning that the experiments that will be flown must require little to no local human intervention. However, the overall budget instability also has affected hardware development funds so that it is more difficult to provide the advanced automation, monitoring, and ground-based control capabilities that are needed.

There are promising applications for biotechnology in the microgravity of space. However, the extent to which these applications will be realized depends on whether they are seen to accelerate the pace of research or whether the situation is viewed as a "zero-sum game" in which resources are diverted that might be better used on Earth. Finally, it remains to be seen whether the political and economic climate will result in an orbiting platform with the staffing and facilities needed to address real research needs. SEE ALSO CRYSTAL GROWTH (VOLUME 3); INTERNATIONAL SPACE STATION (VOLUMES I AND 3); MICROGRAVITY (VOLUME 2); RESOURCE UTILIZATION (VOLUME 4); SPACE STATIONS OF THE FUTURE (VOLUME 4).

*Sherri Chasin Calvo*

**Bibliography**

National Academy of Sciences. *Future Biotechnology Research on the International Space Station.* Washington, DC: National Academies, 2001.

**Internet Resources**

"Success Stories: Biotechnology." *NASA Space Product Development.* <http://www.spd.nasa.gov/biotech.html>.

# Bonestell, Chesley

### *American Artist*
### *1888–1986*

Astronautics is unique among the sciences in that it owes so much of its existence to literature and art. On the one hand was the seminal influence of Jules Verne (1828–1905); on the other, the work of artist Chesley Bonestell, who inspired an entire generation of astronomers and space scientists and may have been instrumental in jump-starting the American space program.

Born in San Francisco on New Year's Day, 1888, Bonestell studied architecture at Columbia University in New York before dropping out to work as a designer and architectural renderer for several New York and California architectural firms. During this period, Bonestell made significant contributions to the design of American icons such as the Chrysler Building and the Golden Gate Bridge. After a stint as an illustrator in London, Bonestell returned to the United States, moving to Hollywood in the late 1930s as a special effects matte artist and working on films such as *Citizen Kane* and *The Hunchback of Notre Dame.* Combining the photorealistic techniques he learned from matte painting with his lifelong interest in astronomy, Bonestell produced a series of paintings of Saturn that were published in *Life* magazine in 1944. Nothing like them had ever been seen before, and Bonestell found himself instantly famous and in demand. More extraordinary magazine appearances eventually led to a book in collaboration with the space expert Willy Ley: the classic *The Conquest of Space* (1949). More

Photographed in his Carmel, California, studio in 1978, Chesley Bonestell specialized in images of outer space.

books followed, as well as work on a series of classic space films for the producer George Pal, such as *Destination Moon* (1950).

Bonestell's greatest influence on public awareness of space travel resulted from his work with Wernher von Braun on a series of articles for *Collier's* magazine (1952–1954). Those articles outlined a coherent, step-by-step space program from robotic satellites, to a piloted lunar landing, to an expedition to Mars. For the first time Americans became aware that spaceflight was not a matter of the far future but was literally around the corner, that it was much less a matter of technology than one of money and will. This came at the most fortuitous time possible: the very beginning of the "space race," when it was imperative to rally public support for what had previously been dismissed as "that Buck Rogers stuff."

Several more books on the future of space exploration followed, extending Bonestell's artistry into hundreds of magazines and other publications. When most people in the 1950s and early 1960s visualized space travel, it was in terms of Bonestell's imagery. His paintings influenced many careers. Carl Sagan once said, "I didn't know what other worlds looked like until I saw Bonestell's paintings of the solar system." Arthur C. Clarke wrote that "Chesley Bonestell's paintings had a colossal impact on my thinking about space travel." In addition to the scientists, astronauts, and astronomers Bonestell inspired, he helped create the genre of illustration called space art. SEE ALSO ARTWORK (VOLUME 1); RAWLINGS, PAT (VOLUME 4); VERNE, JULES (VOLUME 1); VON BRAUN, WERNHER (VOLUME 3).

*Ron Miller*

**Bibliography**

Hardy, David. *Visions of Space.* London: Paper Tiger, 1990.

Miller, Ron, and Frederick C. Durant III. *The Art of Chesley Bonestell.* London: Paper Tiger, 2001.

Ordway, Frederick I., III, and Randy Liebermann. *Blueprint for Space.* Washington, DC: Smithsonian Institution Press, 1992.

# Careers in Space

Humankind is taking its first tentative steps toward a permanent presence in space after retreating from that goal in the late twentieth century, when the American lunar program ended. The goal then consisted only of a piloted round trip to the Moon, a mission prompted by rivalry between the global superpowers of the United States and the Soviet Union. In the future the mission will be the inhabitation of space and other worlds, a mission prompted by a variety of goals.

Since the start of the "space race" in the late 1950s, when the Soviet Union launched the first satellite, Sputnik, and the United States took up the challenge to go to the Moon in the 1960s, each generation has found inspiration that has urged it on towards space and motivated it to join the effort. At each step, a new generation of thinkers and pioneers has come forward to meet the challenge.

The initial inspiration was the beeping signal broadcast from Sputnik. Then came U.S. President John F. Kennedy's challenge to visit Earth's nearest neighbor: "I believe this nation should commit itself to achieving the goal, before this decade is out, of landing a man on the Moon and returning him safely to Earth." It was a momentous achievement when, in 1969, astronaut Neil Armstrong stepped onto the Moon and said: "One small step for man, one giant leap for mankind." However, the piloted effort that culminated with the Apollo Moon landings seemed to flounder and retreat into science fiction, which was where people turned next for inspiration.

That inspiration came from *Star Trek* ("Space: the final frontier.") and *Star Wars* ("In a galaxy, far, far away. . ."), and soon a space industry sprang up. This industry is based primarily on missiles and satellites for military

Mission specialist Linda M. Godwin works during a 4-hour, 12-minute session of extravehicular activity.

and communications purposes. But the desire to return people to space lived on, in part through the development of the shuttle program and through the former Soviet Union, which operated the **space station** Mir. Mir was allowed to fall back to Earth to make way for the International Space Station. The international collaboration involved in the space station reflects the high costs of the effort. This collaboration extends to unpiloted missions. Recent **payloads** to Mars on American, Soviet, Japanese, and European missions have also been international.

To secure an off-world presence, skilled individuals from a variety of professions will be needed to meet the challenges that arise. The next and future generations will require all of the skills that got humanity into Earth orbit and onto the Moon. People from many different professions, some clearly space-related and others less obviously associated, will be needed. Professions that helped humanity reach the Moon include astronautics, rocketry, space medicine, and space science.

Foremost are the dreamers who fire each generation's imagination, including visionary scientists and science fiction writers. They meld what is and what has been with what could be. Using new scientific knowledge, they imagine concepts such as human settlements on planets in this solar system and distant solar systems, propulsion systems capable of near-lightspeed, and years-long missions with crews that are hibernating or even embryonic, to

**space station** large orbital outpost equipped to support a human crew and designed to remain in orbit for an extended period

**payloads** any cargo launched aboard a rocket that is destined for space, including communications satellites or modules, supplies, equipment, and astronauts; does not include the vehicle used to move the cargo or the propellant that powers the vehicle

be raised and educated at the destination in order to minimize the consumption of supplies during the long trip.

Scientific research conducted in space will add fuel to these fires of the imagination, and will provide work for astronomers and planetary scientists. The work of these scientists could lead to discoveries that provide further incentive for a human presence in space. Much of this research will use astronomical observations from new generations of telescopes that look not only at visible light but also at nonvisible portions of the **electromagnetic spectrum** such as **infrared** rays, **ultraviolet** rays, and **X rays**. These space- and Moon-based astronomical observatories will be the successors to the Hubble Space Telescope, which has been used to discover planets in distant solar systems. Free of the fog of Earth's atmosphere, the new observatories will be able to peer farther into deep space and allow chemical analysis of the atmospheres of planets in distant solar systems, an important step toward finding remote worlds capable of sustaining life.

The prophecies of dreamers make their way into people's awareness through the mass media. Journalists, authors, screenwriters, and filmmakers fall into this category, as do those who work in public relations. Although these are broad fields, they include areas of specialty that are space-related. In addition to this role as messengers of new space developments, the media play a vital role in educating the public about ongoing efforts and gathering support for them.

Following close behind the dreamers are the practitioners, the technical and nontechnical workers who turn the dreams into realities. Overseeing the efforts are program managers. These are practical thinkers who strive to make sensible and affordable compromises and alterations to the dreams. Most of these people work in government and defense jobs because the human presence in space is largely the legacy of competition between the United States and the Soviet Union, and remains a risky and extremely expensive enterprise.

## Professions Needed for the Future

Because we want to establish a long-term future in space rather than continue to make short excursions, the projects that will anchor humankind in space will be more ambitious and costly than any single nation can afford. They will therefore need to span national boundaries and rely on international cooperation and participation by commercial enterprises to provide the necessary funding and talent. Like the extensive dam systems and interstate highway networks in the United States that have been funded by the government, these international space efforts will probably be large **infrastructure** projects, such as launch centers, space stations, and new generations of astronomical observatories.

Although early efforts likely will continue to rely on governments and defense departments, in the long run a significant part of this enterprise will probably need to be handled by entrepreneurs who can make the space venture pay its own way and keep it self-sustaining. Such projects will probably depend heavily on the infrastructure built by the international coalition. The mass media will also play a significant role by evaluating the public projects in each country and advertising the products of the private businesses. The teams that will build these projects and populate these companies

**electromagnetic spectrum** the entire range of wavelengths of electromagnetic radiation

**infrared** portion of the electromagnetic spectrum with waves slightly longer than visible light

**ultraviolet** the portion of the electromagnetic spectrum just beyond (having shorter wavelengths than) violet

**X rays** high-energy radiation just beyond the ultraviolet portion of the electromagnetic spectrum

**infrastructure** the physical structures, such as roads and bridges, necessary to the functioning of a complex system

will include engineers, scientists, medical experts, accountants, lawyers, and astronauts.

Current suggestions for space-based industries include mining the Moon, asteroids, and comets for metal ores, water, and isotopes that are rare on Earth and producing materials at sites where the manufacturing process can benefit from the low-gravity characteristics of space. Each type of industry will call for professionals such as geologists (sometimes referred to as planetary scientists in this setting) and engineers specializing in mining, drilling, and chemistry.

Other engineers will design safe space and planetary habitats for the astronauts who will blaze the trail for tourists and businesspeople. Rocketry engineers will design launchers and spacecraft aimed at making space travel inexpensive and routine. There will be an ongoing need for astronauts to pilot existing spacecraft and test new vehicles.

Scientists will continue to research space and near-Earth settings and apply the knowledge gained from those efforts toward making space safer for habitation. Medical experts will determine how to keep bodies and minds healthy during long trips and in the gravitational conditions of space and other worlds. Nutrition scientists will work on making food in space and planetary habitations to avoid having to transport these resources. This will be an important step toward making off-world activities self-sustaining.

Exobiologists—experts on life that could exist beyond Earth—will be needed as people visit planets and moons in the solar system that are capable of supporting some sort of life. The discovery of life in the solar system would be one of the most important events in human history, and this prospect alone is an important incentive to increase the human presence in space.

Business and accounting professions will play a significant role in this effort. These professions include marketing and sales, contract administration, law and licensing, accounting, proposal coordination, and human resources. These professions assure the smooth operation of any endeavor that relies on money and business transactions and will be no less important in space-based efforts. As humankind moves farther from Earth, communications innovators and communications expertise will be at a premium.

There is a lot of work to be done to secure humanity's place in space and on other worlds, and it calls for many types of people. Like the efforts to explore and settle unknown lands, humanity will send out adventurous pioneers and follow them with more ordinary individuals who want to live and work there. SEE ALSO CAREER ASTRONAUTS (VOLUME 1); CAREERS IN ASTRONOMY (VOLUME 2); CAREERS IN BUSINESS AND PROGRAM MANAGEMENT (VOLUME 1); CAREERS IN ROCKETRY (VOLUME 1); CAREERS IN SPACE LAW (VOLUME 1); CAREERS IN SPACE MEDICINE (VOLUME 1); CAREERS IN SPACE SCIENCE (VOLUME 2); CAREERS IN WRITING, PHOTOGRAPHY, AND FILMMAKING (VOLUME 1).

*Richard G. Adair*

**Bibliography**

Goldsmith, Donald. *Voyage to the Milky Way: The Future of Space Exploration.* New York: TV Books, 1999.

Hickam, Homer H. *Rocket Boys: A Memoir*. New York: Delacorte Press, 1998.

Kraft, Chris, with James L. Schefter. *Flight: My Life in Mission Control*. New York: Dutton, 2001.

Mallove, Eugene, and Gregory Matloff. *The Starflight Handbook: A Pioneer's Guide to Interstellar Travel*. New York: John Wiley & Sons, 1989.

Sacknoff, Scott, and Leonard David. *The Space Publications Guide to Space Careers*. Bethesda, MD: Space Publications, 1998.

Stine, G. Harry. *Living in Space*. New York: M. Evans and Company, 1997.

Yanuck, Deborah, and Gary Golter. *Opportunities in High Tech Careers*. Chicago: VGM Career Horizons, 1995.

Zubrin, Robert. *Entering Space: Creating a Spacefaring Civilization*. New York: Jeremy P. Tarcher/Putnam, 1999.

Zubrin, Robert, with Richard Wagner. *The Case for Mars: The Plan to Settle the Red Planet and Why We Must*. New York: Free Press, 1996.

# Chang-Díaz, Franklin

### *American Astronaut*
### 1950–

Franklin Chang-Díaz was instrumental in the formation of the Astronaut Science Colloquium Program and the Astronaut Science Support Group.

Born in San José, Costa Rica, on April 5, 1950, Franklin R. Chang-Díaz immigrated to the United States at the age of eighteen with the goal of someday becoming an astronaut. After learning English as a senior high school student in Hartford, Connecticut, he earned a bachelor of science degree in mechanical engineering from the University of Connecticut in 1973, and a doctoral degree in applied plasma physics from the Massachusetts Institute of Technology in 1977. Chang-Díaz then became an astronaut for the National Aeronautics and Space Administration (NASA) in 1981, and flew on six space shuttle missions.

Chang-Díaz's missions have included the launch of the Galileo spacecraft to Jupiter in 1989 and the final shuttle visit to the Russian Mir space station in 1998. The recipient of numerous medals and awards, Chang-Díaz directs the NASA Advanced Space Propulsion Laboratory at the Johnson Space Center in Houston, Texas. His research team (which includes graduate students at several universities) is developing the Variable Specific Impulse Magnetoplasma Rocket (VASIMR). VASIMR is expected to greatly increase the speed with which humans can travel in space. In addition to his research, Chang-Díaz is organizing more direct involvement in space activities by the countries of Latin America. SEE ALSO ASTRONAUTS, TYPES OF (VOLUME 3); ION PROPULSION (VOLUME 4); JUPITER (VOLUME 2).

*Michael S. Kelley*

### Internet Resources

"Career Astronaut Biographies." 2001. *NASA: Johnson Space Center*. <http://www.jsc.nasa.gov/Bios/astrobio.html>.

**volatile** ices (e.g. $H_2O$ and $CO_2$) that are solids inside a comet nucleus but turn into gases when heated by sunlight

**near-Earth asteroids** asteroids whose orbits cross the orbit of Earth

# Comet Capture

Comets are the most **volatile**-rich minor bodies in the solar system. It has been suggested that impacts with comets and asteroids provided Earth with much of its water. Although most comets are less accessible than **near-Earth**

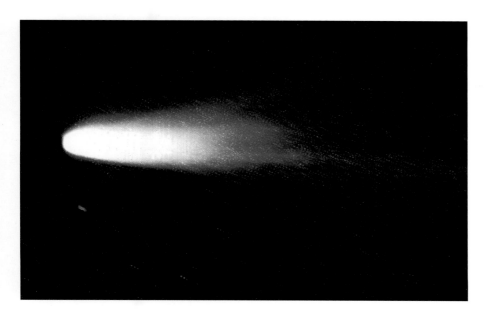

**trajectories** paths followed through space by missiles and spacecraft moving under the influence of gravity

✳ A "sizable" comet in this context means greater than about 100 meters, depending on the density of the material.

**asteroids**, their high water content makes them an economically attractive resource for space mining. The possibility that some near-Earth asteroids are extinct or dormant cometary nuclei means that this water-rich resource may be more accessible than was once thought.

Recent spacecraft- and ground-based studies of comets have confirmed and refined Whipple's "dirty snowball" model for cometary nuclei. Cometary material is composed principally of water ice and other ices (including $CO$, $CO_2$, $CH_4$, $C_2H_6$, and $CH_3OH$) mixed with cosmic dust grains. The passages of most Oort cloud comets through the inner solar system are not predictable. In addition, the highly elongated and inclined **trajectories** of these comets make them difficult targets with which to match orbits. In contrast, Jupiter-family comets tend to have predictable, well-determined orbits with short periods and low inclinations. Therefore, a future mining mission would most likely target a Jupiter-family comet.

The capture of an active comet as a source of water and other volatile elements is a difficult proposition. In the vicinity of Earth the jet-like gas that flows from a comet's nucleus would have a stronger influence on its trajectory than any force humans could apply to the comet. This behavior would make transporting an active comet into a suitable near-Earth orbit, and maintaining it there, very unlikely. The Earth-impact hazard posed by a sizable comet ✳ or comet fragment in an unstable near-Earth orbit would be unacceptable. For example, even if the trajectory of a cometary fragment could be manipulated to produce capture into a high-Earth orbit, bringing the material down to low-Earth orbit (e.g., to the space station) would be difficult. The Moon's gravitational pull would make the trajectory extremely difficult to predict and control.

Capture into a lunar orbit would also be problematical. Lunar orbits tend to be unstable because of gravitational influences from Earth and the Sun. Another difficulty that must be resolved is the current uncertainty about the consistency of cometary nuclei. Not only is the bulk density of cometary nuclei unknown (estimates range from 0.3 $g/cm^3$ to greater than 1 $g/cm^3$;

## WHERE DO COMETS COME FROM?

Comets are thought to have formed in the outer solar system. Two sources have been identified for the comets that are seen today: the Oort cloud and the Edgeworth-Kuiper belt (also known simply as the Kuiper belt). The Oort cloud is a roughly spherical shell located about a third of the distance to the nearest star. The Kuiper belt is a disk-like distribution of icy bodies extending beyond Pluto's orbit. Most bright new comets, such as Comet Hale-Bopp, come from the Oort cloud and have orbits that are highly inclined with respect to Earth's orbit. Most short-period or Jupiter-family comets have low inclination orbits (i.e., their orbits lie nearly in the same plane as Earth's orbit) and are believed to originate in the Kuiper belt.

liquid water has a density of 1 g/cm³), we do not know the cohesiveness of this material. Such uncertainties make it impossible to predict the mechanical properties of cometary material and the way a comet nucleus would react to a "nudge" to change its trajectory. A comet nucleus may or may not behave as a rigid object does; it might instead break up into fragments when a force is applied to change its orbit.

A more attractive approach to harvesting cometary material would be to send a robotic spacecraft to mine the comet. Returning fine-grained material and/or liquid water to Earth orbit would greatly lower the risks. A cargo spacecraft would be easier to control than a comet fragment, and even if an uncontrolled atmospheric entry occurred, the water and/or fine-grained material would vaporize or rain down harmlessly onto Earth's surface. SEE ALSO ASTEROID MINING (VOLUME 4); COMETS (VOLUME 2); KUIPER BELT (VOLUME 2); LIVING ON OTHER WORLDS (VOLUME 4); OORT CLOUD (VOLUME 2); NATURAL RESOURCES (VOLUME 4); RESOURCE UTILIZATION (VOLUME 4); TERRAFORMING (VOLUME 4).

*Humberto Campins*

**Bibliography**

Whipple, Fred Lawrence. "A Comet Model. I: The Acceleration of Comet Encke." *Astrophysical Journal* 111 (1950):375–394.

# Communications, Future Needs in

Space programs, whether unpiloted space probes or human spaceflight missions, must be able to send large amounts of data to and from space. In the past, data might consist of navigational and spacecraft control information, radio conversations, and data collected by onboard experiments. But with today's permanent human presence in space, and for most future missions, the amount of data is much larger. For example, video transmissions are now common, and many spacecraft that conduct experiments are collecting richer sets of data over longer periods, owing in part to greater onboard data storage capacity. Hence, the major challenges in space communications of the future are handling the larger quantities of transmitted data and extending the Internet into space.

## New Generation Satellites

The need to support more data transmissions has spawned the development of a new generation of space communications satellites. The mainstay of space communications since the early 1980s has been the Tracking and Data Relay Satellite System (TDRSS). TDRSS consists of an array of five operational satellites parked in **geosynchronous orbit** over the Earth's equator. Rather than direct communications between a spacecraft and the ground, spacecraft communicate with TDRSS satellites, which in turn communicate with ground stations. As the name implies, these satellites act as a relay point for any communication between the ground and a spacecraft.

Besides forming the main communications link between the space shuttle and National Aeronautics and Space Administration (NASA) ground stations, TDRSS is used by many other NASA and government spacecraft.

**geosynchronous orbit** a specific altitude of an equatorial orbit where the time required to circle the planet matches the time it takes the planet to rotate on its axis. An object in geostationary orbit will always remain over the same geographic location on the equator of the planet it orbits

The Tidbinbilla Deep Space Communication Centre in Australia is one of three communication centers in the world that provide contact with deep space probes and orbiting spacecraft.

These include the Hubble Space Telescope, the Upper Atmosphere Research Satellite, the Earth Resources Budget Satellite, Landsat, the Ocean Topography Experiment, the Earth Observing System, and the International Space Station.

Recognizing it will need more capacity in the near future, NASA has recently embarked on a TDRSS modernization program. In June 2000, NASA launched TDRS-H, the first of its new generation of communications relay satellites. By the end of 2002 it planned to have two more in place: the TDRS-I and TDRS-J. The new satellites will offer the same S-band and Ku-band communications of the original TDRSS satellites. However, the newer generation satellites will also support higher bandwidth links that are necessary for transmitting data such as high-quality video and high-resolution images.

The new generation satellites, like the older satellites, will support S-band communications, which operate at **frequencies** of between 2.0 and 2.3 GHz (gigahertz). Within the S-band communications there exists single access in which there is one back-and-forth link between the ground and spacecraft via the TDRSS satellite. This S-band single access communication channel can support data transmission rates of 300 Kbps (kilobits per second) in the forward direction (from the ground to the spacecraft via the TDRSS satellite) and up to 6 Mbps (Megabits per second) in the opposite direction. Typically, the forward transmission consists of command and control data being sent to the spacecraft, and the return transmission can include data and images.

**frequency** the number of oscillations or vibrations per second of an electromagnetic wave or any wave

TDRSS also supports another S-band mode of operation called multiple access, in which the TDRSS satellite receives data from more than one spacecraft source simultaneously and sends these data to an Earth station. In this multiple access mode of operation, a forward data rate of 10 Kbps and five return data streams of up to 100 Kbps can be supported.

For higher speed transmissions, TDRSS supports Ku-band communications, which transmits at frequencies between 13.7 and 15.0 GHz. The

The Tracking and Data Relay satellite system is a sophisticated network that has granted NASA increased communication abilities between Earth and its low-orbit spacecraft.

Ku-band communications supports forward data rates of 25 Mbps and return rates of up to 300 Mbps. To put this into perspective, this is about 50 times faster than a 56 Kbps dial-up modem, which is commonly used to connect to the Internet.

The new satellites will also support even higher transmission rates such as Ka-band transmissions, which operate at frequencies of between 22.5 and 27.5 GHz. The Ka-band systems will allow forward data transmission rates of 25 Mbps and return rates of up to 800 Mbps. The three new satellites will be phased in as replacements for the originals, some of which have been in space for over ten years.

## Extending the Internet

The new generation TDRSS will handle the larger amounts of data being sent between spacecraft and researchers on Earth. Another effort will try to extend the Internet into space. The Interplanetary Internet Project (IPN), launched in 1998, began to explore the technical challenges to pushing the boundaries of the Internet into outer space. At one end of the spectrum are straightforward matters, such as the top-level domain (TLD) name extensions to be approved for use in space. On Earth, we use country TLD designations such as .uk or .ca (for the United Kingdom and Canada, respectively). In space, the naming structure might be similar including TLD designations for each planet or spacecraft. Other issues that are being investigated are how to handle the basic transmission of data. Existing Internet technology will not work in space applications, largely because of the great distances data must travel. Specifically, many of the underlying communication protocols used to carry Internet traffic, to surf the web, and to access information will not work efficiently over the vast reaches of space.

The downfall of using existing communications technology for an interplanetary Internet is the delay encountered when packets must traverse interplanetary distances. For that reason, the IPN is looking into new protocols and technologies to carry Internet traffic in space. For instance, proposed Interplanetary Gateways could serve regions of space. Combined with perhaps new Internet communications protocols, this potential technology could avoid the problems created by the long distances and transmission times in space. For example, if a person on Earth were communicating with someone on Mars, rather than sending individual communications packets and acknowledgements back and forth between the two, an Earth-based gateway would send the acknowledgement and then pass the packet between Earth and Mars to a similar Martian gateway.

Once such technologies are developed, the next thing needed would be an interplanetary Internet backbone to carry the traffic. NASA is already studying an idea for a Mars network of multiple orbiting satellites. These satellites would be launched over several years, possibly starting in 2005. This system would create high-speed connections between Mars and Earth that could be used as the basis of an interplanetary Internet backbone. SEE ALSO COMMUNICATIONS FOR HUMAN SPACEFLIGHT (VOLUME 3); GUIDANCE AND CONTROL SYSTEMS (VOLUME 3); INTERPLANETARY INTERNET (VOLUME 4); SATELLITES, FUTURE DESIGNS (VOLUME 4).

*Salvatore Salamone*

**Bibliography**

Elbert, Bruce, *Introduction to Satellite Communication*. Boston: Artech House, 1999.

Gedney, Richard T., Ronald Schertler, and Frank Gargione. *The Advanced Communications Technology Satellite: An Insider's Account of the Emergence of Interactive Broadband Services in Space*. Mendham, NJ: SciTech Publishing, 2000.

Heck, André, ed. *Information Handling in Astronomy*. Boston: Kluwer Academic Publishers, 2000.

Kadish, Jules E., and Thomas W. R. East. *Satellite Communications Fundamentals*. Boston: Artech House, 2000.

# Communities in Space

In 1929 Hermann Noording developed the idea of a large wheel-shaped satellite reminiscent of the **space station** in the movie *2001: A Space Odyssey* (1968). In the 1950s Wernher von Braun developed a similar plan for a refueling stop on the way to the Moon. But it was Princeton physicist Gerard K. O'Neill who saw huge orbiting communities as a means of salvation for Earth. Overcoming initial skepticism, he gained support from the National Aeronautics and Space Administration (NASA), organized a series of breakthrough workshops, and set forth detailed plans in his 1976 book *The High Frontier*. Although everyone at that time talked in terms of "space colonies," "colonies," and "colonists," these words evoke images of harsh and repressive governments. For this reason, the terms "settlements" and "settlers" are preferred instead.

**space station** large orbital outpost equipped to support a human crew and designed to remain in orbit for an extended period

## Solving Earth's Problems in Outer Space

Like most proponents of large-scale emigration to space, O'Neill believed that the world, with its rapidly growing population, was entering an era of decline. He noted the heavy consumption of fossil fuels and other resources as well as growing concern about environmental pollution and global warming. By establishing humans in space it will be possible to reduce population pressures on Earth and draw upon the immense natural resources that are available on the high frontier.

O'Neill did not see the Moon or Mars as good destinations for wholesale emigration from Earth. The Moon is small, and it is expensive and time-consuming to get to Mars. Sunlight, the source of power and life, would not be readily available during the two-week lunar night and it would be difficult to collect on Mars. Instead, he recommended human-made communities conveniently located between Earth and the Moon where people could build as many huge settlements as was needed, 500 if necessary.

## Islands in the Sky

O'Neill set forth detailed, phased plans for developing a series of successively larger space settlements. The first construction crews would work out of an orbiting construction shack and at a base on the Moon where they would strip-mine building materials. A device known as a mass driver, which uses electromagnetic propulsion, would accelerate lunar material along a long track. This material, sliced into shapes reminiscent of large, thick plates, would break free of the Moon's weak gravity, and fly through space to be caught at the construction site. There the material could be used like bricks or transformed into other useful materials.

O'Neill envisioned three "islands," ranging from a sphere about 1.6 kilometers (1 mile) in circumference to a cylinder 6.4 kilometers (4 miles) in diameter and 32 kilometers (20 miles) long. These islands would house between 10,000 and tens of millions of people. A shield would protect each community from **meteors** and space debris. Windows and mirrors would fill their interiors with sunlight, and a slow spin would produce artificial gravity. These settlements would be safe from disasters, such as earthquakes and inclement weather, including storms, monsoons, droughts, heat waves, and cold snaps. Insects and other vermin would be left behind on Earth. Clean technologies could prevent pollution and minimize problems associated with environmental health. Settlers would grow their own food (primarily grains and vegetables) and earn money by collecting solar power that would be beamed to Earth.

O'Neill's contribution to the development of space stations involved more than an exploration of the physics and engineering involved: He moved space colony design into the realm of the possible. He attracted support from scientists in many fields and from members of the public who had never before given space settlement serious thought. This interest was sustained in later NASA Ames projects that led to many different designs, which included settlements shaped like doughnuts and paddlewheels. O'Neill's influence is evident in one of the most detailed, bold, and imaginative plans for establishing humans as citizens of the universe. This plan is set forth in Marshall Savage's 1994 book *The Millennial Project: Colonizing the Galaxy in Eight Easy Steps.*

## Making Space Settlements User-Friendly

Early settlers will be a hardy lot. Traditionally, military personnel have been the first to enter new, unusual, and potentially dangerous environments. In recent times, scientists and entrepreneurs have come next. One might expect strong, restless, highly motivated people to follow—the kinds of people who stowed away on ships from Europe and Asia to build new lives in America. In the long run, to establish a permanent human presence in space, settlements will have to be accessible to everyone. Ultimately, they must be inviting communities, not just rough work camps.

Thus, designers avoid the cold, sterile, mechanical look. Some designs incorporate varied architecture, distant horizons, and the use of colors and light to open up areas. They make allowance for ornamental vegetation, including trees, shrubs, and hanging plants. To create a friendly look, buildings may be set off at angles rather than aligned with military precision. Clustering buildings, orienting entrances and exits in different ways, and developing common areas such as neighborhood parks will make it easy for residents to meet, mingle, and develop a sense of community.

The visionaries who foresee space settlements include not just scientists and engineers but social architects as well. Their goal is to establish minimal, low-profile governments that intervene as little as possible. Democracy is the preferred form of government, and "bureaucracy" is considered a bad word. And, as one might suspect, few space settlement enthusiasts propose paying taxes to authorities on Earth.

**meteors** physical manifestations of a meteoroid interacting with Earth's atmosphere

## A Cloudy Crystal Ball

In their 1986 book *Pioneering Space*, James and Alcestis Oberg include a NASA artist's rendition of a huge American space station along with a photograph of a real Russian Salyut station. The flowing lines, spaciousness, and aesthetic appeal of the artist's rendition stand in stark contract to the functional, cluttered look of the real thing. Some day it may be possible to construct large, attractive settlements in space. However, people are notorious for tampering with other people's ideas. Between today's planning efforts and tomorrow's space settlements both technology and people will change. There may be many slips between today's visions and tomorrow's realities. SEE ALSO EARTH—WHY LEAVE? (VOLUME 4); GOVERNANCE (VOLUME 4); HOTELS (VOLUME 4); LIVING ON OTHER WORLDS (VOLUME 4); O'NEILL COLONIES (VOLUME 4); O'NEILL, GERARD P. (VOLUME 4); SETTLEMENTS (VOLUME 4).

*Albert A. Harrison*

### Bibliography

Harrison, Albert A. *Spacefaring: The Human Dimension.* Berkeley: University of California Press, 2001.

Oberg, James E., and Alcestis Oberg. *Pioneering Space: Living on the Next Frontier.* New York: McGraw-Hill, 1986.

O'Neill, Gerard K. *The High Frontier: Human Colonies in Space.* New York: Morrow, 1976; Bantam Books, 1978; Collectors Guide Publishing, 2000.

Savage, Marshall. *The Millennial Project: Colonizing the Galaxy in Eight Easy Steps.* Boston: Little, Brown, 1994.

Schmidt, Stanley, and Robert Zubrin, eds. *Islands in the Sky: Bold New Ideas for Colonizing Space.* New York: John Wiley & Sons, 1996.

Zubrin, Robert. *Entering Space: Creating a Spacefaring Civilization.* New York: J. P. Tarcher, 2000.

# Cycling Spacecraft

The furthering of humankind's expansion into space and establishing of firm footholds on other worlds could depend on a continuously moving, cycling spaceship network. These rapid-transit cycling spaceships would employ the principles of **gravity assist**, which entails taking a slingshot approach to running people and cargo from one locale to another. The motions of the planets and gravity would be used as a natural fuel.

**gravity assist** using the gravity of a planet during a close encounter to add energy to the motion of a spacecraft

It may be possible to establish a "recyclable space program"—a vision that is a far cry from the early days of space exploration. As an example, the Apollo Moon landing effort of the 1960s and 1970s involved tossaway technology. All of the stages of the giant Saturn V booster—except for the return capsule that brought the astronauts back to Earth—were thrown away. Even today, the idea of a fully or partially disposable space program is being perpetuated.

Opening up the space frontier, however, requires transcending reusability and recycling barriers to shape a space agenda for the twenty-first century. Putting into place a fully cycling strategy for travel in the inner solar system travel is likely to happen in phases. The first human missions to Mars will install the early segments of the network.

A champion of the cycling spaceship idea is the Apollo 11 astronaut Buzz Aldrin. Aldrin's vision is to have large cycling spaceships swinging permanently between the orbits of Earth and Mars. A cycling spacecraft in an **elliptical** orbit would transit from Earth to Mars and back again, permanently cycling between the orbits of the two planets. This approach could be used to put in place an interplanetary passenger transport system.

In an Earth-Mars scenario, transfer vehicles ferry passengers from Spaceport Earth to a cycler. At the other end of a Mars cycling trajectory is Spaceport Mars. Cyclers take advantage of the way the Earth, traveling faster on an inside orbit around the Sun, catches up to Mars about every two Earth years. Like a ship using the trade winds, a cycling spacecraft will not follow a linear route to Mars. When the planets are aligned, it will accelerate away from Earth and loop outward, swinging close to Mars five months later.

But instead of stopping, the cycler releases smaller ships that ferry people and supplies to the surface. The cycler acquires some of the planet's momentum using gravity assist and glides on, curving away and eventually back to Earth. It returns home twenty-one months after departure, but it does not stop at that point: With another boost from Earth's gravity it sails onward, and back to Mars. The vehicle becomes a permanent, human-made companion of Earth and Mars, using the free and inexhaustible fuel supply of gravity to maintain its orbit.

The cycler system would eliminate the need to accelerate and decelerate and would also discard the necessity of large and costly spacecraft hardware. Like an ocean liner on a regular route, a cycler would zip perpetually along a predictable orbit. Twin cyclers, one always en route to Mars and the other always in transit back to Earth, would greatly reduce the cost of exploring and, eventually settling, the fourth planet from the Sun: Mars. The pursuit of an economical philosophy may lead to sustainable and recyclable space transportation. Doing so would set in motion expressway traffic carrying humanity into the next great age of exploration, expansion, settlement, and multi-planetary commerce. SEE ALSO ACCESSING SPACE (VOLUME 1); ALDRIN, BUZZ (VOLUME 1); LAUNCH VEHICLES, EXPENDABLE (VOLUME 1); ORBITS (VOLUME 2); VEHICLES (VOLUME 4).

*Leonard David*

**Bibliography**

Aldrin, Buzz, and Malcolm McConnell. *Men from Earth.* New York: Bantam Books, 1991.

United States, National Commission on Space. *Pioneering the Space Frontier: The Report of the National Commission on Space.* New York: Bantam Books, 1986.

# Domed Cities

In the Arizona desert, there is a complex of interconnected domes and glass pyramids known as the Biosphere 2 Center. This structure was originally conceived and built as a sealed environment for the purpose of determining whether a closed ecological system could be maintained and could sustain human beings for long time periods. Eight people lived in the complex for two years, from 1991 to 1992. This was followed by a shorter experiment in 1993 and 1994. However, results from these experiments were not conclusive, partly due to excessive air transfer between the outside environment and the sealed habitat.

The Biosphere ✶ was a practical realization of an idea that has intrigued writers and scientists for hundreds of years—a domed city that would be completely self-sustaining. Science fiction writers have found domed cities to be a fertile ground for imaginative fiction of all types. However, domed cities or variations of domed cities are also seen by some scientists as suitable habitats for humans living on the Moon, on Mars, or in other inhospitable environments.

✶ **An image of this enclosed system may be seen in the Volume 3 article "Biosphere."**

## Science Fiction

Early science fiction stories often emphasized the use of domed cities as space colonies. Various writers placed domed cities on the Moon, Mars, and Venus. Other writers used domed or enclosed cities as metaphors exposing the ills of their own societies. In the short story "The Machine Stops" by E. M. Forster, humans live in a vast complex of rooms inside an enormous subterranean machine that provides everything they need, including vicarious experiences. These people never leave their chambers. However, the machine eventually breaks down, causing the inevitable death of the inhabitants. More recent writers began to see domed cities here on Earth as a retreat—Arthur C. Clarke's *The City and the Stars* (1956) portrayed the domed city as a modern version of Eden.

## Moon and Mars Colonies

The surface of the Moon is uninhabitable. There is no air. However, there may be water locked in permafrost in some deep polar craters. Moreover, there are plenty of raw materials contained in the lunar rocks, including aluminum for structural materials and silicon dioxide for glass. This fact has led to proposals for the construction of permanent colonies on the Moon. Some designs have been suggested for glass-enclosed domed cities although the majority of proposals for lunar habitats feature extended underground bunkers to provide necessary **shielding** from **solar radiation**.

The Moon's surface is an ideal location for many different types of human endeavor. For instance, the Moon's low gravity might provide a suitable environment for hospitals that treat burn patients or patients with limited or painful mobility in Earth's gravity. Moreover, the farside of the Moon is shielded from all artificial radiation originating from Earth, so it would provide an ideal location for radio and optical astronomy.

There are several groups that argue Mars should be colonized. The atmosphere on Mars is so thin that a person walking on the surface of the Red Planet would need to wear a space suit similar to the ones worn by astronauts on the Moon. However, Mars, like the Moon, has ample resources to provide the raw materials for construction of artificial domes. SEE ALSO BIOSPHERE (VOLUME 3); CLOSED ECOSYSTEMS (VOLUME 3); DYSON, FREEMAN JOHN (VOLUME 4); DYSON SPHERES (VOLUME 4); LIVING ON OTHER WORLDS (VOLUME 4); LUNAR BASES (VOLUME 4); MARS BASES (VOLUME 4); O'NEILL COLONIES (VOLUME 4); O'NEILL, GERARD K. (VOLUME 4).

*Elliot Richmond*

**shielding** providing protection for humans and electronic equipment from cosmic rays, energetic particles from the Sun, and other radioactive materials

**solar radiation** total energy of any wavelength and all charged particles emitted by the Sun

## Bibliography

Bacon, Edmund N. *Design of Cities.* New York: Penguin Books, 1974.

Johnson, Richard D. and Charles Holbrow. *Space Settlements—A Design Study.* Washington, DC: Scientific and Technical Information Office, National Aeronautics and Space Administration, 1977.

McCurdy, Howard. *Space and the American Imagination.* Washington DC: The Smithsonian Institution Press, 1997.

O'Neill, Gerard K. *The High Frontier: Human Colonies in Space.* Princeton, N.J.: Space Studies Institute Press, 1989.

### Internet Resources

Planet Mars Home Page. <http://www.marshome.com/>.

Red Colony. <http://www.redcolony.com/>.

# Dyson, Freeman John

### British Space Futurist
### 1923–

Freeman Dyson has written extensively on space, physics, weapons control, and philosophy.

Freeman John Dyson is a space futurist who has envisioned the creation of various human habitats in space. Born December 15, 1923, in Crowthorne, England, he received his bachelor of arts degree from Cambridge University in 1945. From 1943 to 1945, during World War II, he served in Operations Research with the Royal Air Force Bomber Command.

A fellow at Trinity College at Cambridge University in England and a commonwealth fellow at Cornell University, Dyson taught at Princeton University from 1947 to 1949. He was a physics professor at Cornell from 1951 to 1953 and also served as a professor at the Institute for Advanced Study at Princeton University. Since 1994 he has served as professor emeritus at Princeton. Dyson has received many honors and honorary degrees. He is a fellow of the Royal Society, London, and a member of the U.S. National Academy of Sciences and the American Physical Society.

Dyson has written and spoken widely on cosmology, nuclear physics, technology, weapons control, and philosophy. In 1959 he proposed human habitats in space that came to be known as Dyson spheres. Such habitats would surround a star harnessing light and energy to support communities of billions of people. Dyson later developed an interest in asteroids as human habitats in space. Dyson wrote a number of widely read and respected books, including *Disturbing the Universe* (1979); *Weapons and Hope* (1984); *Origins of Life* (1986); *Infinite in All Directions* (1988); *From Eros to Gaia* (1992); *Imagined Worlds* (1997); and *The Sun, the Genome, and the Internet* (1999). SEE ALSO COMMUNITIES IN SPACE (VOLUME 4); DYSON SPHERES (VOLUME 4); HABITATS (VOLUME 3); SETTLEMENTS (VOLUME 4).

*E. Julius Dasch*

## Bibliography

Dyson, Freeman J. *Disturbing the Universe.* New York: Harper & Row, 1979.

———. *From Eros to Gaia.* New York: Pantheon Books, 1992.

———. *Imagined Worlds.* Cambridge, MA: Harvard University Press, 1997.

# Dyson Spheres

While the National Aeronautics and Space Administration (NASA) considers future human trips to Mars and continues to build the International Space Station, some individuals in the field have pushed for even more. They believe that the key to human expansion in space does not lie in the building of colonies on planets or even the building of small **space stations**. Scientists such as Freeman Dyson and Gerard K. O'Neill proposed building gigantic structures for humans to live in. What makes their ideas even more unconventional is the size of their proposed structures. The structures proposed by O'Neill, known as O'Neill colonies, could be a dozen miles long and a few miles wide. Freeman Dyson's structures, called Dyson Spheres or Dyson Shells, would be the size of a planet's orbit. While it would only be a few meters thick, the size of the sphere would stretch for millions of miles.

**space stations** large orbital outposts equipped to support human crews and designed to remain in orbit for an extended period

## Dyson's Vision

In 1959 Dyson hatched the idea of building a huge sphere around a star. In his theory, a shell built at a safe distance away from the star would allow billions of people to live inside while allowing the civilization to harness a large amount of energy, in the form of radiation, from the star. While his vision is fascinating, it poses concerns.

One concern that needs to be addressed involves the materials that could be used to build such a structure. Not only would the shell need to stay together, but it would have to absorb impacts without the inertia pushing it into the star. Creating gravity would be a problem, since spinning the sphere would add more stress to the structure and force everyone to the equator of the sphere. Moreover, the amount of raw materials needed to create a space that would be one billion times bigger than the Earth is enormous. Future engineers would need to be able to deconstruct and process other planets and asteroids to create a sphere.

## The Search for Dyson Spheres

Searches have been conducted using radio telescopes to see if there may be Dyson Spheres already in existence, but none have yet been found. Due to the high level of technical expertise required to build a sphere of this magnitude, some scientists question Dyson's theories. Dyson responds that advanced civilizations would have the ability to build such a device, and that we cannot be biased by our current technological level:

> One should expect that, within a few thousand years of its entering the stage of industrial development, any intelligent species should be found occupying an artificial biosphere which completely surrounds its parent star.

One type of colony Dyson suggested was the "Island Three." This design was an enormous cylinder that was twenty miles long and four miles across. The cylinder would spin to create artificial gravity, but spun slowly enough to prevent harmful **G forces**. The cylinder was designed to contain spaces for agriculture, industrial facilities, and even a place for ships to dock as they transported people from Earth. The Island Three was even designed with huge adjustable mirrors that would move to reflect the light of the Sun to create a daytime and nighttime for the inhabitants of the colony. This

**G force** the force an astronaut or pilot experiences when undergoing large accelerations

design would be capable of holding several million colonists, but not as many as a Dyson Sphere.

Not all proposed Dyson Spheres would need to be complete enclosures. It has been proposed that a smaller series of solar energy collectors could suffice as a first step towards the building of a Dyson Sphere. The collectors would be much larger than standard solar panels, and would therefore allow for a much greater energy gain. In the future, larger solar panels will be useful for extraterrestrial colonization. SEE ALSO DYSON, FREEMAN JOHN (VOLUME 4); L-5 COLONIES (VOLUME 4); O'NEILL COLONIES (VOLUME 4).

*Craig Samuels*

### Bibliography

Dyson, Freeman J. *Disturbing the Universe.* New York: Basic Books, 2001.

O'Neill, Gerard K. *High Frontier: Human Colonies in Space.* Burlington, Ontario, Canada: Collector's Guide Publishing, Inc., 2000.

### Internet Resources

*What's a Dyson Sphere? Astronomy Frequently Asked Questions.* <http://www.faqs.org/faqs/astronomy/faq/part6/section-13.html>.

# Earth—Why Leave?

Only humans have the ability to leave their home planet and explore, settle, and even alter other worlds, and many people want to do all of these things. What is the attraction of these distant worlds that tempts humans to leave the comforts of Earth for uncertain, and probably hazardous, journeys beyond?

The history of human exploration of Earth provides a basis for understanding our motivations for exploring new places. At the same time, humankind's brief experiences with human exploration of the Moon, and the extensive robotic exploration of the solar system, show how space exploration will be different from past voyages of discovery in terms of motivation and operation.

In current and near-term space missions, the search for scientific knowledge has been more prominent, sometimes exclusively so, than it was in historical voyages. Furthermore, unlike the European migrations to the New World, it is unlikely that significant fractions of the population can be transported from Earth because of the limitations and costs of **rockets**. Nonetheless, human and robotic exploration of the other worlds in the solar system might lead to the establishment of permanent human settlements on the Moon, Mars, and elsewhere and eventually to the reconstruction of a planetary-scale **biosphere** on Mars.

**rockets** vehicles (or devices) especially designed to travel through space, propelled by one or more engines

**biosphere** the interaction of living organisms on a global scale

## History and Biology Lessons

Since our ancestors ventured out of Africa, humans have explored Earth. Prehistoric peoples successfully filled every ecological niche available to them on the planet, spreading to every continent except Antarctica. Clearly, this attests to an effective and possibly biologically based drive for exploration and expansion. However, the structure and motivation of prehistoric

This famous view of Earth rising, taken during the Apollo 8 mission, gave people on the planet a new perspective of their place in the universe.

migrations are lost in the depths of time. They probably did not reflect a conscious decision to explore and expand any more than such decisions were part of the spread of the African killer bee through the Americas after its introduction to Brazil in the 1980s. Furthermore, biology is not destiny: Even if there is a biologically based drive to explore and expand, it does not necessarily follow that humans should and will explore and settle other worlds.

The drive to explore in humans can be demonstrated, by counterexample, to be nonobligatory. There are well-known examples of civilizations poised on the edge of great epochs of exploration and expansion that turned inward and developed cultural blocks to exploration and contact with foreigners. In a frequently told tale there is a striking parallel between the expansion of the Portuguese in the fifteenth century and the abortive voyages of the Chinese under the Ming emperors just a few decades before that time. After an impressive series of sea voyages far greater in scope than anything Europe could achieve, the Chinese withdrew, destroyed their seagoing vessels, and left the age of exploration to the Europeans.

There is a clear lesson in this parallel to space exploration, which shows that initial voyages of discovery do not automatically lead to subsequent exploration and expansion. If there is a biological drive to explore, it is greatly influenced, if not dominated, by cultural traditions and myths. In this regard there is general agreement that Western culture has a historical tradition and a collection of myths that inspire and reward exploration.

## To Expand Scientific Knowledge

Many space scientists have argued that the fundamental motivation for a space program is the scientific understanding that it generates. In this view, the performance criterion for any mission is the scientific return compared to the cost. Certainly space missions have contributed to an understanding of Earth through studies of **greenhouse effects** on Venus, Mars, and Titan; the photochemistry of the acid clouds on Venus; the dust storms on Mars; and impact hazard assessments and prevention. Impact by an asteroid is the single most devastating natural hazard known, as testified by the extinction of the dinosaurs 65 million years ago. Through the exploration of space for scientific understanding and the development of space technologies, an asteroid on a collision course with Earth could be detected in advance and methods could be devised for deflection of the asteroid to prevent impact.

Perhaps the most compelling scientific motivation for space exploration is the search for a second genesis of life that has independently begun on another planet. More than being a matter of simple scientific curiosity, the question "Are we alone?" is asked by every person. The search for life is best conducted in space, whether this involves missions to search for biologically produced compounds in the subsurface of Mars, Titan's organic haze, or Europa's frozen oceans or telescopes probing the atmospheric composition of **extrasolar planets**. Space exploration, specifically the human exploration of planets and planetoids that are hospitable to life, is key in the search for life in the solar system and, by extrapolation, the universe.

But common sense and recent history show that space exploration is not about science alone. If science was the only important motivation for space exploration, the world's space programs would be placed within the basic science agencies and would compete directly with programs involving disciplines such as oceanography, particle physics, and geology. Yet clearly this is not the case. Space programs enjoy a special status, usually within a separate agency. This reflects a broader motivation base for space than science alone.

## Beyond Science

Clearly there are significant nonscientific issues of a national and international nature that drive the current space programs of the world. At the highest levels these issues deal with national self-image, international political competition, economic competition, and national technological development. On a more direct level national space programs are perceived as having tangible benefits in terms of the level of education and the overall perception of technology as a positive force in society. For all these reasons there seems to be a consensus that a vigorous space program is in the national and international best interests.

**greenhouse effect**
process by which short wavelength energy (e.g., visible light) penetrates an object's atmosphere and is absorbed by the surface, which reradiates this energy as longer wavelength infrared (thermal) energy; this energy is blocked from escaping to space by molecules (e.g., $H_2O$ and $CO_2$) in the atmosphere; and as a result, the surface warms

**extrasolar planets** planets orbiting stars other than the Sun

Economics has been suggested as a possible motivation for the exploration and utilization of space. Communication satellites, the mining of helium-3 on the lunar surface and metals on asteroids, and oxygen production on the Moon have received the most attention. **Microgravity** manufacturing and space tourism also reflect economic incentives for space missions. From this list the only two that have proven profitable so far have been telecommunications satellites and space tourism. Space tourism has only three examples in its support: the flights of a Japanese reporter, a wealthy American businessman, and a South African Internet tycoon, all on Russian missions. From this humble beginning could come luxury hotels in orbit and on the Moon and possibly eco-tourism to Mars.

## Reasons for Not Exploring Space

Many past migrations of human populations were driven by acute local problems such as dire economic conditions, famine, warfare, overpopulation, and environmental degradation. It is sometimes suggested that other worlds may provide similar relief when Earth becomes overpopulated or uninhabitable as a result of human actions. However, the limitation of space transport makes these motivations for settling other worlds irrelevant in the near-term. Space exploration and settlement may help solve problems on Earth by providing useful knowledge but is unlikely to provide an escape valve for mismanagement of this planet.

## From Exploration to Settlement

The exploration of environments, such as the surface of Mars, that are instantly lethal to humans naturally leads to the question: Does exploration lead to settlement? Historically it has, but the historical record is based upon the exploration of the surface of Earth and, in particular, of environments in which premodern peoples with a rudimentary technology base could thrive. The only example of exploration not based on this model was the exploration of Antarctica. Although permanent scientific research bases have been established in Antarctica and some nations have made legalistic gestures toward inhabitation, there is no effective human settlement in Antarctica. Similarly, but less telling in light of the limited time spent on undersea exploration, there are no human settlements below the water. Human activity on the Moon could be expected to follow the Antarctic model, with the establishment of long-lived research stations and observatories but without a permanent population. Commuting to the Moon from Earth is not out of the question, but travel to Mars is likely to be a different case for two reasons. First, the long trip time and the intermittent nature of Earth-Mars transfer would favor more permanent, self-sufficient settlements than those on the Moon. Second, Mars may allow for the creation of a habitable environment through terraforming efforts.

## From Settlement to Terraforming

The presence of humans on another planet will inevitably alter that world's environment, but this can also be done in a purposeful fashion, resulting in a planet that is capable of supporting a rich biosphere—a process called terraforming. The ultimate motivation for terraforming and for space exploration itself is enhancing the abundance and diversity of life in the universe

**microgravity** the condition experienced in free-fall as a spacecraft orbits Earth or another body; commonly called weightlessness; only very small forces are perceived in freefall, on the order of one-millionth the force of gravity on Earth's surface

and enriching the lives of humans. These are goals worthy of an advanced civilization. SEE ALSO COMMUNITIES IN SPACE (VOLUME 4); ENVIRONMENTAL CHANGES (VOLUME 4); HUMAN MISSIONS TO MARS (VOLUME 3); IMPACTS (VOLUME 4); LIVING ON OTHER WORLDS (VOLUME 4); LUNAR BASES (VOLUME 4); LUNAR OUTPOSTS (VOLUME 4); MARS BASES (VOLUME 4); MARS MISSIONS (VOLUME 4); SCIENTIFIC RESEARCH (VOLUME 4); SETTLEMENTS (VOLUME 4); SOCIAL ETHICS (VOLUME 4); SPACE INDUSTRIES (VOLUME 4); SPACE TOURISM, EVOLUTION OF (VOLUME 4); TERRAFORMING (VOLUME 4); TOURISM (VOLUME 1).

*Christopher P. McKay and Margarita M. Marinova*

**Bibliography**

Clarke, Arthur C. *The Snows of Olympus: A Garden on Mars.* New York: Norton, 1995.

McKay, Christopher P. "Let's Put Martian Life First." *Planetary Report* 21 (July/August 2001):4–5.

———. "Flowers for Mars." *The Planetary Report* 20 (September/October 2000):4–5.

———. "Does Mars Have Rights? An Approach to the Environmental Ethics of Planetary Engineering." In *Moral Expertise*, ed. Donald MacNiven. New York: Routledge, 1990. Pp. 184–197.

McKay, Christopher P., and Margarita Marinova. "The Physics, Biology, and Environmental Ethics of Making Mars Habitable." *Astrobiology* 1, no. 1 (2001):89–109.

Zubrin, Robert, with Richard Wagner. *The Case for Mars: The Plan to Settle the Red Planet and Why We Must.* New York: Free Press, 1996.

# Ehricke, Krafft

### Aeronautical Engineer, Physicist, and Author
### 1917–1984

Krafft A. Ehricke was a rocket pioneer and visionary who made significant contributions to the technology and philosophical basis of space development. Ehricke was born in 1917 in Berlin, Germany. At the age of twelve he founded a rocket society, and he later studied celestial mechanics and nuclear physics at Berlin Technical University. During World War II, Ehricke became a key member of the Peenemuende rocket development team, specializing in the propulsion system for the V-2 rocket. At Peenemuende, he also worked on future space projects and developed theories on human space operations and nuclear propulsion.

After immigrating to the United States in 1947, Ehricke worked for the U.S. Army Ordnance Department, where he pursued the development of ballistic missiles and space vehicles. In the 1950s he joined the General Dynamics Astronautics Division, where he helped develop the Atlas rocket and the Centaur upper stage. Many early U.S. planetary probes were launched using the Centaur, which was the first liquid hydrogen–propelled vehicle. In the 1970s Ehricke led advanced studies at Rockwell International on the use of space for the benefit of humankind and refined ideas for interplanetary travel, manufacturing facilities in space, and mining on the Moon and the other planets. He is remembered for saying, "If God meant us to explore space, he would have given us a moon."

Ehricke died in 1984. He was survived by his wife and three daughters, who founded the nonprofit Krafft A. Ehricke Institute for Space Development in 1985. SEE ALSO CAREERS IN ROCKETRY (VOLUME 1); MOON (VOLUME 2); ROCKETS (VOLUME 3); VEHICLES (VOLUME 4); VON BRAUN, WERNHER (VOLUME 3).

*John F. Kross*

**Bibliography**

Ordway, Frederick I., and Mitchell R. Sharpe. *The Rocket Team.* New York: Crowell, 1979.

# Environmental Changes

There are many causes of environmental changes on Earth. Natural events cause changes in climate. For example, large volcanic eruptions release tiny particles into the atmosphere that block sunlight, resulting in surface cooling that lasts for a few years. Variations in ocean currents such as El Niño can also change the distribution of heat and precipitation. Over longer time spans, tens to hundreds of thousands of years, natural changes in the geographical distribution of energy from the Sun and in the amounts of greenhouse gases and dust in the atmosphere have caused the climate to shift from ice ages to relatively warmer periods. On a longer timescale the presence of life on Earth has changed the environment of the planet radically, transforming a predominantly reducing atmosphere made up of methane and ammonia to today's oxygen-rich gaseous envelope.

Human activities can also change the environment. Orbiting satellites have photographed the transformation of deserts into productive agricultural areas. Conversely, satellites have tracked the advance of deserts (desertification) and the loss of forests (deforestation) as a result of human activity. One root cause of desertification and deforestation is the use of wood as the basic source of energy, with the consequent loss of trees and degradation of the soil. The most obvious impact of desertification is the degradation of rangeland and irrigated cropland and the decline in soil fertility and soil structure. Desertification affects about one-sixth of the world's population and affects 70 percent of all dry lands, amounting to 3.6 billion hectares (8.9 billion acres), or one-quarter of the total land area of the world.

Turning deserts into farmland via irrigation is one way humans have significantly changed Earth's environment. This strip of farmland is in the Atacama Desert in Chile.

## The Greenhouse Phenomenon

In addition to desertification, changes caused by human activities include recent increases in the atmospheric concentrations of both greenhouse gases and sulfate particles ("aerosols"). Greenhouse gases such as carbon dioxide cover the atmosphere's "infrared window," and trap heat. Data from satellites can trace changes in the globally averaged surface temperature of Earth and can be used to predict temperature changes in the future. According to some models, if current trends continue, the amount of carbon dioxide in the atmosphere will double during the twenty-first century, and the average rate of warming of Earth's surface over the next hundred years will probably be greater than it was at any time in the last 10,000 years. The current best estimate of the expected rise of globally averaged surface temperature relative to 1990 is 1°C to 3.5°C by the year 2100, with continued increases thereafter.

Because seawater expands when heated and some glacial ice will melt, the global sea level is expected to rise a further 15 to 95 centimeters (6 to 37.5 inches) by 2100 as a result of global warming. Since 1978 satellite technology has been used to monitor the vast Arctic Sea ice cover on a routine basis. More recently, the Topex/Poseidon satellite has been instrumental in observing the global climate interaction between the sea and the atmosphere. In 2001 a joint U.S.–French oceanography mission, Jason 1, was scheduled to be launched to monitor world ocean circulation, study interactions between the oceans and the atmosphere, improve climate predictions, and observe events such as El Niño.

## Ozone Depletion

Around 1985 scientists taking ozone ($O_3$) measurements in the Antarctic detected an alarming decrease in stratospheric ozone concentrations over the South Pole. This decline in atmospheric ozone was verified by instruments aboard the National Aeronautics and Space Administration's (NASA)'s Nimbus-7 satellite. Under usual circumstances **ultraviolet radiation** helps create and destroy ozone molecules. It is strong enough to break both ozone and oxygen molecules into individual oxygen atoms. This destruction of molecules allows the free oxygen atoms to bond with other oxygen molecules and form more ozone. However, chlorofluorocarbon (CFC) compounds such as the freon used in refrigeration systems upset this balance and destroy ozone (CFCs also are greenhouse gases). The depletion of ozone caused by CFCs results in increased ultraviolet radiation at Earth's surface that could be highly damaging to sensitive Arctic life forms. Ozone losses over the Arctic could also reduce ozone levels over the middle latitudes as a result of the mixing of air masses.

Although some forms of ozone-destroying CFCs have been banned, Arctic ozone depletion might be increased over the next few decades by further accumulations of greenhouse gases in the atmosphere. By trapping more heat near Earth's surface, these gases cause the **stratosphere** to become cooler and produce more stratospheric clouds, which have been implicated in rapid ozone loss.

## Colonization and Terraforming of Planets

Although human-induced changes to Earth's environment are increasingly apparent, humans have also altered the environment of the Moon and the neighboring planets in very small ways. The footprints left by Apollo astronauts and atmospheric gases released by their landing craft produced infinitesimal alterations in the Moon's environment. Similarly, tire tracks and shallow trenches left on the surface of Mars by landers, such as Pathfinder and Viking, have changed the environment of that planet on a minute scale. However, greater environmental changes are almost inevitable as humans venture into the solar system.

Colonization of other worlds will affect those environments, but humans may also undertake the premeditated terraforming of planets to deliberately make them more Earth-like. Making Mars habitable will in many ways restore that planet's climate of billions of years ago, creating a thick atmosphere and a warm surface with bodies of liquid water. Ironically,

**ultraviolet radiation** electromagnetic radiation with a shorter wavelength and higher energy than light

**stratosphere** a middle portion of Earth's atmosphere above the tropopause (the highest place where convection and "weather" occurs)

greenhouse gases such as carbon dioxide and CFCs, which have undesirable effects on Earth, could be instrumental in terraforming Mars. Some researchers have proposed melting the southern polar ice cap on Mars to release large quantities of carbon dioxide into the atmosphere to heat up the planet. Others have suggested the use of super greenhouse gases for that purpose. Warming the atmosphere by using specially designed CFCs would be desirable and would not cause adverse affects on ozone formation.

Over time, Earth's environment has been changed for the better (e.g., transforming deserts to agricultural areas) and the worse (e.g., the ozone hole, greenhouse warming, desertification, etc.). In the future, the challenge will be to remain aware of the accompanying changes to the environment and responsibly guide and monitor those changes on the home planet and beyond. SEE ALSO ASTEROID MINING (VOLUME 4); LIVING ON OTHER WORLDS (VOLUME 4); NATURAL RESOURCES (VOLUME 4); PLANETARY PROTECTION (VOLUME 4); RESOURCE UTILIZATION (VOLUME 4); SETTLEMENTS (VOLUME 4); TERRAFORMING (VOLUME 4).

*John F. Kross*

Computer-enhanced image of Earth from space showing global warming "hot spots," with gas plumes at the poles.

**Bibliography**

Lewis, Richard S. *Appointment on the Moon.* New York: Viking, 1968.

McKay, Christopher P. "Bringing Life to Mars." *Scientific American Presents* 10 (1999): 52–57.

———. "Changing the Face of Mars." *Astronomy Now* 13 (1999):18–21.

Shelton, William R. *Man's Conquest of Space.* Washington, DC: National Geographic Society, 1975.

**Internet Resources**

"The Physics and Biology of Making Mars Habitable." Massachusetts Institute of Technology. <http://web.mit.edu/mmm/www/summary.html>.

U.S. Global Change Research Information Office. <http://www.gcrio.org>.

**light year** the distance that light in a vacuum would travel in one year (about 5.9 trillion miles [9.5 trillion kilometers])

# Faster-Than-Light Travel

Whether science fiction novels refer to it as warp speed, hyperspeed, or lightspeed, the prospect of traveling at the speed of light or faster has enthralled humanity for decades. The possibility of traveling at speeds millions of times faster than those at which people travel today has been the focus of much debate and research. Faster-than-light travel is necessary for space journeys because of the huge distances between stars and star systems. The nearest star to Earth, not including the Sun, is 4.3 **light-years** away. This means that at the speed of light it would take 4.3 years to get there and 4.3 years to return. The Milky Way Galaxy is more than 100,000 light-years across and is only one galaxy in what is believed to be billions. No human could survive for 100,000 years with current medical techniques, and so faster-than-light propulsion would be necessary to make such a trip.

The science of faster-than-light travel is based on the equation $E = mc^2$ determined by physicist Albert Einstein. According to this equation, energy (*e*) is equal to mass (*m*) multiplied by the speed of light (*c*) squared, meaning that energy and matter can be converted from one to the other. A major tenet of physics is that matter can neither be created nor destroyed. Nuclear explosions are a prime example of matter being converted into energy. Amazingly, however, atomic weapons have a very low rate of matter-to-energy conversion.

Using this equation, one can see the near impossibility of faster-than-light travel with today's technology. To travel in a ship at that speed or faster requires a great deal of energy. But according to Einstein's special theory of relativity equation, mass will increase as an object goes faster. As one approaches the speed of light, one will become so heavy that no fuel will be able to propel the ship fast enough to keep up. That rapid increase in mass prevents faster-than-light travel for humans aboard starships today, yet research is under way to determine ways to get around this limitation.

Small subatomic particles such as photons, particles of light, and hypothetical particles called tachyons—faster-than-light travelers with no mass— seem to have no problem reaching lightspeed. In fact, tachyons are widely believed to be a science fiction concept because it would take an infinite amount of energy to *slow down* a tachyon to the speed of light. Whether or not tachyons exist, the ability of particles to travel at higher speeds has not gone unnoticed by scientists. If a bubble could be created around a space-

ship, it is hoped that the weight of the object could be lowered while its speed increased. SEE ALSO ACCESSING SPACE (VOLUME 1); ANTIMATTER PROPULSION (VOLUME 4); INTERSTELLAR TRAVEL (VOLUME 4); LASER PROPULSION (VOLUME 4); POWER, METHODS OF GENERATING (VOLUME 4); SCIENCE FICTION (VOLUME 4); VEHICLES (VOLUME 4).

*Craig Samuels*

Space travel in science fiction, like in the movie *Star Wars,* depends on the ability to move at speeds millions of times faster than possible in reality.

### Bibliography

Bodanis, David. $E = mc^2$: *A Biography of the World's Most Famous Equation.* New York: Walker & Co., 2001.

Greene, Brian. *The Elegant Universe: Superstrings, Hidden Dimensions, and the Quest for the Ultimate Theory.* London: Vintage, 2000.

Krauss, Lawrence M. *The Physics of Star Trek.* New York: Basic Books, 1995.

### Internet Resources

"Ask a High-Energy Astronomer." *Imagine the Universe.* NASA Goddard Space Flight Center. <http://imagine.gsfc.nasa.gov/docs/ask_astro/ask_an_astronomer.html>.

"Ask the Experts." *Scientific American.* <http://www.sciam.com/askexpert/physics/physics57/physics57.html>.

*The Speed of Light.* University of Tennessee. <http://csep10.phys.utk.edu/guidry/violence/lightspeed.html>.

*Warp Drive, When? Frequently Asked Questions.* NASA Glenn Research Center <http://www.grc.nasa.gov/WWW/PAO/html/warp/warpfaq.htm#tach>.

# First Contact

Over a century ago, the astronomer Percival Lowell thought that he had glimpsed artificial canals on Mars and the radio pioneer Nikola Tesla believed that he had intercepted a Martian radio broadcast. Later attempts to signal Mars by means of huge bonfires and powerful radio broadcasts proved unsuccessful. Today people realize that although remnants of microbial life

We do not know if and how we will first discover extraterrestrial intelligence, but most scientists do not expect it to happen quite like it does in the movie, *E.T. The Extra-terrestrial* (1982).

may exist within the solar system, the search for extraterrestrial intelligence (SETI) must extend to distant stars.

## Search Strategies

Microwave SETI, which uses radio telescopes, was popularized in Carl Sagan's novel *Contact* (1985) and in the 1997 Jodie Foster movie of the same name. Dish antennas collect faint microwaves that are fed into receivers that scan billions of channels simultaneously. Computers flag the signals that merit a closer look. Some astronomers have employed optical SETI and use optical telescopes fitted with special devices to hunt for flashes from extraterrestrial lasers pointed toward Earth. There are other search strategies, but because these two are in widespread use, they have the greatest chance of success. Most likely, first contact will involve intercepting a faint signal from a civilization many light-years away.

## Initial Reactions

So many people have become used to the idea that "we are not alone" that intercepting a signal from another solar system is unlikely to cause widespread psychological meltdown or social collapse. Indeed, when a prankster convinced the media that a microwave search had located ET, the public was not upset. An authenticated discovery would prove that humans are the product of processes that are not limited to Earth. Scientists estimate that the average extraterrestrial civilization could be about a billion years older than that on Earth. Finding such an old-timer would prove that civilizations can survive population growth, resource depletion, atomic warfare, and other threats. This would renew hope for the future of human society.

## What We Might Learn

In light of the likely differences between two civilizations that are located in different parts of the galactic neighborhood, those civilizations may have trouble recognizing each other, let alone communicating. Still, an ancient civilization may have solved the problem of communicating with a civilization such as Earth's, or after years of research, humans may learn to communicate with creatures that are not from around here. Our reactions will be shaped by our impressions of the alien civilization's capabilities, intentions, and desire to travel to Earth. These reactions will depend on our expectations, whether the discovery occurs during a time of peace or war, how the media handle the story, as well as other considerations.

Most discussions of first contact are optimistic and suggest benefits for humankind. Earth's new acquaintances might share practical ways to solve energy needs, cure illnesses, and eliminate crime. Their advanced ideas could have a deep and lasting impact on our philosophy, science, religion, and the arts. Learning about their ways could transform the way people think about themselves and prompt humans to redefine their place in the universe. Of course, contact may never occur or may proceed in a less pleasant way. If generations of searches fail, people will come to grips with the reality that humans are alone. Perhaps in the very distant future, as an advanced space-faring civilization, humankind will fill the universe with intelligent life. SEE ALSO LIFE IN THE UNIVERSE, SEARCH FOR (VOLUME 2); SETI (VOLUME 2).

*Albert A. Harrison*

### Bibliography

Billingham, John. *Societal Implications of the Detection of an Extraterrestrial Civilization.* Mountain View, CA: SETI Institute, 1999.

Dick, Steven J. *The Biological Universe: The Twentieth Century Extraterrestrial Life Debate and the Limits of Science.* Cambridge, UK: Cambridge University Press, 1996.

Harrison, Albert A. *After Contact: The Human Response to Extraterrestrial Life.* New York: Plenum, 1997.

Shostak, Seth. *Sharing the Universe: Perspectives on Extraterrestrial Life.* Berkeley, CA: Berkeley Hills Books, 1998.

# Food Production

Space explorers and settlers who are far from the farms and fields of Earth will need a reliable way to produce food. A continuous supply of nutritious, safe, and appealing food is essential for people who are living and working under unusual conditions that require peak physical condition. Food also plays an important role in the psychological welfare of crewmembers by providing familiarity and variety in the diet. The ability to continually produce food is an important element of long-term survival in space that cannot be accomplished by physical or chemical means. Food will have to be grown as quickly, reliably and efficiently as possible.

## Methods of Production

Astronauts on long-duration space missions or settlers on other planets will have to maintain crops in growth chambers protected from the outside environment, but they will still need to supply adequate lighting, nutrients, and a suitable atmosphere. Natural sunlight in transparent greenhouses or artificial lights could satisfy the lighting requirement, but there are tradeoffs. On Mars, for example, sunlight is available for only half of each Martian day,

In space, plant growth requires a controlled, closed environment, and the output emissions of the light emitting diode are conducive with high rates of plant photosynthesis.

'Yecora Rojo'
83 days old

**hydroponics** growing plants using water and nutrients in solution instead of soil as the root medium

**porous** allowing the passage of a fluid or gas through holes or passages in the substance

**regolith** upper few meters of a body's surface, composed of inorganic matter, such as unconsolidated rocks and fine soil

and more light is required for optimal growth of many plant species. In addition, the Sun can be obscured for months by giant dust storms. Higher radiation doses and possible damage from meteoroid impacts are other dangers. On the other hand, artificial lighting systems would be costly to transport and may require a great deal of energy.

Nutrients could be provided to crops by a form of **hydroponics**, with the roots in contact with a thin film of liquid or a **porous** material such as vermiculite. Alternatively, the surface **regolith** of the Moon or Mars could be used as soil after any hypersalinity or toxic materials are washed out. Organic wastes and microbial soil communities could be added to the regolith to render it closer to the fertile soil found on Earth. On-site resources could also be processed to provide air and water for growing crops. On Mars, water can be extracted from the regolith and condensed from the atmosphere. Carbon dioxide could be taken directly from the Martian atmosphere. Atmospheric nitrogen could also be extracted and reacted with hydrogen to produce ammonia for fertilizers. Nitrogen-fixing microorganisms could be added to the soil to chemically alter this gas into a form usable by the plants.

## What Kinds of Food Would Be Produced?

Foods produced in space will be carefully balanced for caloric content, nutritional quality, and palatability. Some plants may be genetically modified to alter or enhance their nutrient composition, and efforts will need to be made to optimize conditions for plant growth. Processing will also be required to convert crops into palatable, safe, and satisfying foods. In addition, processing will be needed to preserve food for storage in case of crop failure. The chosen foodstuffs will have to be versatile and capable of being converted into different types of foods. For example, soybeans can be pressed to release oils, and the remaining high-protein soybean meal can be manipulated to provide different foodstuffs. Soy milk can be used in place of cow's milk or can be used to make curd in the form of tofu or tempeh.

Adding different plant food will enhance the palatability of the diet. For example, various brassicas (similar to wild mustard) produce oils similar in quality to that of canola, and peanuts have an interesting flavor. Black-eyed peas are a good low-fat complement to oily legumes such as soybeans and peanuts. Besides being heat and drought tolerant, cowpeas are a staple crop eaten in Africa as a dry bean, snap bean, or raw salad green. In addition, their low oil content allows cowpea meal to be incorporated into formed or extruded vegetarian food products.

Rice is an excellent cereal crop to complement protein from legumes in a balanced vegetarian diet. Rice protein is tolerated by virtually all people, and it is more versatile than most other cereal grains. Wheat in the form of breads and pastas is a very important and common foodstuff in many cultures. In addition, the plants can be grown in high density, and the grain is very versatile. Potatoes, whether white or sweet, can make good and hearty additions to the diet. Much of the potato plant is edible, and the tubers are versatile and consumed throughout the world. Other crops such as tomatoes and lettuce may also be grown. Tomatoes can be used in stews, sauces, and salads, while lettuce makes good salad greens and can be grown efficiently. Spices and herbs will surely be grown to make the diet seem more varied, and hot peppers could enrich mealtime. Apples, oranges, and other fruits, however, will probably be rare because many fruits grow on bushes or trees that use space inefficiently and are comparatively nonproductive relative to the resources required for cultivation.

## Other Uses for Plant Material

Despite efforts to maximize crop yields, about half of the plant material produced cannot be digested by humans. However, indigestible cellulose can be converted into sugars for use as food or as nutrients to grow yeasts, fungi, or plant **cell cultures**. Cellulose-digesting animals could also be raised on a small scale. While they would not be raised primarily for food, animals could on occasion provide high-quality protein and would make creating a balanced diet easier. At the other end of the spectrum, "microbial crops"

**cell culture** a means of growing mammalian (including human) cells in the research laboratory under defined experimental conditions

**algae** simple photosynthetic organisms, often aquatic

could be good source of single-cell protein. For example, brewer's yeast and **algae** could be used as a dietary supplement, and green algae are a good source of protein as well as essential fatty acids and vitamins. In addition, algae can help provide oxygen to the atmosphere. Although not suitable as the only source of food, algae could be grown very quickly in an emergency and provide needed sustenance for the crew. SEE ALSO BIOTECHNOLOGY (VOLUME 4); FOOD (VOLUME 3); LIVING ON OTHER WORLDS (VOLUME 4).

*John F. Kross*

### Bibliography

Boston, Penelope J., ed. *The Case for Mars.* San Diego, CA: American Astronautical Society, 1984.

Eckart, Peter. *Spaceflight Life Support and Biospherics.* Torrence, CA: Microcosm Press, 1996.

Nelson, Allen J. *Space Biospheres.* Malabar, FL: Orbit Book Co., 1987.

Oberg, James E. *Mission to Mars: Plans and Concepts for the First Manned Landing.* Harrisburg, PA: Stackpole Books, 1982.

### Internet Resources

"Growing Crops in a CELSS." Purdue University. <http://www.bio.purdue.edu/nscort/cea.html>.

"Plant Physiological Research in the KSC-Breadboard Project." Kennedy Space Center. <http://bioscience.ksc.nasa.gov/oldals/plant/physio.htm>.

# Glaser, Peter

## *Mechanical Engineer and Space Technology Pioneer*
## *1923–*

Peter E. Glaser conceived the solar power satellite as a means of capturing solar energy in space for transmission to Earth. In the next few decades this concept may be implemented as part of the solution to the pressing human need for more and cleaner energy.

Glaser was born September 5, 1923, in Zatec, Czechoslovakia. He moved to the United States in 1948 and went on to earn both his master's of science and doctoral degrees from Columbia University in New York City. In addition to his seminal role as inventor of the solar power satellite, Glaser has made many outstanding contributions to space technology during his illustrious career. Until retirement in 1994, Glaser led advanced technology work at Arthur D. Little, Inc. His wide-ranging interests included thermal protection systems, lunar surface properties, lunar laser ranging, and space solar power systems. He directed studies for the National Aeronautics and Space Administration (NASA) and the U.S. Department of Energy, served on several NASA task forces, and testified on numerous occasions before committees of the U.S. Congress.

Glaser has more than 150 publications, books, and patents. He served as president of the International Solar Energy Society and as editor in chief of the *Journal of Solar Energy.* He founded the Sunsat Energy Council in 1978 and was its president until 1994. He is currently the council's chairman emeritus. Glaser has been a prominent member of leading professional organizations in science, technology, and astronautics and has been the recipient of numerous awards and honors, including the Space Technology Hall of Fame in the United States Space Foundation. SEE ALSO SOLAR POWER SYSTEMS (VOLUME 4).

*R. Bryan Erb*

### Internet Resources

Glaser, Peter. "The World Needs Energy From Space." *Space.com.* <http://www.space .com/opinionscolumns/opinions/glaser_000223.html>.

# Governance

The idea of governance within space, on planets, or in space stations has raised many questions. For example, would the laws of the launching country apply in settling a legal matter that occurred in outer space, or would only the laws adopted independently by the space settlement be valid? And, if more than one country sponsored the expedition, which country's laws would be binding and who would enforce these laws? Furthermore, is it realistic to expect space settlers to defer to the authority of a country that it may take months to reach by space travel? These are only a few of the questions that the concept of space governance generates.

## Political Philosophies and Self-Governance

Because of Earth's problematic history with colonization it is thought that some degree of self-governance would likely be suitable for space settlements. The following political philosophies demonstrate the broad spectrum of views as related to self-governance.

**Libertarian.** Libertarians believe in self-governance as related to both personal and economic issues. According to libertarians, the government's only role is to provide protection from coercion and violence. Libertarians value self-responsibility and tolerance of diversity.

The Libertarian view assumes a high level of individually motivated honest behavior. There is no strong deterrence to criminal activity apart from contending with one's own conscience. But the Libertarian approach could potentially find acceptance in space settlements where populations will initially be small and the degree of self-responsibility high.

**Left-Liberal.** The political philosophy of Left-liberals is self-governance in personal matters accompanied by a mechanism for central government to make decisions on economic issues. Among Left-liberals, there is a strong agenda to have government provide for the needs of the disadvantaged. Left-liberals would likely allow self-governance in space to the extent that government sponsored social programs could still be financed.

**Centrist.** Centrists support government intervention on some issues but stress pragmatic solutions to social problems. Centrists would probably see self-governance as a practical strategy to governing small space settlements but would defer to more government intervention as the settlements grew and public problems increased.

**Conservative.** Right-conservatives have essentially the opposite philosophy of Left-liberals. Right-conservatives want people to exercise self-governance when it comes to economic issues, but still want the government to protect society from threats to morality.

The current fiscal situation for many space expeditions and settlements involves a hefty price tag. It takes large groups, either private or public to plan and implement projects such as the settlement of Mars. Therefore, the Right-conservative desire for self-governance in economic matters may not be compatible with the high expenditures that would accompany space colonization. At some point in the future, conservative religious groups may seek to advance their moral agenda through space settlement, as did religious groups such as the Puritans and Quakers of colonial America.

**Authoritarian.** Authoritarians do not see self-governance as a practical alternative, as they would prefer that the government foster advances to humankind by central planning. Left-authoritarians are also referred to as socialists, Right-authoritarians as fascists.

An authoritarian approach to space government would involve either deference to a political government on Earth (i.e., no self-governance) or the establishment of a central government power in outer space. Resource concerns would apply to the latter because a dedicated central government in space would add to the costs of the space settlement.

## Free-Governance in Outer Space as Compared to Governments Used in Colonized Countries

We can look to history to learn how colonization has been handled, at what point power may have shifted from a distant sovereignty to governance by the occupants of the territory, and what the implications are for the colonization of space. At this time we do not have any indigenous, or pre-existing populations on other planets, so at least for now the topic of governance in space refers to the legal issues of persons coming from Earth. Maybe at a future time settlers from Earth will become the indigenous population of a space settlement in free space or of a planet.

**Settlement Colonization.** The original European colonies in the Americas were treated as the property of each respective colonizing European country (Great Britain, Spain, France). Laws were changed, as they would likewise need to be changed in space environments, to take account of special environmental conditions. Generally, however, colonists maintained whatever legal and political rights they had possessed in the colonizing country. This resulted in the colonial governments and laws differing greatly in the Americas, as they did between countries in Europe. Space governance may also differ between space settlements and levels of self-governance are likely to also vary.

Because Great Britain had a representative parliament and a monarchy with limited authority, settlement colonies adopted cabinet governments, and after 1931 became sovereign states, keeping only an allegiance to the crown. Likewise, in the realm of space governance, allegiance to original colonizing countries is likely to exist as well as a certain degree of representation in a legislative body. Perhaps a representative from a space settlement will hold a seat in a national or international legislative body on Earth and will participate in hearings remotely.

Natural conditions may modify laws in space. For example, the remoteness created by the Atlantic and consequently, the length of time it took to transmit communications, made control of Great Britain's colonies in America impractical. The setting produced a tough individualism with inhabitants making their own decisions. Government reached the frontier only gradually, and conditions of anarchy often prevailed. A rugged individualism like in the pioneer days of America could also happen in space. Technology exists to maintain communications, but there may be issues of enforcement because travel takes months to maybe years to accomplish. SEE ALSO COMMUNICATIONS, FUTURE NEEDS IN (VOLUME 4); INTERPLANETARY INTERNET (VOLUME 4); LIVING ON OTHER WORLDS (VOLUME 4); POLITICAL SYSTEMS (VOLUME 4); SOCIAL ETHICS (VOLUME 4).

*Nadine M. Jacobson*

**Bibliography**

Fawcett, James E. S. *Outer Space: New Challenges to Law and Policy.* Oxford, UK: Clarendon Press, 1984.

# Hotels

For the general public, the concept of space tourism continues to be an exciting dream. The first stage of space tourism would consist of very simple low-Earth orbit treks: tourists would orbit Earth several times on a spaceship and then return to the planet in a one-day tour. Even these short tours would be sufficiently adventurous to attract many civilian space travelers in the near future.

The next phase of orbital tourism would consist of "space stays" of one or two nights. If people could reside in space for two or three days, public travel above Earth would be much more enjoyable. Space tourists would then be able to watch Earth, the Moon, and the stars for long periods. It would be possible to produce many interesting materials in **microgravity**,

**microgravity** the condition experienced in freefall as a spacecraft orbits Earth or another body; commonly called weightlessness; only very small forces are perceived in freefall, on the order of one-millionth the force of gravity on Earth's surface

The interior design of a proposed guest room of a space hotel.

An artist's depiction of a space hotel in low Earth orbit.

some of which would be very valuable souvenirs from space. Also, it would be possible for tourists to have many kinds of interesting physical experiences in microgravity.

For people to stay in space for two or three days, "space cottages" would be essential. Those cottages would be small but would have to have minimum habitation systems for hygiene, dining, and sleeping, among other functions. One interesting proposal is the use of the habitation module of the International Space Station to provide room for space tourists after the station's formal planned mission has ended.

Eventually larger space hotels that would have many more functions for enjoying hotel life like those found in terrestrial resorts would be constructed. The accompanying picture shows an example of a space hotel of the future designed by Shimizu Corporation more than ten years ago.

The space hotel shown above has sixty-four guest rooms and a microgravity hall. All of the guest rooms are located on a circle with a radius of 70 meters (230 feet) that rotates three times a minute to produce 0.7 G artificial gravity. Therefore, in a guest room a hotel guest could stand, walk, and sleep normally. The figure on page 51 shows the interior design of a guest room. In the microgravity hall a guest could enjoy an environment in which it is possible to eat, drink, and play. In the future, space resorts will inspire the creation of many appealing microgravity games. SEE ALSO HABITATS (VOLUME 3); LIVING IN SPACE (VOLUME 3); SPACE TOURISM, EVOLUTION OF (VOLUME 4); TOURISM (VOLUME 1).

*Shinji Matsumoto*

### Internet Resources

"Space Tourism." *Texas Aerospace Scholars.* NASA. <http://aerospacescholars.org/Cirr/Em/l8/Tourism.htm>.

# Impacts

Earth's surface undergoes many kinds of environmental changes that affect human life and the evolution of all living things. Some are caused by human beings, and others result from natural processes; some evolve slowly, whereas others are sudden: "accidents" (if caused by humans) and "natural disasters." Since life can adapt to slow changes, the most disruptive changes are sudden calamities. The worst calamity occurs when a large, errant asteroid or comet collides with Earth.

## Sizes of Near-Earth Objects

Fragments of asteroids and comets pervade interplanetary space. Modest cosmic impacts occur all the time. On a dark, clear night one can see a flash of light (a meteor or "shooting star") every few minutes as an interplanetary grain of dust or sand strikes Earth's upper atmosphere. More rarely, larger space rocks cause brilliant "fireballs" when they crash to Earth, perhaps leaving **meteorites** in the ground. Every few years, Earth-orbiting surveillance satellites record multi-kiloton upper atmospheric explosions when a house-size cosmic object impacts. This happened over the Yukon Territory in January 2000, lighting up the night sky ten times more brilliantly than full daylight.

**meteorite** any part of a meteoroid that survives passage through Earth's atmosphere

Objects 50 meters (164 feet) across strike Earth every few centuries, causing airbursts that rival the effects of large thermonuclear bombs. The last one exploded over the Tunguska region of Siberia in 1908, toppling trees over a region the size of Washington, D.C. A similar-sized object composed of solid metal rather than rock struck northern Arizona about 50,000 years ago, forming Meteor Crater.✱

✱ An image of Meteor Crater can be found in the volume 2 article "Meteorites."

Far larger asteroids and comets can strike Earth. About 1,000 asteroids larger than 1 kilometer (0.62 mile) in diameter approach within 45 million kilometers (28 million miles) of Earth; any one of these near-Earth asteroids (NEAs) could impact Earth in the next few million years. Most will crash into the Sun, strike another planet, or be flung by Jupiter's gravity into interstellar space. But every 100,000 years or so a kilometer-sized NEA does crash into Earth, exploding with a force approaching 100,000 megatons—more powerful than all the world's nuclear bombs together.

A few NEAs are much larger than 1 kilometer (0.62 mile). Eros, which was visited by the NEAR Shoemaker spacecraft in the year 2000, is 34 kilometers (21 miles) long. Studies of its orbital path show that Eros cannot hit Earth in the near future, but millions of years from now there is a 5 percent chance that Eros will crash into Earth; the devastation would greatly exceed the impact 65 million years ago of a 10- to-15 kilometer (6 to 9 miles)

A small asteroid hitting an ocean on Earth would cause little damage, but one measuring 200 meters across could cause cataclysmic floods.

**planetesimals** objects in the early solar system that were the size of large asteroids or small moons, large enough to begin to gravitationally influence each other

diameter asteroid or comet that caused 70 percent of all species of plants and animals recognized in Cretaceous fossil beds to suddenly go extinct, including dinosaurs.

Even larger calamities happened early in the planet's history as life tried to gain a foothold on Earth. The circular dark patches on the full Moon are great circular impact basins formed when 100-kilometer-size (60 miles) **planetesimals** struck the Moon 3.9 to 4.2 billion years ago. Earth is a larger target than the Moon; it was surely bombarded by such projectiles during that epoch. It is unlikely but possible that Earth will be struck by such a large object again. If this were to occur, it could sterilize the world of all life. In 1997 Comet Hale-Bopp came inside Earth's orbit; its diameter was 25 to 70 kilometers (15 to 45 miles).

## Risks and Consequences

Impacts do not happen regularly. Earth is in an essentially random, cosmic shooting gallery. Kilometer-size asteroids impact every 100,000 years "on

average." However, that means there is a 1 in 100,000 chance that one will hit "next year," or a 0.1 percent chance during the twenty-first century. A much larger, mass extinction impact is a thousand times less likely than a 1-kilometer (0.62-mile) NEA impact, but even that is not inconceivable in the very near future.

The consequences of impacts vary enormously, depending on the size and **velocity** of the impacting bodies. A Tunguska-like event, which happens somewhere on Earth every few centuries, could happen in the next fifty years. If it exploded unexpectedly over a major city, it would be a catastrophe in which hundreds of thousands might die. However, only a tiny fraction of Earth's surface has urban population densities. A sparsely populated area is a more likely target, such as Tunguska, where only one or two people may have been killed. Even more likely, the explosion would happen harmlessly over an ocean.

A larger body, perhaps 200 meters (124 miles) in diameter, would be catastrophic no matter where it struck. It would certainly penetrate the atmosphere and strike land or water. Indeed, impact into the ocean would be devastating, generating a tsunami (tidal wave) larger than any ever recorded. Such an event might account for some flood myths from ancient times. Astronomers have discovered and tracked only a small fraction of these comparatively small asteroids, and so an impact like this (about a 1 percent chance of happening in this century) probably would occur without warning. Tsunami-warning systems most likely would be ineffective in alerting people to evacuate to high ground. Massive destruction of property along the shores of the impacted ocean would be certain, with an enormous death toll. A similar impact on land would form a crater far larger than Meteor Crater, but the death and destruction would be restricted to within a couple hundred kilometers of ground zero.

**velocity** speed and direction of a moving object; a vector quantity

As frightening as impacts by bodies tens to hundreds of meters in size are to contemplate, more usual natural catastrophes capable of killing just as many people happen 100 times as often. During the twentieth century a dozen natural catastrophes (floods, earthquakes, and the like) each killed between 100,000 and 2 million people. Thus, these "smaller" impacts represent only about 1 percent of the danger.

Impacts by comets and asteroids over 2 kilometers (1.24 miles) in diameter have consequences that exceed those of a nuclear war. There are upper limits to the effects of earthquakes, storms, floods, and exploding volcanoes, which are restricted to localities or regions of the planet. A 2-kilometer (1.24-mile) asteroid, however, would throw enormous quantities of dust and aerosols high in the **stratosphere**, darkening the Sun, leading to the failure of global agriculture for a year or more, and resulting in mass starvation. A billion people might die, and civilization would be threatened. Such impacts are rare, having 1 chance in 10,000 of happening in this century. However, the consequences would be enormous, including possible permanent loss of the accomplishments of modern civilization, and the quantitative risk to human life ranks with other hazards (such as airline safety) that society takes seriously.

## Mitigation

The impact hazard has a hopeful feature: Human beings (unlike dinosaurs) could avert such a catastrophe if it were about to happen. Less than half of the 1- to 2-kilometer (0.62 to 1.24 miles) NEAs have been discovered, and so one could strike without warning. However, an international astronomical program (so far based mostly in the United States) called the Spaceguard Survey employs modest-size wide-field telescopes equipped with charge-coupled devices to search the skies for NEAs larger than about 1 kilometer (0.62 mile). Within less than a decade the paths of about 90 percent of these NEAs will have been charted and it will be known whether one is headed toward Earth in the next decades. A few NEAs will remain undiscovered, and comets from beyond Neptune's orbit will continue to arrive in the inner solar system with only months of advance warning. Thus, there will always be a small chance that humankind will be caught unprepared.

However, current space technology could in principle save the world from an impact catastrophe. Depending on the warning time and the size of the threatening body, several low-thrust propulsion technologies could be used to nudge the object away from its Earth-targeted trajectory. These schemes include solar sails, ion drives, mass drivers, and chemical **rockets**. If the warning time were too short or the object too large, nuclear bombs might be required. Specific engineering designs for these technologies (for example, how to couple the devices to the surface of the NEA) have not been worked out. However, there probably would be enough time to study the body and work out the engineering. Care would have to be taken to deflect the body intact rather than break it into pieces because a swarm of fragments might be more destructive than a single object.

National and international agencies and governments are starting to listen to astronomers, who have been trying to raise the awareness of politicians and emergency management agencies to the impact hazard. However,

**stratosphere** a middle portion of Earth's atmosphere above the tropopause (the highest place where convection and "weather" occurs)

**rockets** vehicles (or devices) especially designed to travel through space, propelled by one or more engines

apart from the modest ground-based Spaceguard Survey, little official action or coordination has been undertaken. Comets and small asteroids are being missed in the Spaceguard census, and the major space and military agencies have paid little attention to the impact hazard. Also, there has been no contingency planning by emergency managers to store food supplies or evacuate people from ground zero in the event of a threatening body. This lack of action represents an implicit political decision to largely ignore the unlikely threats from space in favor of dealing with more near-term issues. SEE ALSO ASTEROIDS (VOLUME 2); CLOSE ENCOUNTERS (VOLUME 2); COMETS (VOLUME 2); ENVIRONMENTAL CHANGES (VOLUME 4); METEORITES (VOLUME 2); MOVIES (VOLUME 4).

*Clark R. Chapman*

### Bibliography

Gehrels, Tom, ed. *Hazards Due to Comets and Asteroids.* Tucson: University of Arizona Press, 1994.

### Internet Resources

"Asteroid and Comet Impact Hazards." NASA Ames Research Center. <http://impact.arc.nasa.gov/index.html>.

"Near-Earth Object Program." NASA Jet Propulsion Laboratory. <http://neo.jpl.nasa.gov/>.

"Report of the U.K. Task Force on Near Earth Objects." <http://www.nearEarth objects.co.uk/>.

"Tumbling Stone." Spaceguard Foundation. <http://spaceguard.ias.rm.cnr.it/tumbling stone/>.

**International Regimes** *See Governance (Volume 4); Political Systems (Volume 4).*

# Interplanetary Internet

Imagine a future in which human intelligence is scattered all over the solar system. That intelligence may take the form of incredibly capable robots that allow us to be "telepresent" in remote parts of the solar system without ever leaving Earth, or perhaps remote space outposts on the Moon or Mars where human beings are learning to live on other worlds. In some of these places there may be thousands or millions of intelligent systems that need to exchange information not only with other intelligence on Earth but also among themselves. How would such communication occur, and how would it differ from the information transfer across the terrestrial Internet that we know so well?

We are all familiar with the explosive growth of the Internet, and the way in which it has entered our daily lives. We log on and expect to instantly access information from all over the world. This is enabled by a vast global network of computers that exchanges information over high-speed communications links. They do this by formatting messages to each other according to highly structured rules or protocols, much the same way that humans talk to each other using highly structured language. Supporting every web page download, every electronic-mail (e-mail) message, and every piece of streaming audio are dozens of computers that are chatting back and forth with each other in the background in order to transfer messages from the source to the destination. They accomplish this by breaking the messages themselves up into little "packets" of data that are routed over the Internet. This "chatty" computer dialog is very similar to a telephone call, where two people are simultaneously online and conducting a conversation.

But what happens when we try to extend the scope of the Internet into space? On Earth, electronic signals zip around the Internet at the speed of light with negligible delay and almost no errors because the distances are short and it is easy to provide strong signals. But as one ventures farther into space the distances become large and delays and errors are introduced. It would be very difficult to conduct a phone call between Earth and the Moon, where it may take five seconds for a signal to make the round-trip. At Mars, where the delay may easily be half an hour, it would be impossible. Furthermore, a continuous connection between Earth and a remote space location is very hard to provide—the radio links are noisy and prone to errors, spacecraft disappear behind the Sun for days on end, planets rotate, and spacecraft on and around them can only occasionally see Earth. The whole nature of communications changes—no longer chatty, with lots of instant feedback, but far more like the letter writing days of the Victorian era in the nineteenth century.

So will we ever be able to talk to other planets using the Internet? The answer is yes, and a small team of engineers at the California Institute of Technology's Jet Propulsion Laboratory in Pasadena, California—the National Aeronautics and Space Administration's lead center for deep-space exploration—is making it happen. New communications protocols are under development that form messages into autonomous "bundles" of information—much like letters or e-mail—that will allow human or robotic users all over the solar system to exchange information across the vast and hostile distances of space even though they may never be simultaneously connected. Deployment of these new capabilities will begin during the period of intensive Mars exploration in the early twenty-first century. The Interplanetary Internet is just around the corner. SEE ALSO COMMUNICATIONS, FUTURE NEEDS IN (VOLUME 4); LIVING ON OTHER WORLDS (VOLUME 4); O'NEILL COLONIES (VOLUME 4); SETTLEMENTS (VOLUME 4); SPACE STATIONS OF THE FUTURE (VOLUME 4); TELEPRESENCE (VOLUME 4).

*Adrian J. Hooke*

**Internet Resources**

InterPlaNet. <http://www.ipnsig.org>.

# Interstellar Travel

Fast, routine travel from one star to another has long been a staple of science fiction. However, interstellar travel would be extremely difficult with current technologies because of the tremendous distances to even the nearest stars, the amount of energy required, and the constraints imposed by the laws of physics. Although there are no specific plans in place for interstellar missions, and there are only a few spacecraft that are heading into interstellar space, a number of concepts for human and robotic spacecraft that could travel from this solar system to another star have been developed.

## Challenges

The greatest challenge of interstellar travel is the enormous distances between stars. Proxima Centauri, the nearest star to the Sun, is about 4.2 **light-years** away, more than 9,000 times the distance between Earth and Neptune. Voyager 2 took twelve years to travel to Neptune, but at the same speed it would take a spacecraft over 100,000 years to reach Proxima Centauri. However, accelerating spacecraft to speeds that would allow them to reach the stars in decades, let alone years, requires energy levels far beyond the capabilities of chemical propulsion systems today.

Travel at high speeds presents several challenges. At extremely high velocities even tiny objects have large amounts of **kinetic energy**. A collision with a speck of dust could be powerful enough to destroy a spacecraft traveling at a significant fraction of the speed of light if the spacecraft is not properly shielded. Relativistic effects also become significant as a spacecraft approaches the speed of light, causing time dilation as well as increasing the mass of the spacecraft.

Regardless of the energy available to accelerate a spacecraft, the speed of light remains the ultimate speed limit that no spacecraft can surpass, according to modern physics. Barring major innovations in physics, it will require years, if not decades, to travel from one star to another. This requires that interstellar spacecraft be able to work for long periods of time, far longer than the short-duration missions common for spacecraft today. Human interstellar missions may require suspended animation or the development of "generation ships," in which the descendants of the original crew members will arrive at the destination.

## Interstellar Propulsion Technologies

Because current chemical propulsion systems are inadequate, scientists have turned their attention to a number of other means to propel spacecraft at the speeds necessary for interstellar travel. Although the technologies needed to make these spacecraft a reality do not exist yet, they are based on well-known laws of physics.

One of the first realistic designs for an interstellar spacecraft was Orion, whose design dates back to the 1950s. Orion would work by ejecting nuclear bombs out the rear of the spacecraft at a rate of five bombs per second. The bombs would explode and push against a shock plate attached to the rear of the spacecraft, accelerating the vehicle. Orion was originally designed as an interplanetary spacecraft for missions to the Moon or Mars, but the design was adapted for interstellar travel. However, the use of such a spacecraft would violate existing treaties that forbid nuclear explosions in space.

The British Interplanetary Society revisited the Orion concept and refined it, creating an interstellar spacecraft design called Daedalus. Daedalus would generate thrust through small **fusion** explosions, using hydrogen scooped up from Jupiter's atmosphere before leaving the solar system. The force of the explosions would be channeled out of the spacecraft through the use of magnetic fields. The spacecraft would be able to reach Barnard's Star, about 6 light-years away, in fifty years.

It took Voyager 2 twelve years to travel from Earth to Neptune (pictured). Current technology does not allow for the speeds needed for travel to other stars and galaxies.

**light year** distance that light in a vacuum would travel in one year (about 5.9 trillion miles [9.5 trillion kilometers])

**kinetic energy** the energy an object has due to its motion

**fusion** the act of releasing nuclear energy by combining lighter elements such as hydrogen into heavier elements

Both Orion and Daedalus require the spacecraft to carry all the fuel needed to cross interstellar distances, a significant fraction of the mass of the vehicle. An alternative proposal, the Bussard Interstellar Ramjet, would circumvent this problem by using the trace amounts of hydrogen in interstellar space. A laser on the front of the spacecraft would fire ahead to ionize hydrogen atoms, which would be scooped into the spacecraft by means of magnetic fields. The hydrogen would then be used in the vehicle's fusion engine to generate thrust. The spacecraft would have to go at least 6 percent of the speed of light for the ramjet to work; to reach this speed, the spacecraft would have to carry some hydrogen of its own. There are a number of potential problems with this concept, including how effectively the ramjet could scoop up hydrogen without slowing down the spacecraft as a result of magnetic field drag. Another major problem is the fact that there are currently no fusion engines.

Another alternative is the use of lasers to propel spacecraft. An interstellar laser sail proposed by scientist Robert Forward would shine an Earth-based laser on a sail attached to a spacecraft, accelerating the craft out of the solar system and towards another star. Forward's original proposal would use a 10-million-gigawatt laser shining on a 1,000-kilometer (62,000 miles) sail attached to a 1,000-ton spacecraft, sending the craft to Alpha Centauri in just ten years. However, the laser would be thousands of times stronger than all of the power used on Earth today, and so Forward revised the concept to use a 10-gigawatt laser on a 16-gram (0.57-ounce), 1-kilometer (0.62-mile) sail embedded with sensors to make observations as it flew by another star.

The best systems for interstellar travel, however, may come from aspects of physics that are not yet known. The National Aeronautics and Space Administration has funded a small project called Breakthrough Propulsion Physics that supports researchers looking into new concepts that could lead to effective interstellar propulsion systems. Research in this area features a number of esoteric topics, from **quantum vacuum** energy to antigravity.

**quantum vacuum** consistent with the Heisenberg uncertainty principle, vacuum is not empty but is filled with zero-point energy and particle-antiparticle pairs constantly being created and then mutually annihilating each other

## Destinations

Where the first interstellar missions will go is an open question. The most likely destinations are the stars closest to Earth, such as Alpha Centauri and Proxima Centauri, Tau Ceti, and Epsilon Eridani. Scientists will probably be most interested in stars that appear to have Earth-like planets, and thus would be likely to have life. Although no Earth-like planets have been discovered, astronomical techniques are improving to the point where such discoveries should be possible within the next few decades. It is quite likely that future interstellar explorers will have a wide range of new worlds to explore. SEE ALSO ANTIMATTER PROPULSION (VOLUME 4); FASTER-THAN-LIGHT TRAVEL (VOLUME 4); LASER PROPULSION (VOLUME 4); POWER, METHODS OF GENERATING (VOLUME 4); SCIENCE FICTION (VOLUME 4); VEHICLES (VOLUME 4).

*Jeff Foust*

**Bibliography**

Mallove, Eugene F., and Gregory L. Matloff. *The Interstellar Handbook: A Pioneer's Guide to Interstellar Travel.* New York: John Wiley & Sons, 1989.

**Internet Resources**

Carter, L. J. "Project Dadedalus—Origins." <http://www.geocities.com/TelevisionCity/2049/DAEDALUS.htm>.

Flora, Michael. "Project Orion: Its Life, Death, and Possible Rebirth." *Encyclopedia Astronautica*. <http://www.astronautix.com/articles/probirth.htm>.

Interstellar-probes.org. <http://www.interstellarprobes.org>.

*Warp Drive, When? Frequently Asked Questions.* NASA Glenn Research Center. <http://www.grc.nasa.gov/WWW/PAO/html/warp/warpfaq).

Woodmansee, Paul. "Interstellar Flight: The Possibilities: Bussard Ramjet." *Rocket Science.* <http://www.woodmansee.com/science/rocket/r-interstellar/r-interstellar-18.html>.

# Ion Propulsion

Ion propulsion is a method of propulsion that uses electrical rather than chemical forces to generate thrust for a spacecraft. Although less powerful than chemical engines, ion propulsion engines are more efficient and can be used continuously for long periods, making them ideal for deep space missions. The concept of ion propulsion has existed for many years, but only recently have ion engine–driven spacecraft been flown.

Ion propulsion works by taking advantage of the very strong repulsive force between two objects with the same electric charge. A cathode emits a stream of **electrons** that collides with neutral atoms of xenon, a gaseous element, in a chamber. The collisions strip the xenon atoms of one or more electrons, converting these atoms into positively charged ions. The xenon ions drift toward a pair of grids, one positively charged and one negatively charged, in back of the chamber. Once the ions are between the grids, the repulsive force from the positively charged grid accelerates them out the back of the chamber at speeds of up to 30 kilometers (18.6 miles) per second. Once the xenon ions are free of the engine, another cathode fires electrons at them to neutralize them and prevent them from being attracted back to the engine. A variation of this design referred to as the "Hall effect thruster," uses a combination of electric and magnetic fields to accelerate ions.

**electrons** negatively charged subatomic particles

A key advantage of ion propulsion is efficiency. The exhaust from an ion engine travels up to 10 times faster than does the exhaust from a chemical engine, generating far more thrust per pound of propellant. However, the thrust from an ion engine is very weak and cannot support the weight of the engine, let alone the rest of the spacecraft. This makes ion propulsion unsuitable for lifting spacecraft off the surface of Earth. In space, however, ion engines can run continuously for weeks, compared to minutes for chemical engines. These engines can build up significant thrust over time.

The American **rocket** pioneer Robert H. Goddard first proposed ion propulsion in 1906. Research started in earnest in the 1950s, and the first suborbital flight tests of ion engines took place in 1964. Although American interest in ion propulsion waned in the late 1960s, the Soviet Union continued to work in this area, flying Hall effect thrusters on a number of spacecraft in Earth orbit. These thrusters allowed the spacecraft to modify their orbits with less propellant than is the case with chemical engines. In the 1990s the American satellite manufacturer Hughes began to include ion thrusters on communications satellites, allowing them to stay in the proper orbit.

**rocket** vehicle (or device) especially designed to travel through space, propelled by one or more engines

Charged atoms emit a faint blue glow from a xenon ion engine tested at NASA's Jet Propulsion Laboratory. Ion propulsion is being researched as an alternative to chemically produced power during space travel.

The most important test of ion propulsion in space has been the National Aeronautics and Space Administration's (NASA) Deep Space One (DS1) spacecraft. DS1 was launched in October 1998 to test a number of advanced technologies, including ion propulsion. A month after launch, and after some initial problems had been overcome, DS1 fired up its ion engine. Working for months at a time, the engine propelled DS1 past the asteroid Braille in July 1999 and the comet Borrelly in September 2001. The engine operated for over 15,000 hours, well over a year, during the mission. SEE ALSO ACCESSING SPACE (VOLUME 1); MARS MISSIONS (VOLUME 4); POWER, METHODS OF GENERATING (VOLUME 4); ROCKET ENGINES (VOLUME 1).

*Jeff Foust*

**Internet Resources**

"Frequently Asked Questions about Ion Propulsion." NASA Jet Propulsion Laboratory. <http://www.nmp.jpl.nasa.gov/ds1/tech/ionpropfaq.html>.

"Ion Propulsion: Over 50 Years in the Making." NASA Marshall Space Flight Center. <http://www.spacescience.com/newhome/headlines/prop06apr99_2.htm>.

"How Does Solar Electric Propulsion (Ion Propulsion) Work?" Northwestern University. <http://www.qrg.ils.nwu.edu/projects/vss/docs/Propulsion/zoom-solar-ion.html>.

# L-5 Colonies

A concept to build giant stations in space far from Earth and the Moon, L-5 colonies would be cities in space, located in a gravitational node in the Earth-Moon system. These colonies would be home to tens of thousands of people each, and serve as bases for building solar power satellites to generate electricity for Earth. L-5 colonies were extensively studied in the 1970s, but the high costs of building them prohibited their construction and they have been largely ignored since.

L-5 is the designation given to one of five Lagrangian points that exist in the Earth-Moon system. These points, also known as libration points, exist where the gravity of Earth and the Moon partially cancel each other out. The first three points, L-1, L-2, and L-3, exist on a line connecting Earth and the Moon. These three libration points are considered unstable: An object placed near them will quickly drift away. The other two points, L-4 and L-5, are in the orbit of the Moon, 60 degrees ahead and behind the Moon. Unlike the other three Lagrangian points, L-4 and L-5 are relatively stable: An object in orbit around either point will remain there.

The first person to propose L-5 colonies was Princeton University physicist Gerard K. O'Neill. Concerned in the early 1970s about both the effects of industrialization on Earth's environment and the energy crisis, he proposed developing giant space stations capable of hosting up to 10,000 people. These space colonies, as O'Neill called them, would be used to support the construction and operation of large solar power satellites that would convert sunlight into microwave energy to be beamed to Earth and converted into electricity.

Many concepts for space colonies✻ were developed in the 1970s, but most shared key characteristics. They had spherical, cylindrical, or wheel shapes, a kilometer (0.6 miles) or more in diameter, and rotated to generate artificial gravity. The interiors were designed to resemble small towns, complete with houses, parks, and farms. O'Neill estimated that one basic design, called Island One, would cost about $100 billion in 1978 dollars (about $275 billion today.)

✻ In the mid-1970s, the U.S. State Department prohibited the use of the term "space colony" because colonialism is a system that denies human equality.

Placing colonies at L-5, rather than on the Moon or in a closer Earth orbit, had a number of advantages. At L-5 the colonies would have continuous sunlight and would be free of the gravity of both Earth and the Moon. The L-5 location would also make it easy to transport building materials from the Moon. At L-5, colonies could be built to support whatever level of gravity was desired, from normal Earth gravity to weightlessness.

The concept of L-5 colonies attracted the attention of the National Aeronautics and Space Administration (NASA), which funded several studies of them and solar power satellites in the 1970s. Interest in such colonies among the general public also led to the creation of the L-5 Society, a precursor to the present-day National Space Society. However, by 1980, NASA's interest in space colonies and space solar power waned and it stopped funding additional studies. Also around this time, supporters discovered that the shuttle would not offer the low launch costs needed to make colonies feasible. There has been only sporadic interest in L-5 colonies since then. SEE ALSO DOMED CITIES (VOLUME 4); DYSON SPHERES (VOLUME 4); O'NEILL COLONIES (VOLUME 4); O'NEILL, GERARD (VOLUME 4); SETTLEMENTS (VOLUME 4).

*Jeff Foust*

**Bibliography**

O'Neill, Gerard K. "Colonization at Lagrangia." *Nature* (August 23, 1974).

———. *The High Frontier: Human Colonies in Space*, 3rd ed. Burlington, ON: Apogee Books, 2000.

Internet Resources

Combs, Mike. "The Space Settlement FAQ." <http://members.aol.com/oscarcombs/ spacsetl.htm>.

# Land Grants

Possession of property in outer space is an area of space law that is complex and controversial. There exists a tension between the desire to encourage scientific exploration that will benefit all humankind and the economic reality that no one wants to invest billions of dollars in a space endeavor that has to be shared with others who have not contributed financially.

Consequently, the question remains: How does one clarify who owns what in space, or, what is called in law, "property rights"? How can an infinite area be divided up? Or should it belong to everyone? If so, how are decisions to be made that involve everyone on Earth? Since the beginning of space exploration nations have been struggling with these questions.

## Treaties

Many countries, through the United Nations General Assembly, have entered into international agreements, international conventions, or charters, which are usually called treaties. A treaty is similar to a law in that it is officially written and is binding, but it is binding only on the states that have signed it.

**The Outer Space Treaty.** The United Nations facilitated the enactment of one of the first treaties that addressed this issue, the 1967 Outer Space Treaty. Operating under the philosophy that "there is a close interrelationship between the prosperity of the developed countries and the growth and development of the developing countries," the treaty holds that space is the heritage of all humankind.

Land grants inherently convey the idea of private property rather than communal or public property. The concepts of community and property have developed over time within most societies. In the majority of societies, possessing land or property is thought of as a natural right that must be protected from intrusion by those who would violate it. However, outer space, which requires enormous financial outlays to even enter, falls between the notions of communal property and private property.

Often, ownership of the high seas is used as an analogy for ownership of space and planets, which are sometimes referred to as "celestial bodies." Maritime law is involved in definitions of and concerns about the utilization and conservation of resources such as fish and oil beneath the seabed. National defense is also a concern in regard to the appropriation of the high seas and outer space.

Resources in outer space could sustain Earth once a growing population has exhausted the planet's natural resources. The Outer Space Treaty addresses the goals of resource management in Article 11 (7):

1. The orderly and safe development of the natural resources of the Moon;

2. The rational management of these resources;

3. The expansion of opportunities in the use of these resources;

4. An equitable sharing by all States Parties in the benefits derived from these resources, whereby the interests and needs of those countries which have contributed either directly or indirectly to the exploration of the Moon, shall be given special consideration.

The Outer Space Treaty prohibits any single country from colonizing outer space but does allow the use of space resources.

**The Moon Treaty.** The 1979 Moon Treaty forbids ownership of the natural resources found on the Moon or other celestial bodies. The purpose of this treaty is to ensure that the wealth of outer space is shared among all nations. Only seven countries have ratified this treaty. Neither the United States nor Russia has agreed with its strict guidelines and thus neither has signed the treaty.

## Comparison of Outer Space and New World Land Grants

Land grants in outer space may seem as alien as the colonization of the New World to us, but some of the concerns are the same. A trip to the New World was costly and required the financial backing of a sovereign nation. Initially, the New World was seen as a source of resources for countries such as Spain and England. With colonization, different groups, such as the Puritans in New England, founded settlements that relied on a philosophy of communal property.

In colonial America an emphasis on agriculture shifted to an emphasis on more commercial endeavors, and so communal rights gave way to speculative land policies that the colonial governments endorsed. Speculators were granted large tracts of land that they then sold to emigrants who had

Who owns the Moon? Possible governmental and commercial uses of resources from the Moon and other planets make this a compelling question.

recently come to the country. The promise of plentiful, cheap land drew groups of colonists from the Old World. A family generally owned its own farm. Land was plentiful, but laborers were lacking.

With the fishing industry came commercialization because many more fish were caught than could be consumed. The fishing industry quickly led to trade for commodities such as molasses, ginger, and sugar, which were sold in the West Indies and Europe. Therefore, it seems possible that as in the initial colonization of the New World, where the backing of countries with large financial resources and a vested interest in lining their coffers with newfound riches derived from resource acquisition, space exploration may require incentives for financial investment.

The history of the western expansion of the United States may parallel the promise of space exploration. During the western expansion speculators were able to purchase for practically nothing vast expanses of land that they soon resold to settlers. But acquisition of a land title was often a dispensable technicality for those too poor to purchase one, or who were not inclined to do so because of the vastness of the land.

Only in the future will it be possible to discover what strategies for granting land ownership in outer space to individuals or groups representing private or national interests will best benefit humankind. Perhaps, as in with the move to the New World, the emphasis will shift from communal property interests to private interests. There is some evidence that the pendulum is swinging in that direction. Space is no longer the exclusive preserve of government programs. Commercial companies launch and operate communications satellites, and other commercial ventures will follow. SEE ALSO Governance (VOLUME 4); Law (VOLUME 4); Law of Space (VOLUME 1); Property Rights (VOLUME 4).

*Nadine M. Jacobson*

**Bibliography**

Fawcett, J. E. S. *Outer Space: New Challenges to Law and Policy.* Oxford, UK: Clarendon, 1984.

Hicks, John D., and George E. Mowry. *A Short History of American Democracy.* Boston: Houghton Mifflin, 1956.

Larkin, Paschal. *Property in the Eighteenth Century with Special Reference to England and Locke.* Port Washington, NY: Kennikat Press, 1969.

Reynolds, Glenn H., and Robert P. Merges. *Outer Space: Problems of Law and Policy.* San Francisco: Westview Press, 1989.

# Laser Propulsion

**rockets** vehicles (or devices) especially designed to travel through space, propelled by one or more engines

The performance of conventional **rockets** is limited by the amount of chemical energy in their fuel. One way to improve the performance of rocket engines is to separate the energy source from the rocket. This can be accomplished by using a laser beam to transfer energy from a stationary source to the rocket. In laser propulsion, the rocket carries a tank of reaction mass, but a stationary laser supplies the energy. The laser can either be located on the ground, and beamed upward at the rocket, or in orbit, and beamed downward.

There are two approaches to laser propulsion to launch from the surface of Earth into space. In laser-thermal propulsion, a laser beam is used to heat a gas, which expands through a rocket nozzle to provide a thrust system. The laser beam is focused on a thermal receiver, consisting of a chamber with pipes through which the reaction fluid can flow. This thermal receiver then heats a fluid to vaporize it into a gas, and the hot gas expands through a conventional rocket nozzle to produce thrust. The advantage of the laser thermal system is that the fluid used for reaction gas can be an extremely light fluid-weight, such as liquid hydrogen, to result in very high performance.

A second approach to laser propulsion for launch is laser-supported detonation. In laser-supported detonation, a repetitively pulsed laser is utilized. Either liquid or solid reaction mass can be used. The reaction mass is vaporized by a pulse of the laser, and then a second laser pulse causes the reaction mass to explode into a high-energy plasma, a gas heated to the point where the **electrons** are stripped from the gas molecules, behind the rocket. The explosion pushes the rocket forward. An advanced laser propulsion system might use air as the reaction mass for the initial portion of the flight, when the rocket is still in the atmosphere. ✳

Laser propulsion systems require a high-power laser, a tracking system to follow the motion of the rocket, a mirror (or "beam director") to aim the laser at the rocket, and a lens or focusing mirror to focus the laser light onto the receiver. The difficulty of laser propulsion is that the system requires a

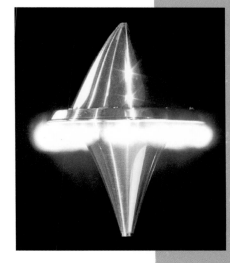

A laser-propelled vehicle is tested in this image.

**electrons** negatively charged subatomic particles

✳ **Low-altitude flight of laser rocket vehicles have been demonstrated by Leik Myrabo at the White Sands Proving Grounds in New Mexico.**

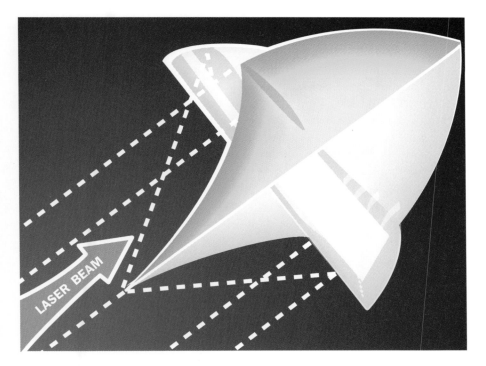

This is a schematic of a "LightCraft" laser-propelled launch vehicle. The propulsive energy is provided by a pulsed laser beam from a ground-based source. The optical rear surface of the lightcraft is used to focus the laser beam into the engine, creating a laser-supported detonation that expands out the rear of the vehicle, producing the thrust that propels the lightcraft into the sky.

laser with higher power than is available in currently existing laser systems. Laser propulsion can also continue to be used once the rocket is in space, to raise the vehicle to a higher orbit, or to boost it to a transfer orbit.

Another propulsion system is laser-electric propulsion, the use of a laser to illuminate a solar array to power an electric thruster. In laser-electric propulsion, a stationary laser (either based on Earth or in orbit) sends a beam of light to a photovoltaic array, which converts the beam into electrical power. This electrical power is then used as the power source for an electric thruster, such as an ion engine.

Further in the future, a laser might also be used to push a lightsail. This propulsion concept could be used as the engine for an interstellar probe. SEE ALSO ACCESSING SPACE (VOLUME 1); ION PROPULSION (VOLUME 4); LIGHTSAILS (VOLUME 4); POWER, METHODS OF GENERATING (VOLUME 4).

*Geoffrey A. Landis*

**Bibliography**

Goldsmith, Donald. *Voyage to the Milky Way: The Future of Space Exploration.* New York: TV Books, 1999.

Myrabo, Leik, and Dean Ing. *The Future of Flight.* New York: Baen Books, 1985.

# Lasers in Space

The word "laser" is an acronym for "light amplification by the stimulated emission of radiation." The laser is a unique device that produces a very pure color of light that is concentrated into a pencil-thin beam that stays concentrated, or focused, as it travels.

Lasers are commonly seen in several ordinary commercial applications, such as bar code scanners, laser pointers, CD players, CD-ROMs, videodiscs, laser surgery, and laser-light shows. However, lasers have many other applications as well. For instance, lasers enable us to communicate and transfer massive amounts of information, monitor our environments, provide protection from aggressive military attacks, and probe the deepest reaches of space and understand the origins of the universe. Lasers will have a myriad of applications in space, the following of which will be highlighted: (1) laser communications, (2) lasers for environmental and remote sensing, (3) space-based laser defense systems, and (4) lasers for astronomical applications in gravity wave detectors.

## Laser Communications

The use of lasers as a tool to transmit information, such as telephone conversations, television programs, and data, is well known. As the **information age** continues to advance, the use of lasers in space as a communication tool will become critical. During the first decade of the twenty-first century, most of the lasers used in communication applications will be associated with optical fiber connections. The growth of the Internet, however, will eventually clog up today's **fiber-optic cables**. This will occur because many people will use computers that send information back and forth to

**information age** the era of our time when many businesses and persons are involved in creating, transmitting, sharing, using, and selling information, particularly through the use of computers

**fiber-optic cable** a thin strand of ultrapure glass that carries information in the form of light, with the light turned on and off rapidly to represent the information sent

each other through fiber-optic phone lines (or fiber-optic cables). This clogging up of the phone lines and cables by computer usage is similar to the clogging up of the phone lines on major holidays, such as Mother's Day.

One way to avoid this problem is to place lasers on satellites in space. In this way, data can be collected from multiple locations that are geographically close to one another and beamed up to a satellite by either a laser or **microwave link**. The satellite can then collect the data and re-transmit the information from one satellite on an ultrahigh-capacity optical data link using lasers.

The importance of using lasers in space for communications is that since light is traveling in space (a **vacuum**) the light signals are not corrupted as much as they would be traveling through optical fiber. In addition, instead of using one color of a laser to transmit information, a satellite could have many different lasers, each transmitting information on a different color. This method of using different colors to increase the amount of information to be transmitted is called "wavelength division multiplexing" and is similar to how conventional radio signals are broadcast on different radio frequencies. With this type of laser technology, optical communication links

Optical films formed with lasers have the potential to replace electronic circuits and wires in optical computers of the future. A space shuttle science team was able to form these films in a purer state than those made on Earth.

**microwave link** a connection between two radio towers that each transmit and receive microwave (radio) signals as a method of carrying information (similar to radio communications)

**vacuum** an environment where air and all other molecules and atoms of matter have been removed

in space could easily handle many tens of trillions of bits of information being sent every second.

## Environmental and Remote Sensing

One of the most common uses of lasers in space is for environmental and remote sensing. In this application, a laser stationed on a satellite can orbit Earth (or other heavenly bodies such as the Moon or Mars) and direct a sequence of short optical pulses onto the surface. These pulses are then reflected from the surface, and the reflected pulses are detected by the satellite that contains the laser. Since the speed of light is known accurately, the time it takes for the light pulses to leave the laser/satellite, travel to the surface, and return can be measured, as can the distance from the satellite to the surface. By repeatedly sending sequences of pulses from the satellite to Earth's surface, a three-dimensional topological map can be generated.

The truly amazing feature of using lasers for this type of geographical mapping is that a distance resolution of a few millimeters can easily be achieved. More importantly, different types of lasers emit different colors of light, and these different colors reflect in particular ways, depending on the type of surface the laser light reflects from. In this way, one can use different types of lasers that not only will map out the geographical terrain but also will be able to measure the composition of clouds and perhaps detect water, **minerals**, and other natural resources underneath the surface.

**minerals** crystalline arrangements of atoms and molecules of specified proportions that make up rocks

## Laser Defense Systems in Space

The prospect of using lasers in space, as part of an overall strategic defense plan of the United States, was gaining significant support in the early twenty-first century. In this scenario, lasers would not be a source of directed energy in an offensive attack, but the lasers would primarily be used in a defensive mode to target, track, and identify potentially hazardous threats that may come in the form of intercontinental ballistic nuclear missiles. The types of lasers used would vary widely, depending on the functions to be performed by the laser. For example, small low-powered lasers would be used to realize **optical radar** functions and to determine the location and **velocity** of moving targets in space. More powerful solid-state or chemical lasers could then be used as a source of directed energy to disable rogue missile attacks. Several plans have been proposed to incorporate lasers in space as part of a unified missile defense plan, including ground-based lasers and orbiting reflectors to assist in tracking and directing the laser radiation. Owing to the harsh environment of space, novel engineering approaches would need to be employed to make these laser systems robust and reliable. In addition, the need for generating power to operate the lasers may easily be accomplished by a combination of solar cells or direct solar-pumped lasers.

**optical radar** a method of determining the speed of moving bodies by sending a pulse of light and measuring how long it takes for the reflected light to return to the sender

**velocity** speed and direction of a moving object; a vector quantity

**optical interferometry** a branch of optical physics that uses the wavelength of visible light to measure very small changes within the environment

**gravity waves** waves that propagate through space and are caused by the movement of large massive bodies, such as black holes and exploding stars

## Gravity Wave Detection in Astronomy

Lasers in space are also used in astronomy. Researchers use ground-based lasers and **optical interferometry** to detect **gravity waves**. Optical interferometry is a technique that splits a laser beam into two beams by using a partially silvered mirror. Each beam travels in a different direction (or arm of the interferometer) and is then reflected back to the silvered mirror. The two beams are recombined and the resulting combined beam can provide information about the differences between the two paths that each beam traversed.

This method is being used on Earth to detect the presence of gravity waves that could have been produced from exploding stars or colliding galaxies. Currently, the limitation in the ground-based approaches is that the sensitivity provided is not sufficient for detecting gravity waves. It should be noted that the lengths of the arms of the interferometer on ground-based gravity wave detectors are on the order of 1 kilometer (0.6 miles). By placing the laser and interferometer in space, the sensitivity can be improved by increasing the lengths of the arms of the interferometer to thousands of kilometers and by removing any disruptions caused by Earth-related effects. The detection of gravity waves would be an incredibly important finding in science, because it would serve as another verification of German-born American physicist Albert Einstein's theory of **general relativity**.

## Outlook Towards the Future

This brief description of the potential applications of using lasers in space shows that these light sources are truly unique and can provide unprecedented performance in specific applications. Scientists and engineers worldwide are researching these and other applications of lasers in space, not only to consider and test the feasibility of specific uses but also to continue to develop state-of-the-art laser systems so that these applications will flourish. What will the newest applications of lasers in space bring? How will these applications change the way humans live their lives? No one can be completely sure, but the new uses that will be discovered will be limited only by the human imagination. SEE ALSO COMMUNICATIONS, FUTURE NEEDS IN (VOLUME 4); LASER PROPULSION (VOLUME 4); MILITARY SPACE USES OF SPACE (VOLUME 4); MINING (VOLUME 4); POWER, METHODS OF GENERATING (VOLUME 4); SCIENTIFIC RESEARCH (VOLUME 4); SPACE INDUSTRIES (VOLUME 4).

*Peter J. Delfyett*

### Bibliography

Bass, Michael, et al., eds. *Handbook on Optics*, 2nd ed. New York: McGraw-Hill, 1995.

Chan, V. W. S. "Optical Space Communications." *IEEE Journal of Selected Topics in Quantum Electronics* 6 (2000):959–975.

Coyne, D. C. "The Laser Interferometer Gravitational Wave Observatory (LIGO) Project." *IEEE Aerospace Applications Conference Proceedings* 4 (1996):31–61.

### Internet Resources

Possel, W. H., and W. C. Martel. "Laser Weapons in Space: A Critical Assessment." <http://www.au.af.mil/au/database/research/ay1998/awc/98-197ex.htm>.

# Launch Facilities

In years past, ships about to sail gathered in port to be fitted and take on their crew and provisions for voyages of exploration or commerce. Today's spaceports have facilities to perform many of these same functions. Of course, launch facilities include the platform from which a rocket is launched, but the most sophisticated facilities also allow state-of-the-art **payload** processing,

**general relativity** a branch of science first described by Albert Einstein showing the relationship between gravity and acceleration

**payload** any cargo launched aboard a rocket that is destined for space, including communications satellites or modules, supplies, equipment, and astronauts; does not include the vehicle used to move the cargo or the propellant that powers the vehicle

A space shuttle slowly moves from the Vehicle Assembly Building on its crawler transporter toward its launch site at the Kennedy Space Center.

**encapsulation** enclosing within a capsule

including fueling and **encapsulation** of satellites and integrating a payload with a launch vehicle. Launch facilities can serve civil, scientific, commercial, and/or military functions.

## Facilities in the United States

The United States has a number of launch sites and associated facilities, located primarily on the East and West Coasts. Perhaps the best known is the National Aeronautics and Space Administration's (NASA) Kennedy Space Center (KSC), where the space shuttle is processed and launched. At KSC are Launch Complex 39's Pad A and Pad B, which were originally built to support Apollo missions but which have been modified for space shuttle launches. Major changes since Apollo include the additions of a Fixed Service Structure (FSS) and a Rotating Service Structure (RSS). Pads A and B are virtually identical and stand almost 106 meters (348 feet) high. At their base are flame trenches, 13 meters (43 feet) deep and 137 meters (449 feet) long, to carry away the flames and exhaust of the shuttle at liftoff.

Because the shuttle stands upright on the launch pad, the RSS is mounted on a semicircular track, which rotates through an arc of 120 degrees and allows payloads to be loaded vertically. The RSS pivots from a hinge on the FSS until the spacecraft changeout room on the RSS fits flush with the orbiter's cargo bay. This room allows payloads to be installed or serviced under contamination-free or "clean room" conditions. A separate Orbiter Access Arm swings out to the orbiter crew hatch. At the end of the arm is the environmentally controlled "White Room" where the ground crew assists astronauts entering the orbiter.

**oxidizer** a substance mixed with fuel to provide the oxygen needed for combustion

Fuel, **oxidizer**, high-pressure gas, electrical, and pneumatic lines connecting the shuttle with ground-support equipment are routed through the

RSS and FSS. There are approximately 400,000 meters (1.3 million feet) of tubing and piping at Launch Complex 39, enough to reach from Orlando to Miami. Not far from Pads A and B are large ball-shaped liquid oxygen and liquid hydrogen storage tanks used to store supercold propellants for the shuttle's external tank.

The shuttle is transported to Launch Complex 39 aboard the Mobile Launcher Platform (MLP), a giant crawler with eight tracks—each 2 meters (6.5 feet) by 13 meters (43 feet)—with cleats that weigh a ton each. Mounted on these eight tracks is a platform, bigger than a baseball diamond, on which the shuttle rides to the launch pad at 1.6 kilometers per hour (1 mile per hour). Once there, six permanent and four extensible pedestals are used to provide support. The MLP starts its trek to Launch Complex 39 from the giant cube-shaped Vehicle Assembly Building (VAB), where the shuttle is mated with its external tank and twin solid rocket boosters (SRB). The VAB was originally built for assembly of Apollo/Saturn vehicles and is one of the largest buildings in the world, enclosing 3.6 million cubic meters (4.7 million cubic yards) of space.

Inside the VAB, integrated SRB segments are hoisted onto the MLP and mated together to form two complete SRBs. The external tank is inspected, checked out, and attached to the SRBs already in place. Next, the orbiter, which is refurbished inside the Orbiter Processing Facility, is towed to the VAB where it is raised to a vertical position, lowered onto the MLP, and mated to the rest of the stack. When assembly and checkout is complete, the crawler-transporter picks up the platform and the shuttle and carries them to the pad.

Adjacent to the VAB is the Launch Control Center, a four-story building that acts as the "brain" of Launch Complex 39. Here are housed four "firing rooms," in addition to telemetry and tracking equipment, plus computers of the Launch Processing System (LPS), a highly automated, computer-controlled system that oversees the entire checkout and launch process. The LPS continually monitors the space shuttle and its ground components, including its environmental controls and propellant loading equipment.

While KSC is widely recognized for its shuttle connection, launch facilities for **expendable launch vehicles** (ELVs) are located at the Cape Canaveral Air Station, south of Launch Complex 39, and at Vandenberg Air Force Base in California. The Cape Canaveral Air Station contains NASA, U.S. Air Force, and contractor facilities for processing ELV hardware and payloads. In addition, Launch Complex 36 is used to launch Atlas II vehicles. This complex has two launch pads (Pads A and B), a blockhouse, and a launch support building and equipment needed to prepare, service, and launch the Atlas vehicles. Pad 36A is used for military launches, and Pad 36B is for commercial launches. Just south of these facilities is Launch Complex 17, which is designed to support Delta II and Delta III launch vehicles.

The primary missions of launch facilities on Vandenberg Air Force Base include military and scientific launchings, and the conducting of missile test flights. There are facilities to support Delta launch vehicles and the Titan rocket, America's largest ELV. The United States also maintains smaller launch facilities, such as the Wallops Flight Facility in Virginia, which typically support scientific research and orbital and suborbital payloads.

**expendable launch vehicles** launch vehicles, such as a rocket, not intended to be reused

The Baikonur cosmodrome has been the launch site of all of the Russian piloted spaceflights, including Sputnik 1 and this Soyuz-TM rocket.

**geostationary orbit** a specific altitude of an equatorial orbit where the time required to circle the planet matches the time it takes the planet to rotate on its axis

**cryogenic** related to extremely low temperatures; the temperature of liquid nitrogen or lower

**fairing** a structure designed to provide low aerodynamic drag for an aircraft or spacecraft in flight

## Major Launch Facilities outside of the United States

The Guiana Space Center, located on the French Guiana coastline, services and launches the European-built Ariane family of rockets. This spaceport was deliberately situated close to the equator to support flights to **geostationary orbit**, the destination of many commercial satellites. The spaceport's ELA-2 Launch Complex supports the Ariane 4 vehicle and has been used for more ninety launches. More recently, Arianespace's ELA-3 Launch Complex was built specifically to serve the new Ariane 5 heavy-lift vehicle. Ariane 5 starts its assembly process at the 58-meter-tall (190-foot-tall) Launcher Integration Building where the main **cryogenic** stage is positioned over Ariane 5's mobile launch table. The Ariane 5 is then transferred to the Final Assembly Building. In this facility, the payload with its **fairing** is mated to the launcher, the attitude control system is loaded with fuel, and the launcher's upper stage is filled with storable propellant. After leaving ELA-3's Final Assembly Building, the completed Ariane 5 arrives at the launch zone, where it is positioned over a concrete foundation and readied for launch.

The Chinese have several launch facilities—Jiuquan, Taiyuan, and Xichang—but the Xichang Satellite Launch Center, which is located within a military installation, supports all **geostationary** missions from its location in southern China. Two separate launch pads support flight operations, and a command and control center is located several kilometers from the launch site. Other facilities include communication systems to provide telephone and data communications.

The Tanegashima Space Center is Japan's largest launch facility. Located on an island 115 kilometers (71 miles) south of Kyushu, this 8.6-square-kilometer (3.3-square-mile) complex plays a central role in prelaunch countdown and postlaunch tracking operations. On-site facilities include the Osaki Range, tracking and communication stations, several **radar** stations, and optical observation facilities. There are also related developmental facilities for firing of liquid- and solid-fuel rocket engines.

Russia launches all of its crewed missions as well as all geostationary, lunar, and planetary missions from the Baikonur Cosmodrome. Baikonur is the launch complex where Sputnik 1, Earth's first artificial satellite, was launched in 1957. It is the only Russian launch site capable of launching the Proton launch vehicle and was used for several International Space Station missions. The Plesetsk Military Cosmodrome, Russia's northernmost launch complex, is used to launch satellites into high-inclination, polar, and highly **elliptical** orbits.

Unique among the world's launch facilities is the floating Sea Launch facility managed by the Boeing Company. Two unique ships form the marine **infrastructure** of the Sea Launch system. The first is a custom-built Assembly and Command Ship (ACS), and the second is the Launch Platform (LP), a semisubmersible vessel that is one of the world's largest oceangoing launch platforms. Both vessels are equipped with spacecraft handling and launch support systems.

The LP—a former North Sea oil-drilling platform—is equipped with a large, environmentally controlled hangar for storage of the Sea Launch rocket during transit, and with mobile transporter/erector equipment that is used to erect the rocket in launch position prior to fueling and launch. Special facilities onboard enable the storage of rocket fuels. Floating nearby is the ACS that serves as a floating rocket assembly factory while in port and also houses mission control facilities for launches at sea. Launch operations begin at home port in Long Beach, California, where satellites are fueled and encapsulated in a payload processing facility and then transferred to the ACS for integration with the launch vehicle.

## Commercial Spaceports

Around the world, steps have been taken to develop commercial spaceports, some at sites of established launch facilities and others unrelated to existing facilities. For example, the Spaceport Florida Authority has created a commercial spaceport where missiles were once launched from the Cape Canaveral Air Station. Launch Complex 46 has been modified to accommodate Lockheed Martin Corporation's LMLV family of launch vehicles and Orbital Sciences Corporation's Taurus launcher.

California's Western Commercial Space Center is planned for Vandenberg Air Force Base. Thousands of kilometers up the coast, the Alaska

Aerospace Development Corporation has built a commercial spaceport at Narrow Cape on Kodiak Island, about 400 kilometers (250 miles) south of Anchorage. The Kodiak Launch Complex is a state-of-the-art launch facility containing all-weather processing adaptable to all current small launch vehicles, and it is the only commercial launch range in the United States not co-located with a federal facility. Other commercial launch facilities have been proposed at various locations around the world, including Australia and the Caribbean. SEE ALSO LAUNCH MANAGEMENT (VOLUME 3); LAUNCH SITES (VOLUME 3); SPACE CENTERS (VOLUME 3); SPACE INDUSTRIES (VOLUME 4); SPACE SHUTTLE (VOLUME 3); TRAFFIC CONTROL (VOLUME 4).

*John F. Kross*

**Bibliography**

Cortright, Edgar M., ed. *Apollo Expeditions to the Moon.* Washington, DC: National Aeronautics and Space Administration, 1975.

Kross, John F. "Fields of Dreams: America's Growing Commercial Spaceports." *Ad Astra* 8, no. 1 (1996):27–31.

Oberg, James E. *The New Race for Space.* Harrisburg, PA: Stackpole Books, 1984.

Shelton, William R. *Man's Conquest of Space.* Washington, DC: National Geographic Society, 1975.

**Internet Resources**

Arianespace. <http://www.arianespace.com/index1.htm>.

Kennedy Space Center. <http://www.ksc.nasa.gov/>.

Russian Space Agency. <http://liftoff.msfc.nasa.gov/rsa/pads.html>.

Sea Launch. <http://www.sea-launch.com/special/sea-launch/facilities.htm>.

*World Space Guide.* Federation of American Scientists. <http://www.fas.org/spp/guide/china/facility/xichang.htm>.

# Law

The birth of the Space Age in the late 1950s opened a new frontier for exploration. It also opened a new arena for law, since existing international laws and treaties did not cover launches or other activities in space. Given the backdrop of the Cold War, there was a concern by some that space could become a new battlefield between the United States and the Soviet Union. In 1959, in an effort to keep space free of conflict, the United Nations established the Committee on the Peaceful Uses of Outer Space (COPUOS), which was charged with, among other things, considering the legal problems that could stem from space travel. COPUOS, through its legal subcommittee, led to the development of several space treaties.

The first international treaty that included specific provisions related to space was a nuclear test ban treaty in 1963. That accord specifically prohibited countries from detonating nuclear weapons in space. The first treaty devoted exclusively to space, though, was the Treaty on Principles Governing the Activities of States in the Exploration and Use of Outer Space, Including the Moon and Other Celestial Bodies, more commonly known as the Outer Space Treaty. This 1967 agreement prevents nations from making territorial claims in space or placing weapons of mass destruction there. The treaty does allow nations to maintain sovereignty over satellites and other vehicles they launch, and requires nations to be responsible for any damage or loss caused by spacecraft launched from their territory, regardless of whether the spacecraft belonged to the government or another organization or company. The Outer Space Treaty also requires nations to treat astronauts as "envoys of mankind" and render them any necessary assistance.

The Outer Space Treaty was seen at the time as a major achievement toward the goal of peaceful exploration of space, at a time when the two major nations involved in space exploration, the United States and Soviet Union, were locked in struggle against each other. By preventing countries from laying claim to the Moon or other bodies, prohibiting the placement of nuclear weapons, and preventing countries from establishing military bases in space, the treaty largely succeeded in its goal of keeping space from being turned into a new battleground. While the militaries of the United States and former Soviet Union, as well as other nations, make extensive use of space, it is for the purposes of **reconnaissance**, navigation, and communication.

**reconnaissance** a survey or preliminary exploration of a region of interest

Some provisions of the Outer Space Treaty were followed up by additional agreements over the next several years. The section of the treaty regarding astronauts was expanded upon with a separate agreement in 1968, the Agreement on the Rescue of Astronauts, the Return of Astronauts and the Return of Objects Launched into Outer Space, regarding the rescue and return of astronauts and objects. This agreement requires countries to assist astronauts who land on their territory and return them to their home country as soon as possible. Another agreement in 1972, the Convention on International Liability for Damage Caused by Space Objects, expanded the section of the Outer Space Treaty that governs the liability a country has for damage that a spacecraft could cause to another country. A 1975 agreement, the Convention on Registration of Objects Launched into Outer Space, requires countries to give the United Nations basic details about each spacecraft it launches.

The last, and most controversial, space treaty was the Agreement Governing the Activities of States on the Moon and Other Celestial Bodies, completed in 1979. This accord, popularly known as the Moon Treaty, requires nations to use the Moon and other bodies for peaceful, scientific purposes and not to damage its environment. The treaty also requires nations to treat the Moon and its natural resources as the "common heritage of mankind"—they do not belong to a single country, organization, or company. Any benefits gained from those resources, according to the treaty, are to be shared with all countries that signed the agreement through an international organization.

The language in the Moon Treaty regarding the use of the Moon's natural resources generated considerable controversy in the United States and other nations, since it would prevent private enterprise from developing in space. The United States did not sign the treaty, in part because lobbying by space activists opposed to the agreement led the Senate to opt against signing it. Only nine nations have ratified the treaty, none of which are major spacefaring nations. While enough nations have ratified the treaty for it to go into effect, the lack of support from major nations means that the treaty has little real power.

The United Nations has developed no additional space treaties since the Moon Treaty. However, there have been a number of minor declarations that COPUOS has approved since then. These declarations cover issues such as the use of television broadcasting and remote sensing satellites as well as the use of nuclear power sources in spacecraft. In recent years there have been discussions about either renegotiating the Outer Space Treaty or developing a new treaty to expressly forbid weapons of any kind in space, including those that might be used in a missile defense system. This effort has been opposed in particular by representatives of the United States, who note that there is no "arms race" in space as of 2002, and no evidence of one for the foreseeable future.

The field of space law is not limited to international treaties. A number of nations, including the United States, have written their own laws governing the use of space by their citizens. Many of these laws are a direct outgrowth of the international treaties, fulfilling some of the provisions in them. For example, in the United States, companies that wish to launch a satellite are required by law to obtain a license from the Federal Aviation Administration to ensure that the launch will be conducted in a safe manner. This law is in place because the Outer Space Treaty makes the U.S. government responsible for all launches from its territory, including those by private parties. SEE ALSO Governance (volume 4); Law of Space (volume 1); Political Systems (volume 4).

*Jeff Foust*

### Bibliography

Reynolds, Glenn H., and Robert P. Merges. *Outer Space: Problems of Policy and Law.* Boulder, CO: Westview Press, 1994.

Von Bencke, Matthew J. *The Politics of Space.* Boulder, CO: Westview Press, 1997.

### Internet Resources

"Frequently Asked Questions about Space Law." International Institute of Air & Space Law. <http://ruljis.leidenuniv.nl/group/jflr/www/faq.htm>.

"International Space Law." United Nations Office for Outer Space Affairs. <http://www.oosa.unvienna.org/SpaceLaw/spacelaw.htm>.

"Space Law." McGill University Institute of Air & Space Law. <http://www.iasl.mcgill.ca/spacelaw.htm>.

# Ley, Willy

### Scientist, Engineer, and Science Writer
### 1909–1969

Willy Ley was born in Berlin, Germany, in 1909. Educated as a paleontologist, Ley chose a career in rocketry and became a tireless advocate of the concept of rocket travel. He founded the German Society for Space Travel in 1927 and attempted to establish that organization as the world's most important society for spaceflight. Among the members he recruited was Wernher von Braun, who later moved to the United States and designed the Saturn series of rockets that carried astronauts to the Moon and space stations into Earth orbit.

Ley emigrated to the United States in 1934 when the German government chose to use rockets as military weapons, a decision he opposed. In the United States he became a popular writer on scientific subjects, includ-

Willy Ley was a tireless supporter of the idea of rocket travel.

ing spaceflight, rocketry, and astronomy. He advised filmmakers, including Fritz Lang and Walt Disney, and helped Disney design a theme park attraction about travel to the planets and a documentary television series. Ley worked with *Collier's* magazine in its special 1947 series about space travel, written by von Braun. The magazine articles and books that followed were a major force in popularizing the idea of spaceflight in the period after World War II. Ley wrote more than nineteen books, including *The Conquest of Space* (1959), *Rockets and Space Travel* (1948), *Kant's Cosmogeny* (1968), and *Rockets, Missiles, and Space Travel* (1961–1969). He died in 1969, a few weeks before the launch of Apollo 11 and the first landing of astronauts on the Moon. SEE ALSO ROCKETS (VOLUME 3); VON BRAUN, WERNHER (VOLUME 3).

*Frank Sietzen, Jr.*

### Bibliography

Ley, Willy. *The Conquest of Space*. New York: Viking Press: 1959.

———. *Rockets and Space Travel*. New York: Viking Press, 1948.

# Lightsails

A beam of light carries both energy and momentum. The momentum of light results in a slight pressure on a surface exposed to sunlight that is known as photon pressure. When light reflects off a mirror, it pushes the mirror slightly. A spacecraft that uses this effect for propulsion is called a lightsail. One that specifically uses light from the Sun to push the sail is called a solar sail spacecraft.

Photon pressure is very weak. At the distance of Earth from the Sun, the pressure produced by sunlight on a mirror with an area of 1 square kilometer (247 acres, or about a third of a square mile) is slightly under 10 Newtons. This pressure would cause an acceleration of about a tenth of a centimeter per second per second on a spacecraft with a mass of 10,000 kilograms (roughly 10 tons). This is not a very high rate of acceleration, but because the mirror does not use up any fuel, the acceleration can be continuous, and speed will build up slowly. In an hour (3,600 seconds) the speed will build up to 3 meters per second (about 10 feet/second); in a day (86,400 seconds) the speed will build up to almost 80 meters per second (260 feet/second); and in a year the speed will build up to 28 kilometers per second—over 96,000 kilometers (60,000 miles) per hour.

## Solar Lightsails

The characteristics of a solar sail spacecraft are extremely light weight, a very large sail area, and low but constant acceleration. Designs for a solar sail spacecraft use a sail that is made out of thin plastic (often Mylar or Kapton), with a thin coating of aluminum to make it reflective. The total sail thickness might be as little as 5 micrometers (1/4000th of an inch). A square meter of this type of sail will weigh only 7 grams (a quarter of an ounce). To keep the thin sail spread, a solar sail spacecraft will use lightweight spars, or else the sail will rotate so that **centrifugal** force keeps it extended.

**centrifugal** directed away from the center through spinning

The light pressure force on a sail, F, can be calculated from the Einstein relation:

$$F = 2P/c$$

A solar sail spaceship uses the Sun's energy to propel it through space.

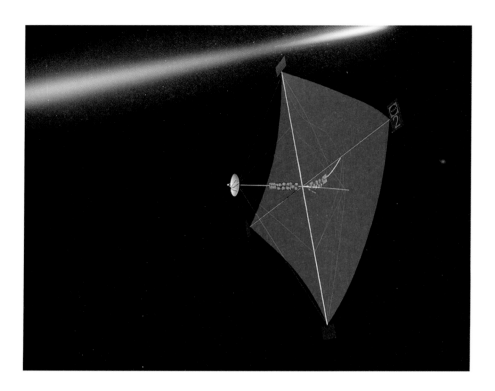

The force produced is equal to two times the power of light reflected, divided by the speed of light. (The factor of two assumes a perfectly reflecting mirror and is derived from the fact that the reflected light is reversed in direction, thus giving the sail a momentum of twice the photon momentum.)

The force of a solar sail need not be directly outward from the Sun. If the sail is tilted, a sideways force can be produced to increase or decrease the **orbital velocity**. If the orbital velocity is increased, the orbit moves outward from the Sun; if the velocity is decreased, the orbit moves inward toward the Sun.

Lightsails have been proposed as a propulsion system for missions to other stars because the fact that a lightsail does not need a fuel tank means that it can continue to accelerate for the extremely long period required to achieve a significant fraction of the speed of light. Since a mission to the stars would move through interstellar space far from the Sun, this type of lightsail-propelled starship would require a large laser to beam the light to push the sail. To make the lightest possible sail (and thus create the highest level of acceleration), proposed laser-pushed lightsails would be designed without the plastic sheet and would have only the thin reflective layer of the sail.

## Solar Wind

The pressure produced by light from the Sun should not be confused with the solar wind. The solar wind consists of a stream of charged particles (mostly **protons**) emitted by the Sun. The solar wind also has a pressure, although because the density of the solar wind is very low, the pressure is also low. Solar-wind pressure is about one-tenth as strong as light pressure.

**orbital velocity** velocity at which an object needs to travel so that its flight path matches the curve of the planet it is circling; approximately 8 kilometers (5 miles) per second for low-altitude orbit around Earth

**protons** positively charged subatomic particles

The use of magnetic fields to sail on this solar wind pressure has been proposed. This is called "magnetic sail" propulsion or "minimagnetospheric plasma propulsion." SEE ALSO POWER, METHODS OF GENERATING (VOLUME 4); SOLAR POWER SYSTEMS (VOLUME 4).

*Geoffrey A. Landis*

**Bibliography**

Clarke, Arthur C. "The Wind from the Sun." In *The Collected Stories of Arthur C. Clarke.* New York: Tor, 2001.

Friedman, Louis. *Starsailing.* New York: John Wiley & Sons, 1988.

Mallove, Eugene, and Greg Matloff. *The Starflight Handbook.* New York: John Wiley & Sons, 1989.

# Living on Other Worlds

Many things about Mars would remind a settler of Earth, but some things are quite different. Except for the lack of any vegetation, the sandy, rock-strewn landscape looks much like an earthly desert. Dust devils and blowing dust storms are often seen. A day on Mars is 24.6 hours, similar to Earth's day, so the **circadian rhythm** of a settler would not be upset. Mars's rotation axis is tilted at 25 degrees compared to Earth's 23.5 degrees, so Mars also has seasons. However, its year is nearly two Earth-years long because Mars is one and a half times farther from the Sun. Therefore, the seasons on Mars are much longer than Earth seasons. Martian gravity is only about four-tenths as great as gravity on Earth. A person weighing 60 kilograms (132 pounds) on Earth would weigh about 24 kilograms (53 pounds) on Mars.

**circadian rhythm** the activities and bodily functions that recur every 24 hours, such as sleeping and eating

The Moon, on the other hand, is extremely different from Earth. It rotates once on its axis in the same time it goes once around Earth. Consequently, the Moon's day is about twenty-seven and one-third days long—two weeks of sunshine followed by two weeks of darkness. Also, the same side of the Moon always faces Earth. To someone standing on the visible side of the Moon and looking up, Earth is always at the same spot in the sky. Although it has phases like the Moon does, it never sets. Gravity on the Moon is only one-sixth of Earth gravity. A person weighing 60 kilograms (132 pounds) on Earth would weigh about 10 kilograms (22 pounds) on the Moon.

In considering how people might live in a settlement on another world, one needs to examine both the necessities of life and the quality of life. The basic necessities are oxygen, water, food, and protection from radiation. Quality of life includes pleasant surroundings, having something worthwhile to do, good health, a general feeling of well-being.

## The Basic Necessities

Oxygen is certainly the most important of human necessities. Humans can live for days without food or water but only minutes without oxygen. Earth is the only known place that has a breathable atmosphere. The Moon has no atmosphere, and the Martian atmosphere is 95 percent carbon dioxide at a pressure only one-hundredth that of Earth's atmosphere.

The housing and equipment needed for settling other worlds would incorporate adaptations made to suit alien environments.

Airtight habitats are necessary. They come in various sizes, ranging from a large dome enclosing an entire settlement to a small space suit enclosing an individual. Inside the habitat, the temperature, pressure, and oxygen content would be controlled. Pressure must be sufficient that lungs operate efficiently and oxygen is absorbed into the bloodstream. On Earth, sea-level pressure is 14.7 pounds per square inch (psi), but people live comfortably in mountain towns where the pressure is less than 10 psi. Pressure in the habitats would probably be less than 10 psi. Lower pressure means less stress on the structure of the habitat and less leakage. Settlers would have to wear a space suit whenever they left the habitat on foot, but rover vehicles for exploration could be pressurized with a breathable atmosphere.

In the list of essentials, water is second only to oxygen. Water was recently detected in sheltered craters in the polar regions of the Moon where the Sun never shines. There is evidence in the images of Mars that water once flowed on the Red Planet. Although the surface of the planet is extremely dry, much of the water may still be frozen in the ground similar to the permafrost in Earth's arctic regions. Dormant volcanoes exist on Mars, and there are probably warm spots underground where liquid water may exist.

An initial supply of food would have to be brought from Earth. A lunar settlement could continue to be supplied from Earth; it is only a three-day trip from Earth to the Moon. A permanent settlement on Mars would construct greenhouses in which to grow its own food supply using the resources of the planet. Plants need carbon dioxide and Mars's atmosphere has plenty. As a by-product, plants produce oxygen.

**minerals** crystalline arrangements of atoms and molecules of specified proportions that make up rocks

Carbon dioxide and noxious gases would be cleansed from the habitat air. Fresh oxygen extracted from Martian **minerals**, water, and atmospheric carbon dioxide would be added to the habitat's air as needed. Lunar settlers could extract oxygen from the minerals ilmenite ($FeTiO_3$) and anorthite ($CaAl_2Si_2O_8$). Everything would be recycled—air and water, in particular. Solid waste would be recycled into fertilizer and other usable products.

Settlers would need protection against the high-energy particles in space, mostly **protons** and **electrons** from the Sun and cosmic rays from beyond the solar system. On Earth humans are protected from these hazardous particles by Earth's magnetic field, which deflects them away, and by the atmosphere, which absorbs them before they get to the ground. The Moon, without a magnetic field or atmosphere, affords no protection against them. Mars also has no current magnetic field. The thin atmosphere of Mars absorbs some of the particles, and a settlement's walls would reduce them to a tolerable level, no greater than living on a mountaintop on Earth. Occasionally **solar flares** on the Sun spew out very-high-speed particles in great number and intensity. For protection during such a storm, settlers would have underground "storm cellars," much as storm cellars are used for protection against tornadoes in the Great Plains of the United States.

From the above it is obvious that Mars is a more desirable place than the Moon to establish a new branch of human civilization.

## A City in a Dome

The enclosure for the settlement would be an inflated sphere with the bottom half buried underground. A simple dome would be difficult to anchor down because the pressure of the air inside would tend to force the dome off its foundation. With a sphere, however, the downward air pressure and the weight of the dirt in the bottom half would hold the upper half in place. The dirt-filled lower half would contain tunnels for rapid transit and chambers for life-support equipment and storage.

To reduce the stress of being on an alien world, the homes should look like terrestrial homes, especially the interiors. Construction material from Earth would be at a premium, so buildings inside the spherical shell would be square. Using the same amount of material, a square building has more floor space than a rectangular building. The citizens of this strange new world would quickly learn to use indigenous materials. They would develop their own ideas of what a Martian home should look like and how to make it comfortable.

Obviously the city in the sphere would have a circular layout. The center of activity would be located in the center of the settlement with a circular street running around the perimeter and linear streets radiating outward from the center. With such a layout, everyone would have about the same distance to walk to reach the center.

## Energy Sources

No oxygen-consuming or polluting fuels would be allowed; only electric energy would be used in the dome. Legs, bicycles, and electric carts would be the primary means of transportation.

Nuclear generators located outside the habitat some distance away would be a primary source of electric power. In addition, electricity could be generated by solar panels during the day when the Sun is shining. Sunlight,

**protons** positively charged subatomic particles

**electrons** negatively charged subatomic particles

**solar flares** explosions on the Sun that release bursts of electromagnetic radiation, such as light, ultraviolet waves, and X rays, along with high speed protons and other particles

however, is only half as intense at Mars than at Earth because Mars is one and a half times farther from the Sun, so the solar panels would have to be twice as large to produce the same electricity. On the Moon, night is two weeks long during which time the Sun could not be a source of electric power.

Once the settlement is well established, indigenous fuels would be used. Methane could be manufactured from the carbon dioxide in the Martian atmosphere. Water can be electrolyzed into hydrogen and oxygen simply by running an electric current through it.

Communications within the settlement would be by cell phone and videophone. Mars and the Moon are both much smaller in diameter than Earth so the horizon is much nearer and line-of-sight television and cell phones would work only for much shorter distances. Low-frequency shortwave radio would work over longer distances on Mars because it has an **ionosphere** to reflect the radio waves beyond the horizon.

Communicating with Earth from Mars involves a time delay because of the distance the radio waves must travel. This means that a Martian settler talking to someone on Earth using a radiophone would have to wait for their response, ten minutes to half an hour, depending on how far apart Mars and Earth are in their orbits. The best way to communicate would be by e-mail.

**ionosphere** a charged particle region of several layers in the upper atmosphere created by radiation interacting with upper atmospheric gases

## The Workforce

From the above description of the settlement one can see the wide variety of jobs that must be done. The atmosphere control equipment, the water pumps and distribution system, the electrical generating and distributing system, the structure of the habitat, the vehicles, and the greenhouses, all require people who can do more than just repair the machinery. Members of the settlement would need to thoroughly understand how the entire system works so they could modify or redesign it to improve its operation. Besides keeping the habitat functioning, scientists and engineers would need to explore the planet to look for resources that can be mined, processed, and fabricated into useful products to build additional habitats for future immigrants.

In the beginning, with only a few settlers, there would be a labor shortage. A person who is expert in several trades and professions would be given the first chance to go. Construction engineers, mechanical engineers, agricultural engineers, and at least one medical doctor would likely be among the first settlers.

Eventually, the settlers would find products that can be manufactured on the Moon and Mars better and cheaper than on Earth, and they would have a surplus to sell to Earth in exchange for equipment that cannot easily be manufactured on other worlds. As the population grows, the settlement would become more self-sufficient, eventually establishing its own political system and declaring its independence from Earth. SEE ALSO COMMUNITIES IN SPACE (VOLUME 4); EARTH—WHY LEAVE? (VOLUME 4); FOOD PRODUCTION (VOLUME 4); GOVERNANCE (VOLUME 4); HABITATS (VOLUME 3); HUMAN MISSIONS TO MARS (VOLUME 3); INTERPLANETARY INTERNET (VOLUME 4); LAND GRANTS (VOLUME 4); LUNAR BASES (VOLUME 4); LUNAR OUTPOSTS (VOLUME 4); MARS (VOLUME 2); MARS BASES (VOLUME 4); MARS

MISSIONS (VOLUME 4); MICROGRAVITY (VOLUME 2); MOON (VOLUME 2); PO-LITICAL SYSTEMS (VOLUME 4); PROPERTY RIGHTS (VOLUME 4); RELIGION (VOL-UME 4); SETTLEMENTS (VOLUME 4); SOCIAL ETHICS (VOLUME 4).

*Thomas Damon*

### Bibliography

Damon, Thomas. *Introduction to Space: The Science of Spaceflight*, 3rd ed. Melbourne, FL: Krieger, 2001.

Lovelock, James, and Michael Allaby. *The Greening of Mars.* New York: St. Martin's/Marek, 1984.

Reiber, Duke B., ed. *The NASA Mars Conference.* San Diego, CA: American Astronautical Society, 1988.

Stoker, Carol, ed. *The Case for Mars III.* San Diego, CA: American Astronautical Society, 1989.

Stoker, Carol, and Carter Emmart, eds. *Strategies for Mars: A Guide to Human Exploration.* San Diego, CA: American Astronautical Society, 1996.

Zubrin, Robert. *The Case for Mars: The Plan to Settle the Red Planet and Why We Must.* New York: Free Press, 1996.

———. *Entering Space: Creating a Spacefaring Civilization.* New York: Tarcher/Putnam, 1999.

# Lunar Bases

When humans return to Earth's Moon, they will probably first live for short periods of time in lunar outposts. Eventually, they will establish lunar bases where they can live for longer periods—months or even years. These bases may result from the growth of lunar outposts, or they may be designed as lunar bases from the outset.

Any successful lunar base must accomplish a few goals. First, it must protect and satisfy the needs of those who live there. Second, it must enable the inhabitants to get some useful work done. Finally, it must minimize the cost of operating it. Sending anything from Earth to the Moon is very expensive, so a high priority for any lunar base will be to minimize the need for resupply from Earth.

An ideal place to meet all these goals might be the Aristarchus Plateau. Located at about 25° north latitude, 50° west longitude, the Aristarchus Plateau is relatively easy to spot from Earth. Aristarchus crater, at the plateau's southeast edge, is the brightest feature on the full Moon. Aristarchus Plateau is covered by fine-grained **pyroclastic** glass beads formed when volcanoes erupted there more than a billion years ago. This material is a good resource, and the area is very interesting to geologists.

**pyroclastic** pertaining to clastic (broken) rock material expelled from a volcanic vent

## Protection of the Inhabitants

The most critically important function of a lunar base is to protect its inhabitants. The Moon has no atmosphere, so a lunar base must be airtight and provide breathable air. Earth's atmosphere is good for more than breathing, though. It protects humans from harmful radiation from space. A lunar base must shield those inside from radiation, and pyroclastic material can do that. From **radar** studies, scientists have found that the pyroclastic deposits on the Aristarchus Plateau are loose and deep enough to be easily

**radar** a technique for detecting distant objects by emitting a pulse of radio-wavelength radiation and then recording echoes of the pulse off the distant objects

While NASA has no formal plans for a human expedition to the Moon or Mars as of 2002, this conception of a lunar base and extra-base activity captures and presents the various theories and possibilities that have developed over the years.

**shielding** providing protection for humans and electronic equipment from cosmic rays, energetic particles from the Sun, and other radioactive materials

dug up and moved around. It would be relatively easy to scoop out a trench, place a habitation module in it, and cover it with several feet of pyroclastic material. That would be enough to protect those inside.

Another way to protect a lunar base from radiation is to put it underground in a lava tube. Photographs of the Aristarchus region show many interrupted channels. These may be lava tubes that have collapsed in places. The interruptions may be places where the lava tubes are still intact. Future lunar explorers might find suitably large, intact lava tube sections that could be turned into next-generation lunar bases.

## Resources to Sustain the Base

Pyroclastic deposits are good for more than just radiation **shielding**. The Sun produces the solar wind—gases that are blown away from the Sun. Earth's atmosphere stops the solar wind before it can reach the planet's surface, but because the Moon has no atmosphere, the solar wind impacts the lunar surface directly. These gases, mostly hydrogen with some helium and other trace components, are sometimes trapped when they hit the surface of the Moon. Because the pyroclastic deposits are fine-grained, they provide a lot of surface area. It would be possible to drive off and collect the solar wind gases from this material by heating it to a few hundred degrees.

The most abundant of the gases, hydrogen, would be very valuable. If the pyroclastic material or other lunar rocks were heated to higher temperatures, the hydrogen could be combined with oxygen to form water vapor. The water vapor could be collected and condensed into liquid water.

Water is necessary to sustain life, of course, but it could also be used as part of the energy system in a lunar base. The Sun is in the Moon's sky for about two weeks, then there is a two-week-long night. During the lunar day, **photovoltaic** panels could convert sunlight into electricity, but storing power for two weeks would require a lot of batteries. A better method would be to use electric power during the day to break water apart into hydrogen and oxygen. During the lunar night, the hydrogen and oxygen could be recombined in a fuel cell to produce water and power.

People living at a lunar base will want to grow as much of their own food as possible. Greenhouses could be built with sufficient radiation shielding, or plants could be grown indoors with artificial lighting. Perhaps plants could be genetically engineered to withstand the intense lunar sunlight. There will be a strong economic incentive to recycle materials as efficiently and completely as possible on the Moon, and plants will play an important role. The goal will be to recycle all human wastes (solid, liquid, and gas) completely through the greenhouses, both to reduce the need for resupply from Earth and to reduce the amount of waste disposal on the Moon. People on Earth might benefit by applying the recycling techniques developed on the Moon.

Lunar base inhabitants will also experiment with other technologies that can reduce the need for bringing materials from Earth. For example, they might be able to produce building materials simply by melting lunar soils and cooling them quickly to form molded glass. Lunar surface gravity is only one-sixth that on Earth, so materials of a given strength could support much more massive structures.

## Science and Exploration from Lunar Bases

One reason to build lunar bases is to study the Moon. The Aristarchus Plateau is very interesting to geologists. The plateau itself may have been raised up by the impact that formed the nearby Imbrium basin, but this is not certain. The volcanic eruptions that produced the pyroclastic material brought material to the surface from deep in the lunar interior. Scientists can learn much by studying the geology near Aristarchus.

Of course, there are many other suitable sites for lunar bases. Many other pyroclastic deposits exist in other parts of the Moon, and scientists would like to have samples from all of them. Other locations that might provide resources for lunar bases include the lunar poles. Because the Moon's polar axis is nearly perpendicular to its orbit around the Sun, sunlight never reaches the bottom of some craters near each pole. If water molecules were deposited there, for example, when a comet hit the Moon, they might remain frozen. The Lunar Prospector spacecraft had an instrument to detect hydrogen, and it did find evidence of more hydrogen near the lunar poles. The instrument could not determine whether the hydrogen was contained in water molecules, but that is the likely explanation. If abundant water is found, a lunar base at one of the poles could get its power from photovoltaic panels located on the rim of a crater at a high point that is always in sunlight, and it could get water from the permanently shadowed bottom of the same crater.

**photovoltaic** pertaining to the direct generation of electricity from electromagnetic radiation (light)

Lunar colonists will handle medical and other emergencies with new technologies and procedures. In this rendering, the crew responds to a colleague who has broken his leg.

Another place that would be interesting for geologists to study is the South Pole-Aitken basin, a giant crater located (mostly) on the lunar farside. This basin is so big that its bottom is about 8 kilometers (5 miles) lower than the average lunar surface. Scientists would like to sample rocks from that deep in the crust.

There are other reasons to establish a lunar base besides studying the Moon. The lack of an atmosphere makes the Moon a very good place to do astronomy. Earth's atmosphere distorts the light that comes through it and even prevents much light from reaching the surface at all. (That is how it protects humans from radiation.) A telescope on the Moon would produce a clear image and could gather light of any wavelength. Because the Moon turns so slowly on its axis, a telescope anywhere on the Moon could observe its target continuously for days at a time, so even a small telescope could do useful work. With no atmosphere to scatter sunlight, observing in the daytime would be possible as well. Radio astronomers on Earth are encountering increasing problems with noise, but the farside of the Moon is the only place in the solar system that is always shielded from the radio noise from Earth. Because of the Moon's lower gravity, telescopes could eventually be built far larger on the Moon than on Earth.

The Moon could also be a good platform for observing Earth and its neighborhood in the solar system. Earth is always in the sky on the lunar nearside (although Earth turns and goes through its phases as it seems to hang in one spot). Because the Moon orbits Earth, and because Earth's magnetic field is affected and distorted by the solar wind, the Moon samples different regions of Earth's **magnetosphere** as it circles Earth every month.

Finally, the Moon can serve as a stepping-stone on humanity's journeys beyond Earth. It took the Apollo astronauts only about three days to travel between the Moon and Earth. A trip to Mars takes at least six months one-way with today's technology. It might be wise to test the abilities of humans to live for an extended period on the Moon before trying to live on Mars. It would be possible to make an emergency return from the Moon in a few days if necessary, but that would be difficult or impossible from Mars. Also, hydrogen and oxygen make excellent rocket fuel, so if there is abundant water at the lunar poles, the Moon may turn out to be the "last chance for gas" on the way to Mars and beyond. SEE ALSO COMMUNITIES IN SPACE (VOLUME 4); DOMED CITIES (VOLUME 4); FOOD PRODUCTION (VOLUME 4); GOVERNANCE (VOLUME 4); HABITATS (VOLUME 3); LIVING ON OTHER WORLDS (VOLUME 4); LUNAR OUTPOSTS (VOLUME 4); MOON (VOLUME 2); POLITICAL SYSTEMS (VOLUME 4); POWER, METHODS OF GENERATING (VOLUME 4); SCIENTIFIC RESEARCH (VOLUME 4); SETTLEMENTS (VOLUME 4); SOCIAL ETHICS (VOLUME 4); SOLAR WIND (VOLUME 2).

*Chris A. Peterson*

**magnetosphere** the magnetic cavity that surrounds Earth or any other planet with a magnetic field. It is formed by the interaction of the solar wind with the planet's magnetic field

### Bibliography

Bova, Ben. *Welcome to Moonbase.* New York: Ballantine Books, 1987.

Burgess, Eric. *Outpost on Apollo's Moon.* New York: Columbia University Press, 1993.

Burns, Jack O., Nebojsa Duric, G. Jeffrey Taylor, and Stewart W. Johnson."Observatories on the Moon." *Scientific American* 262 (1990):42–49.

Chaikin, Andrew. *A Man on the Moon: The Voyages of the Apollo Astronauts.* New York: Viking Press, 1994.

Johnson, Stewart W., and John P. Wetzel, eds. *Engineering, Construction, and Operations in Space II: Proceedings of Space 90.* New York: American Society of Civil Engineers, 1990.

Mendell, Wendell W., ed. *Lunar Bases and Space Activities of the Twenty-First Century.* Houston, TX: Lunar and Planetary Institute, 1985.

Potter, Andrew E., and T. L. Wilson, eds. *Physics and Astrophysics from a Lunar Base.* American Institute of Physics Conference Proceedings 202. New York: American Institute of Physics, 1990.

Spudis, Paul D. *The Once and Future Moon.* Washington, DC: Smithsonian Institution Press, 1996.

Taylor, G. Jeffrey, and Paul D. Spudis, eds. *Geoscience and a Lunar Base: A Comprehensive Plan for Lunar Exploration.* Washington, DC: National Aeronautics and Space Administration, 1990.

Wilhelms, Don E. *To a Rocky Moon: A Geologist's History of Lunar Exploration.* Tucson: University of Arizona Press, 1993.

# Lunar Outposts

Someday humans will live on Earth's Moon. However, before permanent settlements are established, people will probably occupy a series of lunar outposts. Each outpost will be visited one or more times for a few days to as long as a few months so that specific tasks can be performed; when the jobs are finished, the occupants will leave. Visitors to a lunar outpost will have to take with them almost everything they will need there, including the food they will eat and the air they will breathe.

Lunar outposts have potential scientific, commercial, and military uses.

## The Apollo Outposts

The Apollo program of the National Aeronautics and Space Administration (NASA) placed six lunar outposts on the Moon between July 1969 and December 1972. Each one was part of a lunar landing mission during which two American astronauts landed a spacecraft on the surface of the Moon. The astronauts traveled on the surface of the Moon to place scientific instruments and gather geologic samples and then returned to orbit to rejoin the main spacecraft, in which another astronaut had been orbiting the Moon. Part of the landing craft remained on the Moon to be used as a launch platform; the rest was used to carry the astronauts back to lunar orbit. After the astronauts transferred everything necessary back to the main spacecraft, the landing craft was crashed onto the Moon. One reason for crashing the landers was to provide signals for the seismometers the astronauts had placed on the surface to study moonquakes.

## Future Outposts

The Apollo missions were designed as brief visits to a variety of locations, and so there was no reason to establish reusable outposts. In the future, lunar outposts may be designed differently. Scientists have studied the rocks and soil returned from the Moon by the Apollo astronauts and have used telescopic and spacecraft observations to learn a great deal about the lunar environment. It is likely that future outposts will be located in areas that scientists want to study in more detail and will be more permanent facilities that can be visited more than once.

All future lunar outposts will have some features in common. The primary function of each outpost will be to keep the people who visit it alive. This includes protecting them from danger and providing what they need to remain healthy. Dangers in the lunar environment include radiation, extreme temperatures, and the **vacuum** of space. The Moon has almost no atmosphere, so the Apollo astronauts had to wear space suits when they left the landing craft. Any future lunar outpost will need to be airtight so that its visitors will be able to remove their space suits after they enter. An airlock would help reduce the amount of air lost to space each time someone entered or left the outpost.

Earth's atmosphere protects people from much of the harmful radiation produced by the Sun and moderates the temperatures on the planet's surface. The Moon lacks this natural protection, and so lunar outposts must protect their visitors. The longer people stay on the Moon, the more protection from radiation the outpost must provide, because the effects are cumulative. One way to protect against radiation is to shield the outpost with rock or soil. The surface of the Moon is covered by a soil layer called regolith, which has been produced by meteorite impact. This layer can be moved relatively easily to cover the outposts. A layer a few meters thick would protect the people inside from radiation. It also would help insulate the outpost and make it easier to maintain a comfortable temperature inside.

People need to eat food, drink water, and breathe air, and all these things must be taken along with them to a lunar outpost. These materials are all cycled through the body and turned into waste products, and so there must be toilets and air purification equipment to maintain a healthy environment.

**vacuum** an environment where air and all other molecules and atoms of matter have been removed

## The Purpose of Future Outposts

Other features of lunar outposts will depend on the tasks to be performed. Some activities of the Apollo astronauts will probably be repeated at future lunar outposts. Scientific instrument packages will be put in place, maintained, and serviced in order to provide information on the lunar environment, surface, and interior. Geologic fieldwork will be performed; samples of rock and soil will be gathered for this purpose. Some human exploration will be done, although robotic explorers, perhaps controlled remotely by people at the outpost, probably will also be used.

One scientific endeavor for which the Moon is well suited is astronomy. Although the lack of an atmosphere is a problem in terms of life support, it makes the Moon an almost ideal platform for astronomy. Because the Moon turns on its axis only once a month, targets may be observed continuously for many days. Light is not lost or distorted by traveling through air, and so even a small telescope can make useful observations. The farside of the Moon is the only place in the solar system that is always shielded from radio waves coming from Earth, and so it is a perfect place for radioastronomy. The Moon's weaker gravity, only one-sixth that of Earth, will make it possible to build bigger telescopes on the Moon than can be built on Earth.

Some outposts will probably be utilized to test technologies that will be used later in more permanently occupied bases. Some of these technologies

**fusion** the act of releasing nuclear energy by combining lighter elements such as hydrogen into heavier elements

will relate to maintenance of the bases, such as automated greenhouses to grow food and recycle carbon dioxide. Other technologies to be tested will include the extraction of hydrogen, oxygen, and other gases from lunar rocks and soil. The hydrogen and oxygen can be used for fuel, water, and breathing. Helium eventually may be used in **fusion** reactors to produce power.

The next lunar outposts could be constructed by NASA, a cooperating group of nations, a government-industry partnership, or even private for-profit companies. Lunar outposts have been built before, and more can be built in the future. SEE ALSO ASTEROID MINING (VOLUME 4); CLOSED ECOSYSTEMS (VOLUME 3); HABITATS (VOLUME 3); LIVING ON OTHER WORLDS (VOLUME 4); LUNAR BASES (VOLUME 4); MOON (VOLUME 2); POWER, METHODS OF GENERATING (VOLUME 4); RESOURCE UTILIZATION (VOLUME 4); SCIENTIFIC RESEARCH (VOLUME 4); SETTLEMENTS (VOLUME 4); SPACE INDUSTRIES (VOLUME 4).

*Chris A. Peterson*

**Bibliography**

Burgess, Eric. *Outpost on Apollo's Moon*. New York: Columbia University Press, 1993.

Burns, Jack O., Nebojsa Duric, G. Jeffrey Taylor, and Stewart W. Johnson. "Observatories on the Moon." *Scientific American* 262 (1990):42–49.

Chaikin, Andrew. *A Man on the Moon: The Voyages of the Apollo Astronauts*. New York: Viking Press, 1994.

Spudis, Paul D. *The Once and Future Moon*. Washington, DC: Smithsonian Institution Press, 1996.

Taylor, G. Jeffrey, and Paul D. Spudis, eds. *Geoscience and a Lunar Base: A Comprehensive Plan for Lunar Exploration*. Washington, DC: NASA Conference Publication 3070, 1990.

Wilhelms, Don E. *To a Rocky Moon: A Geologist's History of Lunar Exploration*. Tucson: University of Arizona Press, 1993.

# Mars Bases

A Mars base could be the key to making Mars part of humanity's future. Explorers at a base could explore Mars for years or even decades. This is significant because while Mars has only half Earth's diameter, it has as much surface area to explore as Earth has land area. A Mars base might also serve as a stepping-stone to a permanent Mars settlement. Mars is a desirable settlement target because it is the planet in the solar system most like Earth.

## Types of Bases

The form that the first Mars base will take will depend on its ultimate purpose. If established only for brief use with specific objectives in mind, it might resemble a temporary base camp set up to scale Mt. Everest. Alternatively, it might be established for long-term scientific exploration, like McMurdo Base in Antarctica. A base might also be intended as a nucleus around which permanent Mars settlement could grow, much as Jamestown, Virginia, was for the English who settled North America in the early seventeenth century.

In old Mars plans, piloted landing missions, each lasting less than a month, started human exploration of Mars, and any form of base came only later. The Mars exploration plan favored today by the National Aeronau-

Although interplanetary settlement is many years away, Mars is the likely candidate for first settlement since its environment is most like Earth's.

tics and Space Administration (NASA), however, encourages establishment of a temporary base camp on Mars on the first expedition. In NASA's plan, spacecraft use a six-month, low-energy path to travel to Mars. The explorers must then wait at Mars for about 500 days while Earth and Mars move into position so the explorers' spacecraft can follow a six-month, low-energy path home to Earth. This strategy slashes the amount of **rocket** propellant needed, which saves money—less propellant means fewer expensive rockets are needed to launch the Mars mission into space. If NASA's Mars plan becomes the basis for future Mars expeditions, the astronauts are likely to spend most of their time at Mars on the surface, where they can dig in for protection from radiation and explore as much as possible.

**rocket** vehicle or device especially designed to travel through space, propelled by one or more engines

If settlement is the ultimate goal, the base will serve as a "kindergarten" where humanity can learn about settling another planet. Researchers at the base will test human reactions to long exposure to Mars conditions. It is not known, for example, whether humans can survive indefinitely in Mars

This image, taken by Viking Lander 1 just before sunset, shows a landscape dotted with rocks, exposed bedrock, and small depressions.

gravity, which is only one-third as strong as Earth gravity. The base will also develop settlement technologies. For a Mars settlement to be truly permanent, it will need to use Martian resources to sustain itself and grow. The base might, for instance, experiment with processing Mars dirt so it can be used to grow food plants in pressurized greenhouses. Researchers will also experiment with making fuel for surface and air vehicles and with manufacturing building materials.

## Building a Mars Base

Setting up the base will be a step-by-step process. The first step will be to gather data about Mars so that a base site can be selected. Current robotic missions are providing initial data that might eventually be used for base site selection. At minimum, the site must be accessible by spacecraft, with flat places to land, and scientifically interesting sites should be located nearby. If meant for a long-term base or a permanent settlement, the site should be near useful resources, such as underground water or ice, geothermal heat sources, wind for windmills, and latitudes where solar energy can be used year-round. The base should be in a relatively warm area, not prone to dust devils (small whirlwinds of dust) or seasonal dust storms. It might be established on Mars' northern plains or in the southern hemispheric Hellas basin, both places where low altitude means that air pressure is relatively high (though even in such low-lying places it is still barely

1 percent of Earth sea-level pressure). High air pressure means that spacecraft can make fuel-saving parachute-assisted landings and that industrial processes using Martian air as a resource can be more efficient.

The next step will be to build the base. To start, modules built on Earth might land at the chosen site to form a start-up base. In 1965 German-born American rocket pioneer Wernher von Braun described a plan for a "little village" on Mars made up of crew and cargo landers based on Apollo program technology. The second Case for Mars conference, in 1984, envisioned a similar start-up strategy—cargo landers based on space shuttle and **space station** technology would be tipped on their sides to serve as living space.

A temporary base camp might not progress beyond this stage. If, however, the base is meant for the long term or as a settlement nucleus, the astronauts will eventually need to build large, complex structures to supplement modules shipped from Earth. At first, they will probably use prefabricated parts made on Earth. A Mars blimp hangar, for example, would be too large to ship from Earth in one piece, so it would have to be shipped in pieces and assembled on Mars. As new construction equipment arrives from Earth and experience with living on Mars increases, the explorers might begin building using Martian materials. As the Mars explorers become Mars settlers, they might dig tunnels into cliff faces, then progress to erecting clear plastic "tents" over craters and valleys, turning them into huge greenhouses.

**space station** large orbital outpost equipped to support a human crew and designed to remain in orbit for an extended period

## Will We Build a Base on Mars?

These plans assume that we will send people to Mars, and that we will decide to establish a Mars base. History shows that, just because a new world awaits us, it does not follow that we will explore it. Apollo was not followed by a lunar base, even though much remains to be explored on the Moon. If there is life on Mars, we might not build a base—or, indeed, land humans—because to do so would contaminate the planet and possibly destroy its unique biota. We might instead settle worlds without life, such as Earth's Moon or the asteroids. Alternatively, if Mars is lifeless, a base could become life's first foothold on the planet. In time, Mars settlers might begin experiments aimed at remaking Mars' environment—a process called terraforming—so it can support plants and animals from Earth. SEE ALSO EARTH—WHY LEAVE? (VOLUME 4); FOOD PRODUCTION (VOLUME 4); HABITATS (VOLUME 3); HUMAN MISSIONS TO MARS (VOLUME 3); LIVING ON OTHER WORLDS (VOLUME 4); LUNAR BASES (VOLUME 4); MARS (VOLUME 2); MARS DIRECT (VOLUME 4); MARS MISSIONS (VOLUME 4); POWER, METHODS OF GENERATING (VOLUME 4); RESOURCE UTILIZATION (VOLUME 4); SCIENTIFIC RESEARCH (VOLUME 4); SETTLEMENTS (VOLUME 4); SPACE INDUSTRIES (VOLUME 4); TERRAFORMING (VOLUME 4).

*David S. F. Portree*

**Bibliography**

Hoffman, Stephen J., and David I. Kaplan, eds. *Human Exploration of Mars: The Reference Mission of the NASA Mars Exploration Study Team.* Houston, TX: NASA Lyndon B. Johnson Space Center, 1997.

Portree, David S. F. *Humans to Mars: Fifty Years of Mission Planning, 1950–2000.* Washington, DC: NASA History Office, 2001.

Robinson, Kim Stanley. *Red Mars.* New York: Bantam Books, 1993.

von Braun, Wernher. "The Next Twenty Years of Interplanetary Exploration." *Astronautics and Aeronautics* 3, no. 11 (November 1965):24–34.

Welch, S. M., and C. R. Stoker, eds. *The Case for Mars: Concept Development for a Mars Research Station.* Boulder, CO: Boulder Center for Science and Policy, 1986.

Zubrin, Robert, with Richard Wagner. *The Case for Mars: The Plan to Settle the Red Planet and Why We Must.* New York: Free Press, 1996.

**Internet Resources**

Hoffman, Stephen J., and David I. Kaplan, eds. "Human Exploration of Mars: The Reference Mission of the NASA Mars Exploration Study Team." 1997. NASA, Lyndon B. Johnson Space Center. <http://www-sn.jsc.nasa.gov/PlanetaryMissions/EXLibrary/docs/MarsRef/contents.htm>.

# Mars Direct

The Mars Direct concept for a human mission to Mars has been vigorously championed since 1990 by engineer Robert Zubrin, who developed it with fellow Martin Marietta Corporation engineer David Baker. The National Aeronautics and Space Administration (NASA) estimated in 1993 that its plan for Mars exploration, which is called the Design Reference Mission and drew heavily on the Mars Direct approach, could make human footsteps on Mars possible by as early as 2009.

## A Clever Synthesis

Mars Direct originated in a Martin Marietta–sponsored effort to develop plans for U.S. President George H. W. Bush's Space Exploration Initiative (1989–1993), which aimed to return humans to the Moon and land the first astronauts on Mars by 2019. Bush's initiative failed because of excessive cost and lack of political support, but it provided an opportunity to revive many old Moon and Mars exploration ideas. Mars Direct, for example, is a cost-saving synthesis of concepts dating back to the 1950s.

Old concepts in Mars Direct include manufacturing propellants on Mars for the trip home to Earth; splitting the expedition between cargo and crew spacecraft; and a 500-day stay on Mars for the first expedition. The last idea allows the crew to wait for Mars and Earth to move into positions in their orbits around the Sun and enable a propellant-saving low-energy voyage back to Earth. In 1989 NASA's Space Exploration Initiative Mars plan was expected to cost about $400 billion. According to Zubrin's 1990 estimate, Mars Direct might cost a quarter as much.

## The Mars Direct Plan

In their earliest Mars Direct papers, Zubrin and Baker described a Mars expedition kicking off in December 1996. A giant Ares rocket consisting of a space shuttle external tank with four attached space shuttle main engines and two shuttle advanced solid rocket boosters would lift off from Kennedy Space Center in Florida. Atop the external tank would sit a rocket stage and a 40-ton automated cargo lander covered by a streamlined shroud. The cargo lander would include an **aerobrake** heat shield, a descent stage, an Earth-return vehicle (ERV), a propellant factory, 5.8 tons of liquid hydrogen, and a nuclear reactor on a robot truck. The Ares rocket would launch the cargo lander onto a direct course to Mars without assembly in Earth orbit—hence the name Mars Direct.

**aerobrake** technique of using a planet's atmosphere to slow down an incoming spacecraft. Its use requires the spacecraft to have a heat shield, because the friction that slows the craft is turned into intense heat

The 1996-launched cargo lander would land on Mars, then the robot truck would trundle away to safely position the nuclear reactor in a crater. The reactor would then activate to generate electrical power for compressors. These would draw in Martian air to manufacture propellant for the ERV.

The propellant factory would use the Sabatier Process first proposed for use on Mars in 1978 by engineers Robert Ash, William Dowler, and Giulio Varsi at NASA's Jet Propulsion Laboratory. Liquid hydrogen **feedstock** would be exposed to Martian atmospheric carbon dioxide in the presence of a **catalyst**, producing liquid methane and water. The methane would be stored and the water split using electricity to yield oxygen and more hydrogen. The oxygen would be stored and the hydrogen recycled to manufacture more water and methane. In a year this process would manufacture 107 tons of methane and oxygen propellants.

In January 1999 two more Ares rockets would lift off. One would carry a cargo lander identical to the one already on Mars; the other, a drum-shaped, 38-ton piloted spacecraft 8.4 meters (27.5 feet) wide and 4.9 meters (16 feet) tall. Its top floor would house the four-person crew, while its bottom floor would carry cargo, including a Mars rover. The Ares rockets would launch the two spacecraft directly onto six-month transfer paths to Mars.

The 1999-piloted spacecraft would land near the cargo lander launched in 1996. The 1999 cargo lander, meanwhile, would land 800 kilometers (500 miles) from the 1996 cargo lander and begin making fuel for the second crew, which would leave Earth in 2001.

Eleven of the 107 tons of propellants manufactured by the 1996 cargo lander's propellant factory would fuel the rover. The explorers would undertake long traverses, thoroughly studying and recording the characteristics of the region around their landing site. The rover might traverse a total of 16,000 kilometers (10,000 miles) during the explorers' 500-day Mars surface stay.

As Earth and Mars move into position, the 1999 expedition crew would board the 1996 ERV. Rocket engines burning the methane and oxygen propellants manufactured from the Martian atmosphere would place it on direct course for Earth. After six months in the ERV, the crew would reenter Earth's atmosphere and perform a parachute landing.

The most significant difference between Mars Direct and NASA's 1993 Design Reference Mission was the division of ERV functions between two vehicles. In the judgment of many, the Mars Direct ERV was too small to house four astronauts during a six-month return from Mars. It provided about as much room as a phone booth for each crew member. In NASA's plan, therefore, the crew would use a small Mars ascent vehicle to reach Mars orbit. Once there, they would dock with an orbiting ERV.

## Martian Towns

The 2001 expedition crew would land near the 1999 cargo lander, and the 2001 cargo lander would land 800 kilometers (500 miles) away and make propellants for the 2003 expedition. The 2003 crew would land by the 2001 cargo lander; meanwhile the 2003 cargo lander would touch down 500 miles away and make propellants for the 2005 crew; and so on. After several

**feedstock** the raw materials introduced into an industrial process from which a finished product is made

**catalyst** a chemical compound that accelerates a chemical reaction without itself being used up

expeditions, a network of Mars bases would be established. "Just as towns in the western U.S. grew up around forts and outposts," wrote Zubrin and Baker, "future Martian towns would spread out from some of these bases. As information returns about each site, future missions might return to the more hospitable ones and larger bases would begin to form." (Zubrin and Baker 1990, p. 41). SEE ALSO HUMAN MISSIONS TO MARS (VOLUME 3); LIVING ON OTHER WORLDS (VOLUME 4); MARS BASES (VOLUME 4); MARS MISSIONS (VOLUME 4); NATURAL RESOURCES (VOLUME 4); POWER, METHODS OF GENERATING (VOLUME 4); RESOURCE UTILIZATION (VOLUME 4); ZUBRIN, ROBERT (VOLUME 4).

*David S. F. Portree*

**Bibliography**

Hoffman, Stephen J., and David I. Kaplan, eds. *Human Exploration of Mars: The Reference Mission of the NASA Mars Exploration Study Team.* Houston, TX: NASA Lyndon B. Johnson Space Center, 1997.

Portree, David S. F. *Humans to Mars: Fifty Years of Mission Planning, 1950–2000.* Washington, DC: NASA History Office, 2001.

Zubrin, Robert. "The Economic Viability of Mars Colonization." *Journal of the British Interplanetary Society* 48, no. 10 (1995):407–414.

Zubrin, Robert, and David Baker. "Humans to Mars in 1999." *Aerospace America* 28, no. 8 (1990):30–32, 41.

Zubrin, Robert, with Richard Wagner. *The Case for Mars: The Plan to Settle the Red Planet and Why We Must.* New York: Free Press, 1996.

**Internet Resources**

Hoffman, Stephen J., and David I. Kaplan, eds. *Human Exploration of Mars: The Reference Mission of the NASA Mars Exploration Study Team.* 1997. National Aeronautics and Space Administration, Lyndon B. Johnson Space Center. <http://www-sn.jsc.nasa.gov/PlanetaryMissions/EXLibrary/docs/MarsRef/contents.htm>.

Portree, David S. F. *Humans to Mars: Fifty Years of Mission Planning, 1950–2000.* 2001. <http://members.aol.com/dsfportree/explore.htm>.

# Mars Missions

Mars has attracted human interest throughout history. *The War of the Worlds* (1898) by H. G. Wells, about an advanced Martian civilization that came to attack Earth, was inspired by the work of the Italian astronomer Giovanni Schiaparelli, who observed *canali* (channels) on Mars. (The Italian word *canali* was mistranslated as "canals.") This led to interest in the possibility of intelligent life on Mars.

Although it is now known that there is no intelligent life on Mars, planning for exploration of the Red Planet is at an all-time high. The question of whether simple life ever arose on Mars is a strong motivation for exploration. Other questions include how the Martian climate evolved and how it differs from that on Earth and how the surface and interior of Mars evolved.

## Proposed Missions

With the long-term goal of human exploration, many preliminary missions are needed to address these questions and engineering issues. Water is the link between these goals, and the plan of the National Aeronautics and Space

Administration (NASA) is to "follow the water." The strategy will be to sample the Martian environment through **in situ** experiments and by bringing pieces of the planet back to Earth.

The proposed mission plans for the next decade include one or more spacecraft launches every two years. These spacecraft will be designed to address the primary scientific questions and conduct the experiments necessary to prepare for the launching of astronauts to Mars. The vehicles will probably alternate between orbiter and lander spacecraft. Beginning in 2007, there will be less expensive spacecraft, termed "scouts," which will supplement the program by addressing objectives not targeted by the other missions.

## Life and Water on Mars

Life on Earth contains organic carbon and needs water and energy to exist. Searching for carbon in the soil and ice on Mars and understanding how the amount of carbon has changed during that planet's history are primary goals of future Mars missions. It is important to understand where water (ice, liquid, and vapor) exists on Mars today, how much there is, and how it is transported around the planet. There may have been much more liquid water on Mars in the distant past. Flowing water may have deposited sand and silt in the bottoms of lakebeds or oceans. If standing water once existed, these areas will be a primary place to search for fossilized life.

The Mars Odyssey orbiter spacecraft, launched in April 2001, is designed to detect evidence of ancient water on Mars and possible locations of current water in the subsurface. The two rovers that will be sent to land on Mars in 2003 will study rocks and soils to determine whether water was ever present at those sites.

The Mars Reconnaissance Orbiter, planned to be launched in 2005, will have cameras that can see beachball-size rocks on the surface. This will allow scientists to compare surface to orbiter observations and may indicate which parts of the surface were created by volcanic flows and which were created by sand and silt deposited in water.

Scientists would also like to know how the Martian climate has changed since the ancient past. The atmosphere of Mars contains mostly carbon dioxide, with very little water. This means that there are only very thin clouds that occur rarely. Because it is very cold on Mars and the atmosphere is thin, there is no rain. Mars also has severe dust storms during the southern hemisphere summer.

However, if liquid water flowed on Mars in the distant past, the climate might have been very different from what it is today. To understand those changes, it is necessary to understand the present-day climate. The Mars Odyssey spacecraft will gain insight into the climate, but the Mars Reconnaissance orbiter will contain instruments specifically designed to address these issues.

## Astronauts on Mars

Landing astronauts on Mars will not be easy. A spacecraft with humans onboard will be much heavier than any previous spacecraft and thus will enter

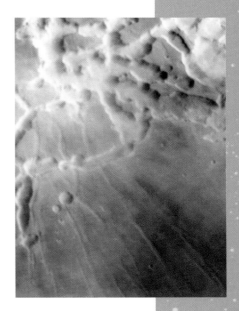

Viking Orbiter I captured this sunrise over tributary canyons in a high plateau region of Mars. The bright white areas are clouds of water ice, which appear starkly set against the rust-colored Martian desert.

**in situ** in the natural or original location

The Mars Reconnaissance Orbiter is expected to launch in 2005. Its main purpose will be to study the Martian surface using a high-resolution camera.

the Martian atmosphere at a very high speed. It therefore will need a new type of aeroshell and a strong parachute to slow it down.

With humans onboard, a safe landing becomes more critical—for instance, it will be important to avoid large rocks or cliff walls. To do that, instruments and software are being developed to view the ground below the spacecraft just before landing and automatically select the safest touchdown spot. The plan is to have the Mars 2007 spacecraft demonstrate these capabilities.

While on the surface, the astronauts will need to have continuous communication with Earth. This will require a network of communication satellites around Mars to provide the connection at all times of the Martian day and night. Most future science orbiters will be designed to continue in use as communications satellites. There is also a plan to have an Italian Space Agency communications satellite at Mars in 2007. Since it is difficult to bring much to Mars, rocket fuel to return to Earth probably will have to be made on the surface.

It will be very difficult for humans to survive on Mars. One of the main concerns is the radiation level on the surface of the planet. The Mars radiation environment experiment, named MARIE, is flying on the Mars Odyssey spacecraft and will help investigate the level of radiation above the atmosphere.

Understanding how much water is present and where it is located will be crucial for human survival. If water is found in deep reservoirs, instruments such as drills will be designed and tested to bring it to the surface. There also may be very small amounts of water in the soil that instruments can separate out.

If enough water and oxygen are not brought to Mars, instruments will be needed to create them on the surface. Bringing enough food will also pose a challenge. It is vital to learn enough about the soil on Mars to determine whether it is safe and can be used for growing plants for food. In addition, the soil may corrode the spacecraft or the space suits. The survival of the astronauts also will depend on having enough power to operate all the necessary machinery.

With more sophisticated instruments on Earth, scientists are certain to learn a great deal from returned Martian rock and soil samples. In the second decade of the proposed Mars plan, NASA intends to return the first sample in 2014 and the second in 2016. SEE ALSO ASTROBIOLOGY (VOLUME 4); HUMAN MISSIONS TO MARS (VOLUME 3); LIVING ON OTHER WORLDS (VOLUME 4); MARS (VOLUME 2); MARS BASES (VOLUME 4); MARS DIRECT (VOLUME 4); NATURAL RESOURCES (VOLUME 4); PLANETARY PROTECTION (VOLUME 4); POWER, METHODS OF GENERATING (VOLUME 4); RESOURCE UTILIZATION (VOLUME 4); SCIENTIFIC RESEARCH (VOLUME 4); TELEPRESENCE (VOLUME 4); TERRAFORMING (VOLUME 4).

*Leslie K. Tamppari*

**Internet Resources**

Brians, Paul. "Study Guide for H. G. Wells: The War of the Worlds (1898)." Washington State University. <http://www.wsu.edu:8080/~brians/science_fiction/warofworlds.html>.

"Marie Instrument." *2001 Mars Odyssey*. Jet Propulsion Laboratory. <http://mars.jpl.nasa.gov/2001/instruments/lander_marie_text.html>.

*Mars Odyssey*. Jet Propulsion Laboratory, 2001. <http://mars.jpl.nasa.gov/2001/>.

**Migration** *See Living on Other Worlds (Volume 4).*

# Military Uses of Space

During human history, the exploration of space has been based on more than just scientific potential. People may like to believe that we are exploring the cosmos purely for academic purposes, but the truth is that space plays a huge role in both offensive and defensive military planning. In fact, much of the exploration that humans have already achieved would not have come to pass if it had not been for the military motives that underpin most space missions. Long before satellites orbited Earth for cell phone calls, **global positioning systems**, or picture taking, the military was interested in space. Commercial interest would not come until years later.

**global positioning system** a system of satellites and receivers that provide direct determination of the geographical location of the receiver

BAGHDAD DIR OF MILITARY INTEL HEADQUARTERS, IRAQ

PRE-STRIKE
AREA 2
AREA 1
AREA 1

POST-STRIKE
AREA 1

AREA 2

The U.S. Department of Defense uses satellite images to monitor foreign military installations and troop movements. This image shows the damage caused to the Baghdad Directorate of Military Intelligence Headquarters by a U.S. missile attack.

**rockets** vehicles (or devices) especially designed to travel through space, propelled by one or more engines

While many countries now have space agencies and conduct missions into space, it was the United States and Russia who first began the competition to reach the stars. In 1957, more than a decade after World War II, and after the Cold War had been in bloom for years, the "space race" began. The Cold War—a war of spies and threats, of moves and countermoves—had reached a new plateau. Nuclear power had been demonstrated by both superpowers and as **rockets** began slowly to become more advanced, space weaponry became the new battleground. Not only could weapons be placed in space, but powerful cameras could be used for spying on the enemy. The potential uses for space during the Cold War were numerous and clearly visible.

Each side believed that having weapons in orbit could mean their success in this war and the destruction of their enemies. Test planes were designed to fly in space, while rockets became more than just short range missiles. Satellites would soon be designed and the launches would lead to panic and confusion.

In 1952 branches of the U.S. military, including the air force and the navy, along with private companies began trying to design planes for space travel. During a time when all planes flew with propellers, these ideas were unheard of. When the experimental X-15 debuted in 1958, the craft was far ahead of other planes. For nine years, these three hypersonic, or faster than sound, planes made more than 200 trips with twelve different pilots. They continued their trips during the Mercury, Gemini, and Apollo missions. These craft would lead designers to create a reusable spacecraft that later became the space shuttle. Amazingly, these planes made it into space and landed back on Earth decades before the space shuttle ever flew.

Ironically, the role these weapons played would become more defensive than offensive. As each superpower increased its stockpile of nuclear arms and continued its space program, it was obvious that an attack and destruction of one would lead to the mutual destruction of the other. Great efforts were made by both sides to keep the mutual destruction from happening while secretly trying to gain the advantage.

In January 1954, U.S. Secretary of State John Foster Dulles announced the new "Massive Retaliation" policy. If the Soviet Union attacked, the United States would return the attack with its huge nuclear arsenal. Despite this, the Cold War would continue to grow in scope, and while no nuclear weapons were fired, there were plenty of times when this Cold War almost became a hot one.

## Russia Takes the Lead

Three years later, in 1957, America went through one of its biggest nuclear scares. On October 4, the Soviet Union launched Sputnik, the world's first artificial satellite. Even though it was only the size of a basketball, many believed that a nuclear warhead was onboard and that this was a Russian attack. During the 98 minutes that it circled Earth, the 83 kilogram (183-pound) ball showed that the space race was no longer theoretical, or even solely missile based.

In reality, the Soviets had simply beaten the United States to the first satellite launch. No nuclear warhead was onboard and the only thing given off by Sputnik was a radio transmitter's beep, proving that the satellite was functioning properly.

The Soviet Union would improve its lead, as it would soon send up Sputnik II, containing a small dog in its cargo. This was still before any U.S. satellite had been launched. The seriousness of the situation led Congress to pass the National Aeronautics and Space Act in July 1958. This act created NASA, the National Aeronautics and Space Administration, on October 1 of that year.

The United States would launch satellites of its own, but for years Russia maintained the lead in the space race. Russia beat the Americans to records for the first person in space, Yuri Gagarin; the first space walk, Alexei Leonov; and the first woman in space, Valentina Tereshkova.

As time went on, the Cold War would continue to visit new levels. A mere year after U.S. President John F. Kennedy had told Americans to begin building bomb shelters in a letter to *Life* magazine, the Cuban missile crisis in 1962 brought the world to the brink of nuclear disaster for two weeks.

## Going to the Moon

It was only the year before when President Kennedy set the bar for the United States—going to the Moon. He said:

> I believe that this nation should commit itself to achieving the goal, before this decade is out, of landing a man on the Moon and returning him safely to the Earth. No single space project in this period will be more impressive to mankind, or more important for the long-range exploration of space; and none will be so difficult or expensive to accomplish.

Great skepticism existed as to whether the United States would be able to perform this task in the time frame that Kennedy had determined. If Americans got there before the Soviets, it would mean the end of the race and a U.S. victory; if Americans did not get to the Moon before the Soviets did, the United States would have lost according to Kennedy. The next year, he further explained his decision, saying: "We have a long way to go in the space race. We started late. But this is the new ocean, and I believe the United States must sail on it and be in a position second to none." Kennedy also uttered this now-famous line: "We choose to go to the Moon. We choose to go to the Moon in this decade and do the other things, not only because they are easy, but because they are hard."

Seven years later, on July 20, 1969, U.S. astronauts Neil Armstrong and Edwin "Buzz" Aldrin would be the first men to land on the Moon, and Armstrong would say the now immortal line: "That's one small step for man, one giant leap for mankind." The United States had successfully sent men to the Moon and back before the Soviets. Despite all the setbacks—President Kennedy's assassination, astronauts who had died in previous Apollo mishaps, and the United States' start from the underdog position—Americans had won. The country rejoiced, thinking it had won the space race. But then a new race began.

## The New Race

No longer was the race about who could get their citizens to what location. Instead, the war became about technology. Defenses against offensive systems, imaging for early warning systems, and weapon ships for ensuring military victory. The Russians would build Mir, and the United States would build its Skylab. When the space shuttle was built, the hope was to have numerous shuttles, keeping one above Earth at all times, and possibly armed with nuclear weapons. Both sides launched satellites for spying, photography, and communication interception.

As the years went on, each division of the military would begin to form its own agenda for space defense and offense. Plans continued to become more complex, until on March 23, 1983, U.S. President Ronald Reagan introduced a plan for a new defense system, nicknamed Star Wars. In his speech, the president spoke of the continuing threat of Soviet attack and raised the question, "What if free people could live secure in the knowledge . . . that we could intercept and destroy strategic ballistic missiles before they reached our own soil. . . ?" The controversy began.

The underlying technology was very new and untested. The idea that the required accuracy to destroy a missile either with a laser or by collid-

President Ronald Reagan introduced a new defense program, "Star Wars," on March 23, 1983. The program was meant to protect U.S. soil from potential Soviet missile attacks.

ing another missile with it was too advanced. The concept was ahead of its time and was never successfully developed during President Reagan's days in office. Ironically, the animations of this shown on television during that time were created by the television networks and not by NASA or the government.

During U.S. President Bill Clinton's administration, tests were conducted to try and shoot down a test missile by hitting it with another. Every test failed. The proposed Missile Defense System or Missile Defense Shield did not look promising. During the office of U.S. President George W. Bush, the Missile Defense Shield again became a priority; despite massive cost overruns and failures, the tests continued.

It was during this time that the Missile Defense Shield had its biggest success and failure. For the first time, the test worked and the missile was successfully destroyed. However, the proposed Missile Defense System is in violation of the 1972 Anti-Ballistic Missile Treaty that the United States and Russia both signed. The treaty was one of many between the 1960s and the present designed to continue moving away from the prospect of nuclear holocaust. President Bush has stated that he believes the treaty is outdated, and will continue tests in spite of it. Russian President Vladimir Putin has not agreed to abandon the treaty and is a strong critic of the plan. As of this writing, each side claims they are willing to make compromises to the treaty, but the exact form those compromises will take has yet to be seen.

Another controversial event occurred during President Clinton's term in office when the armed forces were given the right to attack another spacecraft, whether it be government owned or privately owned, should it "attempt to hinder the ability of U.S. spacecraft to operate freely in space." Any such attempted hindrance is now considered to be an attack on the United States itself. At first, this piece of legislation was destroyed using the line item veto but, on appeal, the U.S. Supreme Court found the line item veto unconstitutional and this new policy replaces the one put in place by President Reagan in 1987.

Ever since the fall of the Soviet Union, Russia has been struggling to try and keep its space program afloat. From the costs of upkeep on the Mir space station to the new International Space Station, the Russian Space Agency has undergone many challenges. In 2001 the organization was restructured again as Russia continued to cut back on its military space program. Between cost concerns for the International Space Station and political feelings about Missile Defense Systems, experts predict that Russia's space program will either undergo a vast transformation in the coming years or a terrible collapse. Russia and the United States are not the only countries, however, with space programs.

Today, many different space agencies exist in numerous countries. France has its agency, the Direction Générale de l'Armement or DGA, while Japan has its own space agency, called NASDA, or the National Space Development Agency, founded in 1969. Even countries without large space agencies still have launch sites for military and commercial satellites. Brazil has prime real estate, near the equator, for launches. (Being closer to the equator means the rocket can leave Earth having used less fuel.) Many countries are joining together and launching satellites and rockets by combining

## USING SATELLITES TO FIGHT

The military's use of space continues to grow with each passing campaign. In January 2002, the final Milstar satellite was launched into orbit. This series of satellites provide more secure data transmission, as well as faster relaying of mission critical data. The system is capable of cutting the transmission time from dozens of hours to a mere few when transmitting photographs taken from orbit. The same imaging sensors are used to help aid precision bomb attacks over enemy targets.

their money and resources. It is in this fashion that the International Space Station is being built. Ironically though, as countries come together to build this station, many still develop and launch satellites designed for defense against other countries. It indicates that space exploration may always include a defensive submotive, at least as long as there is disagreement here on Earth.

Now, many military officers carry specially modified computer laptops that rely on satellite-guided data to ensure the positions of themselves, their allies, and their targets. The accuracy available is so remarkable, it puts the revolutionary GPS to shame. Military satellites with these abilities can map areas on Earth down to the last inch, and possibly even smaller areas. Full information on military space capabilities is not made available to the public. SEE ALSO GLOBAL POSITIONING SYSTEM (VOLUME 1); LAUNCH FACILITIES (VOLUME 4); MILITARY CUSTOMERS (VOLUME 1); SPACE INDUSTRIES (VOLUME 4).

*Craig Samuels*

**Bibliography**

Collins, Martin J. *Space Race: The U.S.-U.S.S.R. Competition to Reach the Moon.* San Francisco, CA: Pomegranate Communications, 1999.

Johnson, Dana J., C. Bryan Gabbard, and Scott Pace. *Space: Emerging Options for National Power.* Santa Monica, CA: Rand, 1998.

Richelson, Jeffrey T. *America's Space Sentinels: DSP Satellites and National Security.* Lawrence, KS: University Press of Kansas, 1999.

**Internet Resources**

National Aeronautics and Space Administration. <www.nasa.gov>.

Universe Today. <http://www.universetoday.com/>.

Scientific American. <http://www.sciam.com/>.

Space.com. <http://www.space.com/>.

SpaceWar. <http://www.spacewar.com/>.

# Miniaturization

Space exploration is an expensive and risky business. All too often, probes malfunction once they leave the ground; launching a satellite costs many millions of dollars at a minimum, and prices increase with **payload** weight. Designers feel constant pressure to keep spacecraft as efficient and cost-effective as possible.

To solve these problems, engineers are finding new ways to miniaturize spacecraft components, often pursuing branches of science that are still in their infancy. But the potential benefits for both the space program and private industry are driving a concerted effort toward smaller, more advanced technology.

## Nanotechnology

The capability to construct nanometer-sized materials promises to have tremendous impact on space exploration and industry. Scientists are still learning to manipulate nanomaterials, but one promising creation is a form of carbon called a nanotube. These cylinder-shaped molecules are not only unusually strong, but also have potential as **semiconductors**, which could

**payload** any cargo launched aboard a rocket that is destined for space, including communications satellites or modules, supplies, equipment, and astronauts; does not include the vehicle used to move the cargo or the propellant that powers the vehicle

**semiconductors** elements with properties intermediate between the metals and non-metals

Advances in nanotechnology at NASA are important in the miniaturization of equipment such as the Sojourner rover. By helping reduce payload weight and size, launch costs can be cut dramatically.

make them ideal candidates for both the next generation of spacecraft hull and the computers inside them. Composite materials that incorporate nanotubes could dramatically reduce the weight of launch vehicles and commercial aircraft, cutting fuel requirements by 25 percent or more. NASA is also trying to develop sensors based on nanoscale devices. These would potentially be sensitive enough to detect a single molecule of a substance, while still being microscopically small.

In the long term, scientists may be able to exploit the characteristics of biological systems to create materials that actually assemble themselves—without need for manufacture. Such materials would also have the ability to "heal themselves" after being damaged, increasing the durability of the aircraft or spacecraft.

## Computer Microsystems

It is predicted that within ten years, the silicon switches on chips will be made of single molecules, at which point silicon will reach its physical limits as a semiconductor. While other materials such as nanotubes could help augment silicon, other innovations in computer design can help shrink systems as well.

Systems on a chip will replace circuit boards with many discrete components, leading to much smaller and lower-power systems with higher reliability. A current example is a digital camera on a chip that includes the imager, all control electronics, and an analog-to-digital converter—all on the same silicon chip. Navigation systems built around this technology can guide spacecraft, and also can help soldiers and firefighters position themselves.

## Micro Power Sources

Powering a spacecraft under the extremes of heat, cold, and radiation levels encountered on a mission has always been challenging, but it is even more so when the power source has a size limitation. The only miniaturized power sources currently available are electrochemical batteries (which have a limited lifespan) and solar cells (which lose their effectiveness when far from the Sun or in a planet's shadow).

**kinetic energy** the energy an object has due to its motion

Two potential solutions are thermoelectric power, which converts heat energy into electricity; and alpha-voltaic power, which converts the **kinetic energy** of alpha particles emitted from a radioactive isotope. While still under development, these methods could produce chip-sized, solid-state power supplies that could have applications on Earth whenever battery lifetime and environmental limitations play a role. SEE ALSO COMMUNICATIONS, FUTURE NEEDS IN (VOLUME 4); MARS MISSIONS (VOLUME 4); NANOTECHNOLOGY (VOLUME 4); SCIENTIFIC RESEARCH (VOLUME 4); SPACE INDUSTRIES (VOLUME 4); VEHICLES (VOLUME 4).

*Chad Boutin*

### Bibliography

*1999 Annual Report of the Center for Integrated Space Microsystems.* Pasadena, CA: Jet Propulsion Laboratory, 1999.

Goldin, Daniel S. *Statement before the U.S. Senate Subcommittee on Science, Technology, and Space, Committee on Commerce, Science, and Transportation.* September 23, 1998.

### Internet Resources

Center for Integrated Space Microsystems. <http://cism.jpl.nasa.gov/>.

Center for Space Microelectronics Technology. <http://csmt.jpl.nasa.gov>.

**Mining** *See Asteroid Mining (Volume 4); Natural Resources (Volume 4); Resource Utilization (Volume 4); Space Resources (Volume 4).*

# Movies

In 1997 astronomer Jim Scotti discovered the asteroid 1997 XF11. Initial calculations predicted that the asteroid would make an extremely close approach to Earth in 2028. A collision would result in a global catastrophe, killing hundreds of millions of people. More accurate calculations of the orbit of the asteroid, however, determined that its probability of colliding with Earth is zero. Nonetheless, Hollywood films such as *Deep Impact* and *Armageddon*, both released in 1998, illustrated the global crisis that a comet or asteroid heading toward Earth would generate. Together with the alarming news about 1997 XF11, these movies heightened public awareness of the threat from an asteroid impact. As a result, the National Aeronautics and Space Administration (NASA) doubled its funding to $3 million a year for searching for near-Earth objects (NEOs). In addition, NASA initiated the Spaceguard Survey, intended to find 90 percent of all NEOs larger than 1 kilometer (0.62 mile) in diameter by 2008. Ultimately, the Torino scale, developed by astronomer Richard Binzel, was released in 1999 as a means of categorizing the likelihood of an asteroid or comet colliding with Earth.

*Deep Impact* and *Armaggedon* are two of over a hundred science fiction films about space that have generated interest in space exploration. For instance, *2001: A Space Odyssey* (1968) illustrated what space travel may have been like in the year 2001. In addition to its artistic use of visual and sound effects, that film introduced fascinating ideas for new technologies. The *Star Wars* trilogy and the *Star Trek* movie franchise also offered ideas for advanced technological devices. Other science fiction films, such as *E.T. The Extra-Terrestrial* (1982) and *Contact* (1997) in which humans make contact with intelligent extraterrestrial life have sparked the imagination and curiosity of viewers, generating excitement about exploring the depths of space.

A year before humans walked on the Moon, *2001: A Space Odyssey* opened in theaters. This movie has had such a great impact on society that a NASA spacecraft en route to Mars was named after it: the 2001 Mars Odyssey. Adapted from the novel by Arthur C. Clarke and directed by Stanley Kubrick, *2001: A Space Odyssey* foresaw a colonized Moon and a piloted mission to Jupiter in the year 2001. While the Moon has not yet been colonized, scientists are looking closely at Mars, where settlement may be easier because of the possible presence of water. Perhaps the enthusiasm generated by the piloted trip to Jupiter shown in the movie will be caused by the first human mission to Mars.

Settling Mars, however, will probably require a process known as terraforming. The atmosphere of Mars is composed of carbon dioxide, which may be converted to breathable air by this process. As an example, the movie *Red Planet* (2000) suggests one possible way of terraforming Mars—using **algae** to create a **greenhouse effect** that would allow life to thrive there. Some ideas for new technologies introduced by *2001: A Space Odyssey* exist today. For example, videoconferencing as shown in the movie is feasible via the Internet along with an inexpensive video camera. However, an intelligent computer such as HAL 9000 is still science fiction, although advances in artificial intelligence have produced expert systems that help professionals make decisions.

## Technology

George Lucas's *Star Wars* trilogy generated another wave of enthusiasm for space travel. The technology of *Star Wars* is highly advanced, although the ideas behind it have caused people to ponder their possibilities. The lightsaber, a powerful energy-based sword, is one example. Today researchers can use lasers to cut through some materials, but there is nothing like the lightsaber. Another interesting concept in those films is the hyperdrive, which can transport a starship at a speed faster than that of light. Scientists are just beginning to ask directed questions about the possibility of lightspeed travel. Similarly advanced is the idea of antigravity. Researchers have been able to simulate antigravity under extremely cold temperatures for small objects, but true antigravity is only a theoretical concept. Other technologies, such as the holocam, the proton torpedo, the blasters, and the electrobinoculars, are high-technology devices that with human ingenuity may become realities.

The *Star Trek* television series and movies offer a myriad of advanced technologies, the most prominent being the transporter and the holodeck. The transporter can convert every atom of an object into a stream of matter and send it to its destination to be reconstructed there. By taking advantage of the properties of quantum mechanics, scientists have been able to "teleport" a photon, or light particle, a promising achievement. The holodeck can produce a holographic environment that feels as real as

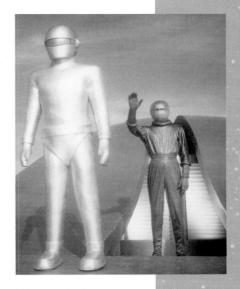

Extraterrestrials emerge from their spacecraft to warn humans of impending nuclear disaster in a scene from the 1951 film *The Day the Earth Stood Still*.

**algae** simple photosynthetic organisms, often aquatic

**greenhouse effect** process by which short wavelength energy (e.g., visible light) penetrates an object's atmosphere and is absorbed by the surface, which reradiates this energy as longer wavelength infrared (thermal) energy; this energy is blocked from escaping to space by molecules (e.g., $H_2O$ and $CO_2$) in the atmosphere; and as a result, the surface warms

The crew of the starship Enterprise in a scene from the 1986 film *Star Trek IV: The Voyage Home.* Fans of the series *Star Trek* successfully petitioned the White House to name the first space shuttle orbiter "Enterprise."

reality. Researchers at the Massachusetts Institute of Technology have been able to make small holographic imaging devices with force-feedback, but holodeck-type rooms are technologies of the future. Like the high-technology devices in *Star Wars*, the tricorder, the warp drive, and the phaser in *Star Trek* remain to be explored.

## Extraterrestrial Life

The discovery of extraterrestrial life would be one of the greatest achievements in human history. As a result, many movies that depict an alien encounter have generated enthusiasm for space exploration. Steven Spielberg's *E.T. The Extra-Terrestrial* touched many viewers' hearts through its depiction of the love of an alien, giving people a motivation to explore outer worlds. Similarly, *Contact*, based on scientist Carl Sagan's novel, motivated space exploration through the words of an advanced alien being. However, the central theme of *Contact* was the process of decoding a message that described how to build a machine with an unknown function. *Contact* illustrated how the message united people around the world for the common goal of building a machine that might reveal the purpose of humanity. Other films, such as *Cocoon*, *The Abyss*, and *Mission to Mars*, have given humans a motive to explore space: the possibility of an encounter with an alien civilization and the rewarding consequences it might have.

Science fiction movies express ideas that may become realities and provide reasons to examine the depths of space more closely. SEE ALSO DOMED

CITIES (VOLUME 4); FASTER-THAN-LIGHT TRAVEL (VOLUME 4); FIRST CONTACT (VOLUME 4); INTERSTELLAR TRAVEL (VOLUME 4); ION PROPULSION (VOLUME 4); LUNAR BASES (VOLUME 4); LUNAR OUTPOSTS (VOLUME 4); MARS BASES (VOLUME 4); SCIENCE FICTION (VOLUME 4); STAR TREK (VOLUME 4); STAR WARS (VOLUME 4); TELEPORTATION (VOLUME 4); TIME TRAVEL (VOLUME 4); VEHICLES (VOLUME 4); WORMHOLES (VOLUME 4).

*Carlos J. Rosas-Anderson*

**Bibliography**

Krauss, Lawrence M., and Stephen Hawking. *The Physics of Star Trek.* New York: Harper/Perennial Library, 1996.

Smith, Bill. *Star Wars: The Essential Guide to Weapons and Technology.* New York: Del Rey, 1997.

Zubrin, Robert, with Richard Wagner. *The Case for Mars: The Plan to Settle the Red Planet and Why We Must.* New York: Free Press, 1996.

# Nanotechnology

Like a swarm of bees, tiny humanmade satellites—called nanosatellites or picosatellites, depending on their size—may one day fly in formation to remote destinations throughout the solar system. Upon reaching their targets, they will spread out to investigate the area, perhaps one satellite landing on each of a thousand asteroids, crawling around its surface, and sending data back to scientists waiting on Earth. Another swarm might cover the surface of Mars with an army of explorers, investigating more area in one day than a standard rover could reach in several years. Alternatively, the group might be designed to stay together to accomplish its mission: a cluster of satellites each carrying a tiny mirror could be coordinated to act as one giant telescope mirror, surpassing the Hubble Space Telescope's light-gathering power by a factor of a thousand.

## Problems with Large Satellites

Typical satellites deployed in the early twenty-first century weigh more than 1,000 kilograms (2,200 pounds). To qualify as a nanosatellite, the device must weigh less than 20 kilograms (or 44 pounds); a picosatellite less than 1 kilogram (2.2 pounds). Such small nano- or picosatellites could address two of the major problems involved with traditional satellite technology:

1. Cost. The major expense of deploying a traditional satellite lies in transportation costs. A ride on the shuttle averages $6,000 per pound, so the lighter the better. Tiny satellites could possibly be launched using small rockets or electromagnetic railguns, bypassing the expensive shuttle ride altogether.

2. Failure due to one faulty system. If the communications system of a traditional satellite fails, or if the satellite is damaged during deployment, the whole mission might be scrapped, at a loss of millions of dollars. But nano- and picosatellites could be designed with distributed functions in mind: Some may be responsible for navigation, some for communication, and some for taking photographs of target sites. Should a problem develop in one of the units, others in the group with the same function would take over. Distributed functions and built-in redundancy would save the mission.

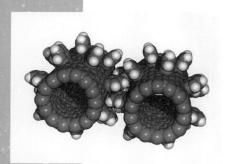

These "Fullerene Nano-gears" were developed by NASA as a prototype for similar future products, constructed of thousands of tiny machines that could adapt to their environment without human interaction and repair themselves.

**transponder** bandwidth-specific transmitter-receiver units

**frequency** the number of oscillations or vibrations per second of an electromagnetic wave or any wave

## Early Attempts: OPAL

Thanks to the miniaturization of off-the-shelf computer components, satellites the size of a deck of cards have already orbited Earth, performing simple tasks, and sending signals back to interested parties on Earth. These include groups of college students at Stanford University in California, who designed and built a satellite "mothership" called OPAL (Orbiting Picosatellite Automatic Launcher) as part of their master's degree program; a group called Artemis at Santa Clara University in California, who designed three of the picosatellite "daughterships" for the mission; and a group of ham radio operators from Washington, D.C., whose StenSat picosatellite was also included aboard the mothership. The Aerospace Corporation in El Segundo, California, manufactured the final two picosatellites for the mission to test microelectromechanical systems (MEMS) technology.

OPAL was launched onboard a JAWsat launch vehicle on January 26, 2000, from the Vandenberg Air Force Base in California. It consisted of a hexagonal, aluminum mothership 23 centimeters (9 inches) tall, weighing 23 kilograms (51 pounds), and containing the six small daughter satellites described earlier, weighing about 0.45 kilograms (1 pound) each. When it reached its orbiting altitude of 698 kilometers (434 miles) above Earth, the picosatellite daughterships were deployed by a spring-launching device.

Once free of the mothership, the picosatellites went into operating mode. One of the three Artemis satellites began transmitting the group's web site address in morse code, while the other two measured the field strength of lightning strikes. StenSat's **transponder** sent telemetry signals to ham radio operators around the world. The two satellites from the Aerospace Corporation were tethered together, and communicated with each other and the engineers on Earth using MEMS switches that selected between various experimental radio **frequencies** for transmission. OPAL was still operating a year after launch.

## Micro- and Nanotechnologies

The technology that made OPAL possible is as near as one's laptop computer or personal digital assistant. Computing power that used to require a mainframe computer in a room of its own can now fit into a laptop, thanks to innovative engineers who continually cram more and more memory onto smaller and smaller silicon chips. The student engineers used a Motorola microcontroller with 1 MB of onboard RAM operating at 8.38 MHz as OPAL's central processing unit. It was powered by commercially available solar panels, and backed-up by rechargeable nickel cadmium batteries.

But off-the-shelf components, while sufficient for student projects, will not survive at the cutting edge of nanosatellite technology; other technologies will be necessary to keep the smaller-and-smaller trend going. MEMS are tiny devices—gears, switches, valves, sensors, or other standard mechanical or electrical parts—made out of silicon. The technology arose out of the techniques used by microchip designers: pattern a wafer of pure silicon with the dimensions of the transistors, resistors, logic gates, and connectors required for the chip, etch away the material surrounding the pattern, and one has the beginnings of an electronic circuit. So why not do the same for mechanical systems? Lay out a pattern for a tiny gear on a silicon wafer, etch

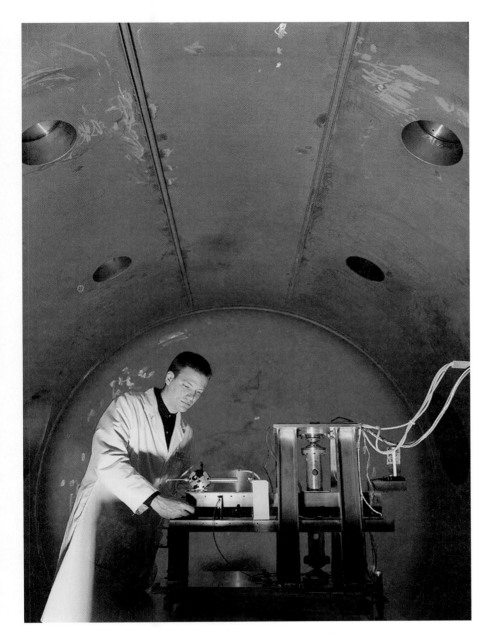

An engineer at the Marshall Space Flight Center tests a micro-thruster model. Through development of this nano-technology, it is hoped that microthrusters will be able to propel future spaceships with a small amount of expended energy.

away the surrounding material, including the material underneath that holds the gear to the wafer and to its axle, and one has a working gear that can mesh with other gears. By making sandwiches of different materials and etching them in a carefully controlled manner, scientists have been able to make gears, valves, pumps, switches, and sensors on a very small scale—the microscale. MEMS technology is often called a "top-down" approach: start with a large wafer of silicon and make microcomponents out of it.

To reach the even smaller nanoscale requires a "bottom-up" approach. Using instruments such as an atomic force microscope that can manipulate individual atoms, engineers can build tiny devices an atom at a time. Or, by understanding how atoms tend to bond together naturally, scientists can create conditions where nanoscale devices "self-assemble" on a patterned surface out of the atoms in a vapor. Such precise control will enable them to build nanostructures 1,000 times smaller than MEMS devices. This level of structural control will be necessary for the next generation of sophisticated nano- and picosatellites currently in the planning stages.

## What Is Next?

The National Aeronautics and Space Administration's (NASA) Space Technology 5 (ST5) mission is scheduled to launch three nanosatellites into low orbit in 2003. The ST5 nanosatellites will be small octagons about 43 centimeters (17 inches) in diameter and 20 centimeters (8 inches) high—about the size of a big birthday cake. They will be complete systems in themselves, each having navigation, guidance, propulsion, and communications abilities. In addition, the ST5 nanosatellites will be test platforms for new space technologies. One of these, called A Formation Flying and Communications Instrument is a communications system designed to monitor the positions of small spacecraft relative to each other and the ground—a first attempt at making satellites fly in formation. Other technologies to be tested on ST5 include a lithium-ion power system that can store two to four times more energy than current batteries, an external coating that can be tuned to absorb heat when the spacecraft is cold or to emit heat when it is too warm, and a MEMS chip that makes fine attitude adjustments to the spacecraft using 8.5 times less power than 2002 devices.

By 2020 NASA hopes to deploy ANTS to the asteroid belt between Mars and Jupiter. ANTS stands for Autonomous Nano Technology Swarm. Each tiny spacecraft would weigh about 1 kilogram (2.2 pounds) and have its own solar sail to power its flight. After a three-year trip, the swarm would spread out to cover thousands of asteroids. The swarm would have a hierarchy of rulers, messengers, and workers. Each satellite would carry one type of instrumentation to perform a specific function: measure a magnetic field, detect gamma rays, take photographs, or analyze the surface composition of an asteroid. Messengers would relay instructions from the rulers to the workers, and also inform the rulers of important information collected by the workers. The rulers could then decide to reassign some of the workers to explore the more promising areas. In the end, a small number of messengers would return to the space station to deliver the data to scientists; the rest of the swarm would perish in space, having finished their duties. Scientists hope to obtain valuable information about the mineral resources of the asteroid belt, which could be a source for metals and other raw materials needed to build colonies in space.

## Future Prospects

Nano- and picosatellites will also be useful in Earth orbit in situations where information from a large area is needed simultaneously. Traditional satellites can only be in one place at a time, but picosatellites can be everywhere, if enough of them are deployed. A swarm of picosatellites equipped with cameras and communications links could gather vital information from a battlefield on Earth, relaying enemy positions and troop counts to generals behind the lines. Or an array of satellites could be launched to gather atmospheric information that could help to predict the formation of hurricanes and tornadoes in time to warn the population. The Earth's entire magnetic field might be captured in one instantaneous "snapshot" by widely scattered swarms of satellites.

Projecting far into the future, perhaps a picosatellite could be made that would travel as far as possible into space, then manufacture a copy of itself before its mechanisms failed. This second generation robot/satellite could then travel as far as it could before making another replica, and so on. By sending out millions of tiny, affordable, self-replicating satellites, humankind's reach might one day extend to the farthest parts of the solar system. SEE ALSO MINIATURIZATION (VOLUME 4); ROBOTIC EXPLORATION OF SPACE (VOLUME 2); ROBOTICS TECHNOLOGY (VOLUME 2); SATELLITES, TYPES OF (VOLUME 1).

*Tim Palucka*

### Bibliography

Booth, Nicholas. *Space: The Next 100 Years.* New York: Orion Books, 1990.

The Editors of Time-Life Books. *Spacefarers.* Alexandria, VA: Time-Life Books, 1990.

**Internet Resources**

*Orbiting Picosatellite Automated Launcher.* Stanford University. <http://ssdl.stanford.edu/opal/>.

*Space Technology 5 (ST5).* New Millennium Program. <http://nmp.jpl.nasa.gov/st5>.

# Natural Resources

Exploration is hard. After all, it involves being in a place where few or none have been before, whether it is the top of a mountain, the bottom of the ocean, or the surface of another world. Historically, part of the reason that exploration is so difficult is because most explorers have had to be self-sustaining; that is, most explorers have had to bring their own provisions, whether it was food or water or heat or tools, and the portage and maintenance of these provisions naturally limits the scope and pace of exploratory activities. The most successful explorers have been those who learned to use the natural resources that they encountered along the way to enable new and unanticipated discoveries and to increase their chances of successfully reaching their goals. This "living off the land" philosophy has been crucial for the exploration of Earth, and it also applies to the exploration of space.

During the latter half of the twentieth century, humans took baby steps out into the solar system. Exploratory ventures ranged from modest robotic missions designed to perform **reconnaissance** of planets, moons, asteroids, and comets to the bold and expensive human missions to the Moon as part of the Apollo program. These initial forays provided a sound foundation of scientific knowledge and tested many of the basic engineering principles required for human spaceflight. However, almost all of those missions were self-sustaining. For example, robotic orbiters and landers had to carry their own propellant, which, when exhausted, meant the end of those missions. The Apollo astronauts had to bring their own oxygen and water, as well as the rocket fuel for the return trip, which ultimately limited their duration on the lunar surface. If humans are to venture farther into the solar system in the twenty-first century, it will be necessary to learn how to identify and exploit the abundant natural resources available in the places they wish to explore.

**reconnaissance** a survey or preliminary exploration of a region of interest

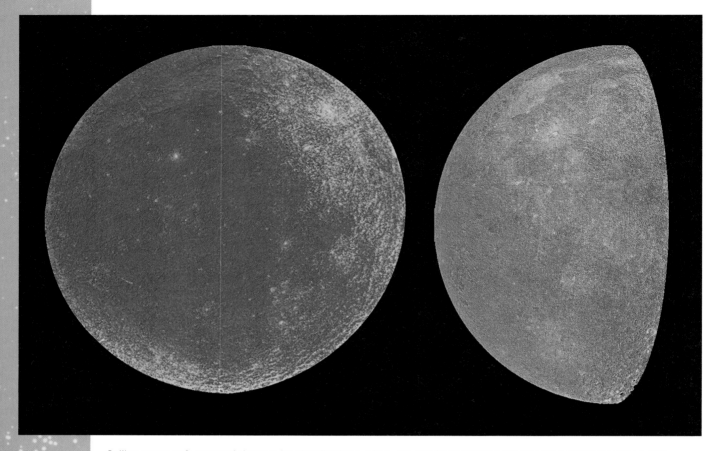

Galileo spacecraft captured these color visualizations, which are helpful in locating the Moon's natural resources. The deeper blue sections are relatively rich in titanium, while the greens, yellows, and light oranges indicate areas rich in iron and magnesium. The yellowish area is part of the South Pole Aitken basin, a large circular crater, which may be rich in iron and magnesium. The reds are cratered highlands, which contain few resources.

**minerals** crystalline arrangements of atoms and molecules of specified proportions that make up rocks

**solar wind** a continuous, but varying, stream of charged particles (mostly electrons and protons) generated by the Sun; it establishes and affects the interplanetary magnetic field; it also deforms the magnetic field about Earth and sends particles streaming toward Earth at its poles

**shielding** providing protection for humans and electronic equipment from cosmic rays, energetic particles from the Sun, and other radioactive materials

## The Moon

The Moon provides a good example to demonstrate this point, because the lunar surface contains a number of natural resources that could substantially enhance both exploratory and commercial space activities. For example, the lunar surface consists of **minerals** containing iron, silicon, titanium, aluminum, oxygen, and other elements. Experiments on the Apollo samples have demonstrated that it is fairly simple to extract these elements from lunar rocks and soils. Oxygen, especially, is a critical resource that can be used for breathing as well as generating rocket fuel. Extracted metals could be used for habitat construction or tool fabrication, and because they are dense, they offer the potential for enormous savings in the mass of raw materials that would have to be sent from Earth.

The Moon is also constantly bombarded by **solar wind** particles that implant hydrogen and helium into the surface. When extracted, hydrogen can be used for propellants or combined with extracted oxygen to make water. Water is another critical resource for life support, radiation **shielding**, and self-sustaining agriculture. Extracted helium could be used for power generation on Earth or the Moon once the technology for large-scale **fusion** power production matures. At a more basic level, unprocessed lunar rocks and soils are a resource that can be used for solar wind radiation shielding, thermal isolation, and heat storage for habitats and other structures built on the Moon. There may be other natural resources on the Moon, such as subsurface water or ice deposited by asteroid or comet impacts, which will be discovered only through continued exploration that is enabled by the utilization of resources that are known to be there.

## Asteroids and Comets

Asteroids and comets are important space exploration targets because of their scientific value as samples of the early solar system as well as the threat to Earth posed by potential impacts. In many ways asteroids and comets are likely to offer more varied and abundant natural resources than the Moon. Like the Moon, asteroids and comets are bombarded by solar wind and have silicate minerals on their surfaces, and those surface materials can be processed to yield oxygen and hydrogen and the other potential resources. However, several asteroids are known to have abundant metallic deposits on their surfaces that are likely to be rich sources of ores for construction materials and shielding. Many asteroids and most comets are also known to be rich in volatile materials such as water ice, dry ice, and hydrated minerals as well as carbon-rich organic compounds. Once extracted, these resources could be used for life support, propellant production, and construction and shielding. Perhaps most importantly, many near-Earth asteroids and some comets are easier to get to and launch from than the Moon because of their small mass and occasional close passes by Earth. Ease of accessibility is itself a natural resource and opens up the economic possibility of efficient exportation of asteroidal or cometary natural resources to Earth and other exploration targets.

## Mars

Finally, Mars will be an important focus of space exploration in the twenty-first century because of its spectacular geology and **meteorology** and the discovery in the twentieth century that it once may have been much more Earthlike and perhaps even hospitable to life. Mars offers abundant natural resources that will almost certainly have to be tapped to enable efficient and long-term exploration so far from Earth. These resources include many materials that are extractable from the silicate-rich rocks and soils. However, Mars is also a volatile-rich planet and has an atmosphere containing carbon dioxide and other gases with resource potential. Water is known to be trapped in a small percentage of the surface soils and is hypothesized to exist either in subsurface liquid water aquifers or in water ice permafrost deposits. Self-sustaining agriculture and oxygen production are possible by extracting or accessing this water and using the abundant atmospheric carbon dioxide to fuel photosynthesis. Light elements such as hydrogen, carbon, nitrogen, and oxygen are much more abundant on Mars than on the Moon or most asteroids, and extraction of these volatiles from crustal rocks and soils could provide raw materials for the production of propellant and manufactured goods. And because of the role of water in its geologic history, Mars is likely to have rich deposits of metals, salts, and other minerals or ores. Even modest initial developments in natural resource usage on Mars, such as those planned for robotic missions, are likely to enormously increase the efficiency and capability of Mars exploration.

**fusion** the act of releasing nuclear energy by combining lighter elements such as hydrogen into heavier elements

**meteorology** the study of atmospheric phenomena or weather

## Issues

There are many other potential sources of natural resources in the solar system, including cosmic dust, solar wind, and the atmospheres of gas giant planets. There are also important political, ethical, technological, and economic issues regarding natural resource exploitation that need to be addressed: What are the most energy-efficient ways to generate propellants from raw materials? Who owns mining rights on Mars and the asteroids? Will extraction activities irreparably harm the environments of other worlds? Given the difficulty of balancing environmental stewardship and natural resource extraction on Earth, this issue is particularly important and will require substantial global cooperation among all of the nations involved in future space exploration. SEE ALSO ASTEROID MINING (VOLUME 4); COMET CAPTURE (VOLUME 4); EARTH—WHY LEAVE? (VOLUME 4); ENVIRONMENTAL CHANGES (VOLUME 4); LIVING ON OTHER WORLDS (VOLUME 4); LUNAR BASES (VOLUME 4); LUNAR OUTPOSTS (VOLUME 4); MARS (VOLUME 2); MARS BASES (VOLUME 4); MARS DIRECT (VOLUME 4); MOON (VOLUME 2); RESOURCE UTILIZATION (VOLUME 4); TERRAFORMING (VOLUME 4).

*James Bell*

### Bibliography

Heiken, Grant H., David T. Vaniman, and Bevan M. French. *Lunar Source Book.* Cambridge, UK: Cambridge University Press, 1991.

Lewis, John S., Mildred S. Matthews, and Mary L. Geurrieri. *Resources of Near-Earth Space.* Tucson: University of Arizona Press, 1993.

Mendell, Wendell W., ed. *Lunar Bases and Space Activities of the 21st Century.* Houston: Lunar and Planetary Institute, 1985.

# Nuclear Propulsion

Nuclear energy remains an attractive potential means of propulsion for future spacecraft. When compared with conventional rocket engines, a nuclear propulsion system would in theory be less massive, and could provide sustained thrust with greater energy. Many believe nuclear-powered spacecraft can and should be built, but first many technical problems and other hurdles must be overcome.

Both the U.S. and Soviet space programs were researching nuclear propulsion as far back as the early 1960s, and since then, dozens of ideas for nuclear propulsion systems—and the spacecraft they would power—have been proposed. Each system, however, is based around one of the two methods of generating nuclear energy: fission and fusion.

## Fission Propulsion

Fission is the act of splitting a heavy **atomic nucleus** into two lighter ones, which results in a tremendous release of energy. Common fuels for fission reactions are plutonium and enriched uranium, a soft-drink sized can of which carries 50 times more energy than the space shuttle's external tank.

Fission has been used to generate electricity on Earth for six decades, often by using the heat from the reactor core to boil water and spin a tur-

**atomic nucleus** the protons and neutrons making up the core of an atom

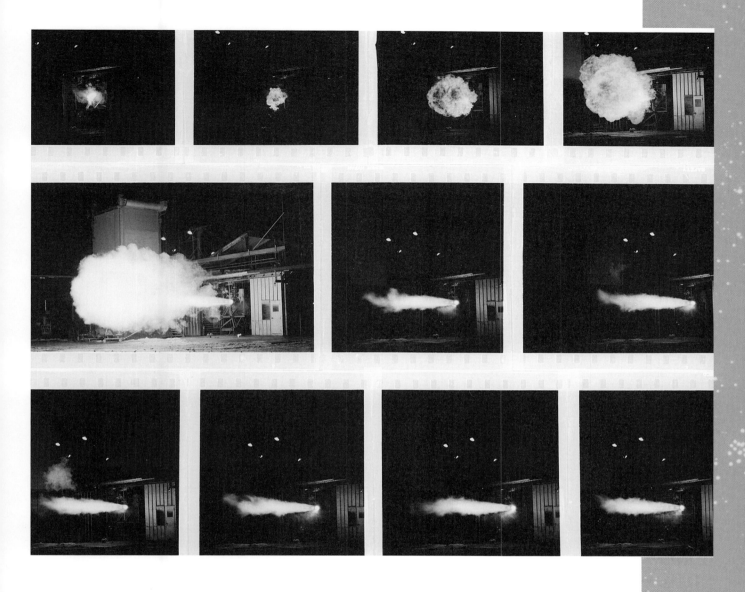

bine. But a reactor core could also be used to heat a propellant such as hydrogen into a super hot gas. The gas could then be expelled out of a nozzle, providing thrust, just like in a conventional chemical rocket. Engines of this type are called nuclear thermal rockets (NTRs), and were ground-tested by the United States in the Rover/NERVA program of the 1960s.

A related method, being studied by the National Aeronautics and Space Administration (NASA) in the early 2000s, would give an NTR the equivalent of a military jet's afterburner. In this scheme, liquid oxygen could be pumped into the exhaust nozzle. This would cool the hydrogen enough that it could combine with the oxygen and burn, providing additional thrust and leaving water vapor as a by-product.

NTRs could produce enough thrust to carry a spacecraft into orbit, but because the propellant itself would quickly run out, they are unsuitable for longer missions to Mars or beyond. An alternative approach to NTRs is to use the reactor to produce electricity, which could power various types of electrical thrusters. Such nuclear-electric propulsion systems (NEPs) would use electric fields to ionize and/or accelerate propellant gas

The Plum Brook Station, at the Glenn Research Center, is the site of the 28,000 pound Nuclear Transfer Copper Engine, used in testing nuclear propulsion, which one day may propel humans to Mars.

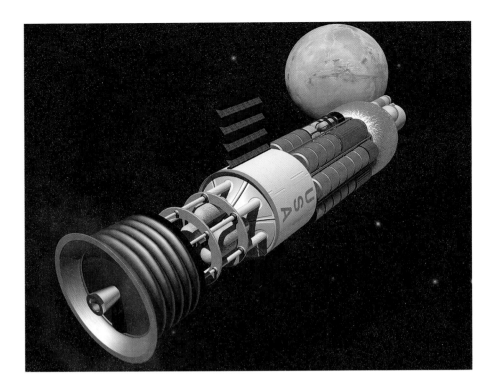

This concept spacecraft was developed under Project Orion in the 1960s by the U.S. government. In theory, small nuclear pulses would propel the craft.

such as hydrogen, argon, or xenon. NASA plans to put development of NEPs on a fast track beginning in 2003.

NEPs would be able to produce smaller amounts of continuous thrust over periods of weeks or months, making them extremely suitable for robotic missions to the outer planets or slow journeys between Earth orbit and the Moon. For human missions, when diminishing supplies for the crew make speed a more important factor, a combination of NTRs and NEPs could be used.

## Fusion Propulsion

We have nuclear fusion to thank for life on Earth: Most solar energy comes from the four million tons of hydrogen that is converted into helium every second in the interior of the Sun. But fusion can only occur in superheated environments measuring in the millions of degrees, when matter reaches a highly ionized state called plasma. Since plasma is too hot to be contained in any known material, controlled nuclear fusion remains one of humanity's great unrealized scientific goals.

However, plasma conducts electricity very well, and it could be possible to use magnetic fields to contain and accelerate it. It might even be more feasible to use fusion in space, where it would not be necessary to shield the reactor from the environment in all directions, as it would be on Earth.

Experiments toward developing a fusion propulsion system are underway at NASA's Marshall Space Flight Center in Huntsville, Alabama. The Gas Dynamic Mirror (GDM) Fusion Propulsion system would wrap a long, thin current-carrying coil of wire around a tube containing plasma. The current would create a powerful magnetic field that would trap the plasma in the tube's center section, while each end of the tube would have special magnetic nozzles through which the plasma could escape, providing thrust.

The amount and efficiency of the energy released by fusion makes it a good candidate for interplanetary travel. As a comparison of their efficiency, if a chemical rocket were an average car, a fusion rocket would get about 3,000 kilometers (1,864 miles) per liter! Fusion also has great potential as an energy source because of the nature of the fuel and reaction—hydrogen is the most common element in the universe, and the by-products are non-radioactive (unlike fission products, which remain hazardous for many years). But until fusion becomes a reality, fission is humanity's sole option for nuclear-powered space travel—and is not without strong opposition.

## Pros and Cons

Plutonium is one of the most poisonous substances known; doses of one millionth of a gram are carcinogenic, and it is difficult to contain the radioactive by-products of fission safely. These dangers have made nuclear fission controversial from the outset, and the prospect of a nuclear reactor reentering Earth's atmosphere and scattering radioactive material over a wide area makes many people nervous.

Many space probes have not carried reactors but are powered by radioisotope thermoelectric generators (RTGs), which derive electrical power from the slow decay of radioactive material. There was concern in 1997 that the Cassini probe to Saturn might meet with an accident as it flew by Earth, scattering its RTG's 33 kilograms (72 pounds) of plutonium into the atmosphere. This did not occur and Cassini continued on its route to Saturn. However, such concerns, along with the high projected cost of research and construction, have been obstacles in the way of nuclear-propelled spacecraft.

Still, nuclear propulsion could dramatically decrease travel time to the planets. A round trip to Mars could be accomplished in half the time with fusion power, which would lessen the crew's exposure to the hazards of weightlessness and **cosmic radiation**. A nuclear-propelled craft could conceivably be used repeatedly for round trips to the Moon and planets, cutting down the cost of operating such a long-term transit system. Funding for the development of new nuclear propulsion will be boosted in 2003 with a view to production of an operational system within a few years. SEE ALSO ACCESSING SPACE (VOLUME 1); ANTIMATTER PROPULSION (VOLUME 4); EXTERNAL TANK (VOLUME 3); FASTER-THAN-LIGHT TRAVEL (VOLUME 4); INTERSTELLAR TRAVEL (VOLUME 4); ION PROPULSION (VOLUME 4); LASER PROPULSION (VOLUME 4); LIGHTSAILS (VOLUME 4); POWER, METHODS OF GENERATING (VOLUME 4).

*Chad Boutin*

**cosmic radiation** high energy particles that enter Earth's atmosphere from outer space causing cascades of mesons and other particles

### Internet Resources

*Advanced Plasma Propulsion.* Space Transportation, Marshall Space Flight Center. <http://astp.msfc.nasa.gov/sciresearch/adv_plas_prop.html>.

*High-Powered Electrical Propulsion.* Space Transportation, Marshall Space Flight Center. <http://astp.msfc.nasa.gov/sciresearch/nuclear_prop.html>.

# O'Neill Colonies

Gerard K. O'Neill (1927–1992), a particle physicist who spent most of his career at Princeton University, was the driving force behind the first serious space colony design study. Conducted in 1975, this study took the form

Settlers would reside in the ring circling the central hub of the colony, while a large circular mirror with a hole in its middle would be positioned directly above the settlement to beam sunlight into the structure for power.

of a ten-week program held jointly at the National Aeronautics and Space Administration (NASA) Ames Research Center and at Stanford University, outside San Francisco, California. NASA and the American Society for Engineering Education sponsored the program. The program's work laid out the basic requirements for large-scale human settlement of the solar system. As technical director, O'Neill guided the study towards its basic conclusion that the best way to begin the human colonization of space was to build a large space colony at **L-5**, with the colony being dedicated to using lunar materiel to build a series of solar power satellites to beam electricty down to an energy-hungry planet.

**L-5** the gravitationally stable Lagrange point 60 degrees behind the orbiting planet

## Colony Basics

The colony would be a home for 10,000 people living and working in a round tube 130 meters (425 feet) across and 1,790 meters (5,870 feet) in diameter. The ring would rotate around a central hub, providing artificial gravity. It would be shielded from **solar radiation** by 9.9 million metric tons (10.9 million tons) of lunar material, built up as a stationary ring—stationary relative to the habitation structure. At the center of the ring would be a hub where spaceships would dock and where cargo and passengers would be transferred back and forth.

**solar radiation** total energy of any wavelength and all charged particles emitted by the Sun

**photovoltaic cells** cells consisting of a thin wafer of a semiconductor material that incorporate a p-n junction, which converts incident light into electrical power; photovoltaic cells connected in a series make up a solar array

A large circular mirror with a hole in its middle would be positioned directly above the colony to beam sunlight into the structure, bypassing the shielding and providing both light and solar energy to power the **photovoltaic cells** arrayed around the hub. Underneath the main structure would be a large heat radiator that would collect and expel waste heat generated by the colony. At the bottom of the structure, at the end of a long access tube, would be a solar furnace where lunar ore (or ore from elsewhere in the solar system) would be converted into material with which to build solar power satellites and other space habitats.

## What Motivated O'Neill's Vision?

At the time of the initial study, O'Neill was partly motivated by the worldwide energy crisis of the early seventies and the popular "Limits to Growth" movement. This movement was embodied in such documents as the famous Club of Rome report, which summed up Limits to Growth's attitude with the declaration that "the world has a cancer and the cancer is man." O'Neill rejected the grim future implied by this group. He saw that this powerful movement required that future "limits will almost surely be more than physical, and that in the long run the freedom of the human mind will have to be limited also. . . . For me the age old dreams of improvement, of change, of greater human freedom are the most poignant of all; and the most chilling prospect that I see for a planet bound human race is that many of those dreams will be forever cut off for us." (O'Neill 1982, pp. 39–40).

As he refined his vision, O'Neill began to ask basic questions about the world: "Is a planetary surface the right place for an expanding technological civilization? There is no clear answer except to say that my own interest in space as a field for human activity went back to my own childhood, and that I have always felt strongly a personal desire to be free of boundaries and regimentation. The steady state society, ridden with rules and laws, proposed by the early workers on the limits to growth was, to me, abhorrent" (O'Neill 1982, p. 279).

In order to make his vision of the humanization of space plausible, O'Neill had to invent a new way of looking at the resources and the economics of human space activity. He imagined a space economy in which 90 percent or more of the raw materials needed for survival would come from the Moon, the asteroids, or elsewhere in the solar system. Only an indispensable small amount would have to be brought up from Earth.

## Obstacles to Permanent Space Colonies

Then, as now, the greatest obstacle to building a permanent human colony in space was the expense of getting into **low Earth orbit**. In the late 1970s and the early 1980s it was thought that NASA's space shuttle would provide reliable, relatively inexpensive, access to space. O'Neill expected that there would be a minimum of twenty-five shuttle flights a year. The reality is that in the early twenty-first century NASA is struggling to fly the shuttle more than six or seven times a year at a cost of between $300 million and $400 million per flight.

**low Earth orbit** an orbit between 300 and 800 kilometers above Earth's surface

O'Neill accurately foresaw that the shuttle could be improved. The weight of the main fuel tank has been considerably reduced, the main engines have been made lighter and more efficient, and, after the Challenger disaster in 1986, the whole system has been made safer and more reliable. Unfortunately, this has not been enough to make the space shuttle into the all-purpose, reliable vehicle that NASA had promised. The heavy-cargo version of the shuttle, the so-called Shuttle-C, which O'Neill had been depending on to build the initial elements of his dream, never materialized.

For moving large tonnages of material from the Moon's surface to the space colonies, O'Neill imagined a mass driver, a type of electromagnetic catapult. Powered by solar-generated electricity, this machine would have very low operating costs and would be the centerpiece of lunar mining. Longer term, mass drivers would be used to move heavy loads of material throughout the solar system.

## O'Neill's Ultimate Dream

Ultimately, O'Neill imagined that humanity would gradually move out into the solar system, leaving Earth with a much smaller population that was dedicated to tending the planet's magnificent, unique environment and its historical treasures. Thousands, perhaps millions, of visitors would come to see the wonders of humanity's original home world. The vast majority of the human race would live, work, and thrive elsewhere in the solar system.

The resources needed to accomplish this goal and to fulfill O'Neill's great dream already exist. O'Neill concluded that space "is nothing less than a rich, wholly new frontier—a new ecological range for humankind. . . .The untapped resource of clean, unvarying solar energy waiting on that frontier is more than a hundred million times as much as the sunlight we intercept on Earth. The material resources waiting there, in the form of small asteroids whose diameters have been measured and whose orbits have been plotted, are enough to let us build Earth-like colonies with a total land area of three thousand Earths. So much for the limits to growth" (O'Neill 1982, p. 321). SEE ALSO COMMUNITIES IN SPACE (VOLUME 4); O'NEILL, GERARD K. (VOLUME 4); SETTLEMENTS (VOLUME 4).

*Taylor Dinerman*

### Bibliography

Harrison, Albert A. *Spacefaring: The Human Dimension*. Berkeley, CA: University of California Press, 2001.

O'Neill, Gerard K. *The High Frontier: Human Colonies in Space*. Garden City, New York: Anchor Books, 1982.

# O'Neill, Gerard K.

## *American Physicist and Visionary 1927–1992*

Gerard K. O'Neill is sometimes considered the father of space colony design. Born in Brooklyn, New York, O'Neill served as a **radar** technician in the navy, then earned a bachelor's degree from Swarthmore College in 1950 and a doctoral degree in physics from Cornell University in 1954. Upon earning his doctorate, O'Neill joined the faculty of Princeton University's physics department, where he remained until his retirement in 1985.

O'Neill's early research focused on experiments in high-energy particle physics. He invented the colliding-beam storage ring and developed the technology that is now the basis of all high-energy particle accelerators. By the end of the 1960s, O'Neill became very interested in the idea of space colonization. In 1977 he founded the Space Studies Institute at Princeton, the purpose of which was to develop tools for space exploration. The insti-

**radar** a technique for detecting distant objects by emitting a pulse of radio-wavelength radiation and then recording echoes of the pulse off the distant objects

tute today is a major source of funds for research on space resources and manufacturing. O'Neill became world-famous in 1977 with the publication of his book *The High Frontier*. It was here that he described plans for the construction of large, cylindrical space colonies. Such a colony, O'Neill said, could become self-sustaining when placed in a stable orbit between Earth and the Moon. This was the first serious description of how a space colony could be sustained and it continues to serve as a model as such settlements are planned. SEE ALSO DYSON SPHERES (VOLUME 4); DYSON, FREEMAN JOHN (VOLUME 4); O'NEILL COLONIES (VOLUME 4); SPACE STATIONS OF THE FUTURE (VOLUME 4).

*Michael S. Kelley*

### Bibliography

Dyson, Freeman J. *Physics Today* 46, no. 2 (1993):97–98.

O'Neill, Gerard K. *The High Frontier: Human Colonies in Space.* Garden City, New York: Anchor Books, 1977.

# Planetary Protection

Since the early days of the space program, there has been concern about planetary protection: the prevention of human-caused biological cross-contamination between Earth and other bodies in the solar system. After the launch of Sputnik in 1957, scientists cautioned about the possibility of contaminating other places in the solar system with microbes from Earth: "Hitchhiker" bacteria and other organisms on spacecraft and equipment might cause irreversible changes in the environments of other planets. Moreover, these changes could also interfere with scientific exploration. In addition, it was felt that spacecraft or extraterrestrial samples returned from space might harm Earth's inhabitants and ecosystems.

The Outer Space Treaty of 1967 requires that exploration of outer space and other celestial bodies "avoid their harmful contamination" and "adverse changes in the environment of Earth" caused by the "introduction of extraterrestrial matter." In practical terms, the concerns are twofold: avoiding (1) forward contamination, the transport of terrestrial microbes on outbound spacecraft, and (2) back contamination, the introduction on Earth of contamination by life-forms that could be returned from space.

## Protection Policies

The issues involved in planetary protection are similar to those associated with environmental and health policies. Just as there are rules and laws about moving certain types of organisms from one place to another on Earth, so it is with space exploration. But there is a difference. On Earth, those regulations are intended to prevent the spread of serious disease-causing microbes (e.g., HIV/AIDs, tuberculosis, or Dutch Elm disease) or limit the movement of invasive pests (e.g., Medflies, gypsy moths, zebra mussels, kudzu vine, or water hyancinth). In space exploration, the issues are the same, although the existence of extraterrestrial organisms is unknown. Nonetheless, in space exploration there are domestic and international policies to regulate spacecraft and mission activities before launch and upon return to Earth.

President Richard Nixon greets the successful Apollo 11 astronauts who, upon their return from the Moon, were placed inside a hermetically sealed trailer to prevent possible cross-contamination.

**synthesis** the combination of different things so as to form new and different products or ideas

**trajectories** paths followed through space by missiles and spacecraft moving under the influence of gravity

Worldwide, planetary protection policies are recommended by the international Committee on Space Research (COSPAR), which reviews the latest scientific information. In the United States the National Aeronautics and Space Administration (NASA) issues guidelines and requirements for solar system exploration missions. Planning planetary protection measures requires **synthesizing** information about biological systems and extraterrestrial environments while acknowledging uncertainties about the conditions that exist in the locations that spacecraft will visit or where samples might be collected. Planetary protection policies must take into account these uncertainties, even while exploration tries to determine whether life exists elsewhere. It is necessary to be conservative to prevent the act of exploration from disrupting or interfering with extraterrestrial life.

Controls to implement planetary protection policies may consist of procedures and measures that depend on the solar system body that will be explored and whether its environment could harbor living organisms or support Earth life. For example, before launch, spacecraft are assembled in clean rooms and scientific instruments may be heat treated or specially packaged to reduce the bioload, or the number of microbes they carry. Spacecraft **trajectories** are designed to avoid unintended impacts on other bodies. For round-trip missions to places such as Mars, returned samples are treated as potentially hazardous until proven otherwise.

In addition to extensive cleaning and decontamination of the outbound spacecraft, the return portion of the mission requires a fail-safe durable container that can be remotely sealed, cleanly separated from the planet, monitored en route, and opened in an appropriate quarantine facility. If containment cannot be verified during the return flight to Earth, the sample and any spacecraft components that have been exposed to the extraterrestrial environment will be sterilized in space or not returned to the planet. Pristine sample materials will not be removed from containment until they are sterilized or certified as nonhazardous, using a rigorous battery of life detection and biohazard tests. Although the likelihood of releasing and spreading a contained living organism is low, special equipment, personnel, and handling are warranted to minimize harmful effects if a life-form is discovered.

## The Apollo Missions

A similar approach to extraterrestrial quarantine was used during the Apollo program, when lunar samples were returned to Earth along with lunar-exposed astronauts. Before the first Moon landing, the Interagency Committee on Back Contamination (ICBC) was formed to coordinate requirements for the quarantine of astronauts, spacecraft, and samples returned from the Moon. The ICBC also developed and oversaw plans for a special Lunar Receiving Laboratory (LRL) at what is now the Johnson Space Center in Houston, Texas. At the LRL, an elaborate series of tests and analyses were conducted before astronauts and samples could be released from quarantine. Strict quarantine testing ended with the Apollo 14 mission because lunar samples were determined to be lifeless and not biohazardous. There were a variety of problems in implementing the Apollo quarantine, but it provided a wealth of information useful in planning future missions that will require planetary protection and quarantine on Earth.

## Future Missions

Future round-trip missions to Mars or other extraterrestrial locations will differ from Apollo in several ways. Because no astronauts will be involved in the initial sample-return missions and because sample amounts are anticipated to be limited (less than 1 kilogram [2.2 pounds] of rocks and soils), quarantine procedures and flight operations will be less complex. However, the missions will still be challenging because of the distances involved. In addition, advances in microbiological and chemical techniques since Apollo have increased knowledge about life in extreme environments on Earth and expanded the ability to detect life or life-related molecules in samples. A heightened awareness of microbial capabilities and microbe-caused diseases has developed, with corresponding public concern about the risks of sample-return missions.

As solar system exploration continues, so too will planetary protection policies. Revisions to planetary protection policies will depend on an improved understanding of extraterrestrial environments and the emerging awareness of the tenacity of life in extreme environments on Earth. It appears increasingly likely that there are extraterrestrial environments that could support Earth organisms. Equally important, future missions may find distant environments that support their own extraterrestrial life. Planetary protection provisions will be essential to the study and conservation of such environments. SEE ALSO ASTROBIOLOGY (VOLUME 4); ENVIRONMENTAL CHANGES (VOLUME 4); HUMAN MISSIONS TO MARS (VOLUME 3); MARS MISSIONS (VOLUME 4).

*Margaret S. Race and John D. Rummel*

**Bibliography**

Task Group on Issues in Sample Return, Space Studies Board, National Research Council. "Mars Sample Return: Issues and Recommendations." Washington, DC: National Academy Press, 1997. <http://www.nas.edu/ssb/mrsrmenu.html>.

Task Group on Planetary Protection, Space Studies Board, National Research Council. "Biological Contamination of Mars: Issues and Recommendations." Washington, DC: National Academy Press, 1992. <http://www.nas.edu/ssb/ssb.html>.

Task Group on Sample Return from Small Solar System Bodies, Space Studies Board, National Research Council. "Evaluating the Biological Potential in Samples Returned from Planetary Satellites and Small Solar System Bodies." Washington, DC: National Academy Press, 1998. <http://www.nas.edu/ssb/ssb.html>.

"Planetary Protection: Safeguarding Islands of Life." *Planetary Report* XIV, no. 4 (1994):3-23.

Rummel, John D. "Planetary Exploration in the Time of Astrobiology: Protecting against Biological Contamination." *Proceedings of the National Academy of Sciences* 98 (2001):2,128–2,131. <http://www.pnas.org/cgi/content/abstract/98/5/2128>.

# Political Systems

As space is the heritage of all people, so the political systems of Earth are our heritage for governance in outer space. There are many questions that remain to be answered when it comes to maintaining law and order in space's vast territory. Which of Earth's political systems will be molded to fit into the unique requirements of space law? Will controversy over governance cause international disputes on Earth? Which system will prevail?

Currently, we can only speculate about how a political system in space would operate. These theoretical systems are informed by Earth's various political models as well as modern international space treaties, which are indicative of what the international community has or has not been able to agree upon regarding the space infrastructure.

## Types of Political Systems

The purpose of political systems is to address any conflicts that may arise in a relatively peaceful manner. One type of governmental system that may be adopted for space governance would be one that is organized with a constitution that establishes a legislature, a court system, and police powers charged with protecting us. The following are some political systems that are derivable from the experiences of humankind that could pertain to space society.

**Democracy.** There exist two different kinds of democracies. One is government by the people, whereby the people retain supreme power and directly exercise it. The other type is government by popular representation, whereby the people retain supreme power but indirectly exercise it by delegating their power to delegates who represent the people. This second type of governmental system would most likely be the one adopted for governance of the entirety, but self-governance could be more appropriate to space settlements that are small and isolated.

**Socialism.** Many developed countries have a "quasi-socialist" system. Consequently, some socialist ideals are likely to be a part of any space system of government. Socialism is a political system wherein the methods of production, distribution, and exchange are mainly state-owned. The state distributes the wealth among all members of society. The influence of socialism is evident in some of the United Nations' space treaties, particularly the Moon Treaty of 1979. The United States and Russia have not signed the Moon Treaty because of the issue of space being the "common heritage of mankind" and what that means for the development of lunar resources that all people are to benefit from.

**Libertarianism.** Central to American government is the philosophy of freedom. The libertarian viewpoint emphasizes the concept of liberty, particularly freedom from any unnecessary restraints that a government might impose on it. A problem with libertarianism is the absence of police powers and how to address crime. A small society in space could possibly adopt a libertarian approach. This system could be appealing to individualistic types of people who would likely be interested in space exploration, settlement, and development.

Any further advances in the realm of space governance will most likely continue to be under the auspices of the United Nations' Office of Outer Space Affairs, as well as its Committee on Peaceful Use of Outer Space. SEE ALSO GOVERNANCE (VOLUME 4); LEGISLATIVE ENVIRONMENT (VOLUME 1); LIVING IN SPACE (VOLUME 3); LIVING ON OTHER WORLDS (VOLUME 4).

*Nadine M. Jacobson*

### Bibliography

Fawcett, James E. S. *Outer Space: New Challenges to Law and Policy.* Oxford, UK: Clarendon Press, 1984.

O'Donnell, Declan J. "Metaspace: A Design for Governance in Outer Space." *Space Governance* 1, no. 1 (1994):8–15.

# Pollution

Pollution and other environmental impacts have been unwelcome companions in humanity's voyage to space. They shadow all stages of the journey, from manufacturing, to launch, and even to space and other worlds, as debris may be strewn along the way to a planet, causing navigational hazards in Earth orbit and possibly contaminating the other world with chemicals and infection. Awareness of these problems has grown as a concern about global environmental problems has spread across the world.

## Government Regulations

In the United States and many other nations, government regulations are the first line of defense against these problems. These regulations control manufacturing-related pollution in industries, including space-related ones, and are designed to prevent or reduce the escape of toxic chemicals into the environment and protect groundwater, the air, and the quality of life.

The regulations cover routine releases of propellant combustion products during testing, which in addition to their effects on human health can contribute to the formation of acid rain. Also, noise levels generated by the testing are strictly limited to prevent harm and disruption to people, animals, and property. The regulations also cover the disposal of **rockets** and

**rockets** vehicles (or devices) especially designed to travel through space, propelled by one or more engines

Government regulations exist as a defense against excessive pollution caused by testing, launching, and disposing of NASA rockets.

missiles at the end of their useful lives. This too can involve harmful air emissions and hazardous chemical spills.

These environmental protections extend even to the early launch period. For example, the heat, vapors, and intensity of the space shuttle launch pose problems for the environment around the launch pad. In response, the National Aeronautics and Space Administration (NASA) ensures that the coastal wetlands and estuaries surrounding the launch center are not stressed beyond recovery. Trenches at the launch facility divert the boiling, mildly toxic ground cloud made of water from the main engines, which use the energy that results when hydrogen and oxygen combine to form water, and the more complex and damaging cloud from the boosters, which burn a solid propellant. The solid propellant cloud damages vegetation, increases water and soil acidity, and kills fish, but alternating launches between two pads and treating the soil and water reduces these problems and keeps them from expanding. Innovative reprocessing programs also lessen the impact. At the shuttle launch facility some of the launch emissions are rendered into a fertilizer used in local orange groves. But there are some environmental hazards rarely found outside the space industry that are associated with rocket exhaust and space debris.

## Rocket Exhaust

**ultraviolet** the portion of the electromagnetic spectrum just beyond (having shorter wavelengths than) violet

**stratosphere** a middle portion of Earth's atmosphere above the tropopause (the highest place where convection and "weather" occur)

Chlorine, nitrogen, and hydrogen compounds in both liquid and solid rocket propellants, such as the propellant used in the shuttle's boosters, were recognized in the early 1970s as agents of ozone destruction. Ozone protects us by absorbing the Sun's harmful **ultraviolet** rays and is concentrated between 15 and 30 kilometers altitude (9.4 and 18.8 miles), in the **stratosphere**.

Recent work indicates that significant ozone destruction resulting from rocket exhaust is brief and short-lived because launches are infrequent. Instead, the ozone loss is dominated by other sources of atmospheric pollution, such as the chlorofluorocarbon compounds used as a refrigerant and to make plastic foam. But other aspects of rocket exhaust affect the climate. Combustion products in the exhaust such as carbon dioxide, nitrous oxide, and water vapor are greenhouse gases and may contribute to global warming.

Particulates in the exhaust can interfere with the passage of sunlight and promote cloud formation, leading to unforeseen effects on the climate. These particulates can provide sites for ozone-depleting chemical reactions and thus boost the destructive power of the reactions.

Some propellants are highly toxic. Spills of the propellant heptyl left over in Soviet booster stages that have fallen to the ground in Russia's Altai Republic for decades may have caused unexplained medical and environmental problems there. Solving problems related to propellant characteristics will be done on both regulatory and technological fronts. The best solution may be the creation of new, less harmful propellants and the transfer of bases of operation into space.

## Space Debris

Space debris is space travel's other major pollution problem. Also called space junk, it fills the near-Earth orbit and poses a threat to current and future efforts above Earth. Missions to other worlds also have the potential for contamination.

Space debris is the accumulation of rubbish since 1957 from rockets and satellites, some exploded and some obsolete. It includes discarded hardware no longer needed by piloted missions and gumball-size spheres of coolant that escaped from satellite reactors and froze in space.

Because of high speeds relative to a passing satellite, spacecraft, or **space station**, collisions with even small bits of this debris can do serious damage. Shields offer protection from the smallest pieces, and ground-based tracking systems provide advanced warning of the biggest hunks, allowing time for evasive action. But the most troublesome pieces fall between these sizes, ranging from a 1 centimeter (a half inch) to 10 centimeters (4 inches). These pieces are hard to track and plentiful, numbering more than 150,000.

A ground-based laser that destabilizes the orbit of this intermediate-size junk is one promising solution to this problem. Studied since the late 1970s, this approach would vaporize a thin layer of a piece of space junk as it approached, effectively creating a retrorocket that would slow it down. The laws of physics, which dictate a lower altitude when a body's orbital speed drops, then drop the piece into the atmosphere, which slows it more, eventually causing it to burn up in the atmosphere. Studies of the concept, planned for a test by 2003, estimate that Earth orbit could be cleansed of junk this size within two years.

## Current Protocols

Protocols exist for avoiding pollution of other worlds. **Payloads** are scrupulously sterilized. Rocket stages that loft probes toward these targets are diverted to avoid trajectories that would follow the probe. SEE ALSO SPACE DEBRIS (VOLUME 2).

*Richard G. Adair*

**space station** large orbital outpost equipped to support a human crew and designed to remain in orbit for an extended period

**payloads** any cargo launched aboard a rocket that is destined for space, including communications satellites or modules, supplies, equipment, and astronauts; does not include the vehicle used to move the cargo or the propellant that powers the vehicle

**Bibliography**

Bendisch, Joerg, ed. *Space Debris 1999: Proceedings of the Space Debris Sessions, the International Academy of Astronautics.* San Diego: Univelt, 2001.

Jackman, C. H., D. B. Considine, and E. L. Fleming. "A Global Modeling Study of Solid Rocket Aluminum Oxide Emission Effects on Stratospheric Ozone." *Geophysical Research Letters* 25 (1998):907–910.

Johnson, Nicholas L., and Darren S. McKnight. *Artificial Space Debris.* Melbourne, FL: Krieger, 1991.

Phipps, C. R., H. Friedman, D. Gavel, J. Murray, G. Albrecht, E. V. George, C. Ho, W. Priedhorsky, M. M. Michaelis, and J. P. Reilly. "ORION: Clearing Near-Earth Space Debris Using a 20-kW, 530-nm, Earth-Based, Repetitively Pulsed Laser." *Laser and Particle Beams* 14, no. 1 (1996):1–44.

Ross, M. N., J. R. Benbrook, W. R. Sheldon, P. F. Zittel, and D. L. McKenzie. "Observation of Stratospheric Ozone Depletion in Rocket Plumes." *Nature* 390 (1997):62–65.

Ross, Martin N., and Paul F. Zittel. "Rockets and the Ozone Layer." *Crosslink* 1, no. 2 (2000):4–10. <http://www.aero.org/publications/crosslink/pdfs/Crosslink-vol1-2.pdf>.

Somerville, Richard C. J. *The Forgiving Air: Understanding Environmental Change.* Berkeley: University of California Press, 1998.

# Power, Methods of Generating

All space vehicles, whether robotic probes or vehicles for human exploration, require electrical power. Electrical power is required to run the computers and control systems, to operate the communications system, to operate scientific instruments, and to power the life support equipment to keep humans alive and healthy in space. For missions to the surface of the Moon or the planets, power may be required to run rovers, or to process material into useful products such as fuel or oxygen. Advanced **rocket** engines such as ion drives also run on electrical power.

Electrical power sources can be categorized into three basic types: batteries and **fuel cells**, solar power systems, and nuclear power systems.

For short missions, power can be provided by batteries or fuel cells, which produce power from chemical energy. Fuel cells are similar to batteries, producing electricity from a fuel and an oxidizer, stored in separate tanks. The space shuttle power system, for example, uses fuel cells that combine hydrogen and oxygen to produce electrical power, as well as by-product water. Primary cells produce power only until the chemical **feedstock** that powers the reaction is used up. The space shuttle's fuel cells consume about 150 kilograms (330 pounds) of hydrogen and oxygen per day.

A battery that can be recharged with an external source of power is called a rechargeable (or "secondary") battery. A fuel cell is called regenerative if it can electrolyze the by-product water back into hydrogen and oxygen. Rechargeable batteries or regenerative fuel cells can thus be used to store energy from a solar array.

## Solar Power Generation

Solar arrays produce electrical power directly from sunlight. Most long-duration space missions use solar arrays for their primary power. Most designs use **photovoltaic cells** to convert sunlight into electricity. They can be made from crystalline silicon, or from advanced materials such as gallium arsenide

**rocket** vehicle (or device) especially designed to travel through space, propelled by one or more engines

**fuel cells** cells that react a fuel (such as hydrogen) and an oxidizer (such as oxygen) together

**feedstock** the raw materials introduced into an industrial process from which a finished product is made

**photovoltaic cells** cells consisting of a thin wafer of a semiconductor material which incorporates a p-n junction, which converts incident light into electrical power; a number of photovoltaic cells connected in series makes a solar array

(GaAs) or cadmium telluride (CdTe). The photovoltaic cells with the highest efficiency use several layers of semiconductor material, with each layer optimized to convert a different portion of the solar spectrum. The solar intensity at Earth's orbit is 1,368 watts per square meter, and the best photovoltaic cells manufactured today can convert about a third of the solar energy to electrical power. For electrical power when the Sun is not available (for example, when a space vehicle is over the night side of Earth), solar power systems typically use rechargeable batteries for storage.

Solar power systems can also be designed using mirrors or lenses to concentrate sunlight onto a thermal receiver. The heat produced by the thermal receiver then is used in a heat engine, similar to the steam turbines used in terrestrial power plants, to produce power. Systems of this type can store power in the form of heat, instead of requiring batteries, but have not yet been used in space.

## Nuclear Power

Since solar power decreases with the square of the distance from the Sun, missions to the outer planets require an alternate power source. Nuclear power systems can provide power even when sunlight is unavailable. Nuclear generators are categorized as "radioisotope" power systems, which generate heat by the natural radioactive decay of an isotope, and "reactor" power systems, which generate heat by a nuclear chain reaction. For both of these power systems types, the heat is then converted into electrical power by a thermal generator, either a thermoelectric generator that uses thermocouples to produce power, or a turbine. For radioisotope power systems, the most commonly used isotope is Plutonium-238. The plutonium is encapsulated in a heat-resistant ceramic shell, to prevent it from being released into the environment in the case of a launch accident. Such isotope power systems have been used on the Pioneer, Voyager, Galileo, and Cassini missions to the outer planets (Jupiter and beyond), where the sunlight is weak, and also on Apollo missions to the surface of the Moon, where power is required over the long lunar night.

## Solar Power Satellites

Scientist Peter Glaser has proposed that very large solar arrays could be put into space and the power generated by the solar arrays can be transmitted to the surface of Earth using a microwave or laser beam. Glaser argues that such a "solar power satellite" concept would be a pollution-free source of low-cost solar power, and that by putting the solar power system above the atmosphere, 24-hour power could be produced with no interruptions by clouds or nighttime. To be practical, such solar power satellites will require a reduction in the cost of manufacturing solar cells, and new methods of low-cost launch into space. SEE ALSO SOLAR POWER SYSTEMS (VOLUME 4).

*Geoffrey A. Landis*

### WHAT ARE RADIOISOTOPES?

Atoms of an element that have the same atomic number but a different atomic weight are referred to as isotopes. Radioisotopes are unstable isotopes that spontaneously decay into a different atom, releasing energy. This radioactive decay energy can be converted into electrical energy.

**Bibliography**

Glaser, Peter, F. P. Davidson, and K. I. Csigi. *Solar Power Satellites: The Emerging Energy Option.* New York: Ellis Horwood, 1993.

Green, Martin. *Solar Cells: Operating Principles, Technology, and System Applications.* Englewood Cliffs, NJ: Prentice-Hall, 1982.

Landis, Geoffrey A., Sheila G. Bailey, and Barbara I. McKissock. "Designing Power Systems." In *Human Spaceflight: Mission Analysis and Design*, eds. W. J. Larson and L. Pranke. New York: McGraw-Hill, 1999.

# Property Rights

The right to own land and other property is taken for granted in many countries. It is one of the cornerstones of private enterprise and capitalism, and makes it possible for people to control where they live and work. In space, however, this right is an open issue. International treaties appear to bar people from making ownership claims to property on celestial bodies but do not explicitly prohibit it. Although the topic of property rights in space is not yet a major issue, it is something that will have to be resolved before major commercial development of space, particularly the Moon and other nearby celestial bodies, can proceed.

## Treaties and Property Rights

Two international treaties address, at least to some extent, the question of property rights in space. The Outer Space Treaty of 1967, the first treaty to deal exclusively with space, specifically prohibits nations from making claims in outer space. Article 2 of the treaty states: "Outer space, including the moon and other celestial bodies, is not subject to national appropriation by claim of sovereignty, by means of use or occupation, or by any other means." This provision is similar to one in the Antarctic Treaty of 1959, which prevented countries from making new claims on territory in Antarctica, although that treaty allowed existing claims to stand.

The Outer Space Treaty does not specifically prohibit nongovernmental organizations, including individuals and businesses, from making claims to or owning property on other worlds. However, because no nation can claim another body, it becomes much more difficult for private claims to be enforced. If two people have a dispute over the ownership of a parcel of land in the United States, that dispute can be resolved through American courts because the United States clearly has jurisdiction over that parcel. However, since no nation has jurisdiction over land on another celestial body, it is unclear how disputes, registration of deeds and claims, and other aspects of property rights could be managed.

The United Nations made an effort to eliminate this concern in 1979 through a separate treaty that is known popularly as the Moon Treaty. This treaty, like the Outer Space Treaty, prohibits countries from claiming property on other worlds. However, the Moon Treaty also bars nongovernmental organizations from owning property on other worlds. The treaty considers the Moon and the celestial bodies of the solar system the "common heritage of mankind" and would require an international organization of some kind to oversee development on other worlds. That organization also would be responsible for the distribution of the benefits realized from any such development among all nations.

Although the Moon Treaty could settle the question of property rights in space, the accord has been largely ignored. Only nine nations have ratified the treaty, none of which play a significant role in space exploration. The United States and other major spacefaring nations have never signed,

Although the United States was the first country to land on the Moon, no country, private corporation, or individual may lay claim to private ownership of the Moon or any other celestial bodies.

let alone ratified, the treaty. Although the treaty technically has gone into force because of the small number of nations that have ratified it, the agreement has very little real power. This has left the question of private property rights in space unsettled.

## Private Property Right Claims

Despite the current ambiguity regarding private property in space, some companies and individuals have attempted to make claims on celestial bodies. One of the best-known claims was made by Dennis Hope, an American entrepreneur. In 1980 Hope filed a claim for the surface of the Moon, the other planets in the solar system (except for Earth), and their moons. The claim was filed with a claim registry office of the U.S. government under the Homestead Act of 1862. Hope also sent copies of the claim to the United Nations and the Soviet Union, neither of which, according to Hope, contested the claim. Hope has been selling property on the Moon and other solar system bodies since he registered the claim through a company called Lunar Embassy.

Many space law experts do not believe that Hope's claim is valid. They contend that it runs afoul of Article 2 of the Outer Space Treaty, which prevents nations from claiming territory in space. Because no nation can claim the Moon or another world, there is no nation that would have jurisdiction over such a claim. Moreover, there is more than one claim to ownership of the Moon: A German, Martin Jürgens, has a declaration given to one of his ancestors by the Prussian king Frederick the Great that gives that person ownership of the Moon. While maintaining the legitimacy of his claim, Hope carefully skirts around the legal issues by noting that the deeds he sells for property on other worlds are "novelty items."

In February 2001 the National Aeronautics and Space Administration's (NASA) Near Earth Asteroid Rendezvous (NEAR) spacecraft landed on the surface of the asteroid Eros after orbiting the body for a year. Shortly afterward Gregory Nemitz, chief executive officer of Orbital Development, a San Diego company, submitted a letter to NASA headquarters. That letter stated that Nemitz and Orbital Development had filed a claim in 2000 for the asteroid with the Archimedes Institute, which maintains a registry of such claims but is not supported or endorsed by any government entity. Nemitz asked NASA for a nominal "parking/storage fee" of $20 per century for landing NEAR on the surface of Eros.

In response, NASA General Counsel Edward Frankle said that the agency would not pay the fee. Frankle cited Article 2 of the Outer Space Treaty, which prohibits nations from claiming celestial bodies, as the main reason why he believed Nemitz's claim was not valid. Although Nemitz made a number of arguments stating why he believed that article of the treaty did not apply, NASA was not swayed. The space agency continued to decline to pay the fee, saying that the claim was not sufficiently established. NASA declined to take a position on whether Article 2 of the Outer Space Treaty applied to individuals or whether the treaty should be amended to deal specifically with this issue.

Other companies have taken a more circumspect approach to the question of property rights. Applied Space Resources, an American company that is planning to land a spacecraft on the Moon, has made a conscious decision not to claim any territorial rights on the Moon. The company is concerned that any near-term debate over property rights could prove detrimental for commercial efforts because it believes that one possibility would be a moratorium on commercial space projects until the legal questions about property rights are resolved.

## The Future of Property Rights in Space

A complete solution to the question of private property rights in space probably will require either changes to the Outer Space Treaty or an entirely new accord. As of this writing, however, there are no efforts under way to amend existing treaties or write new ones. In light of the relative lack of activity in commercial space enterprises to date, it may be some time until nations take action on this issue.

However, there have been some low-key efforts to address the property rights issue. Attorney Wayne White has drafted a proposed treaty that deals with property rights on the Moon and other bodies. Under his proposal, private entities—individuals or companies—that operate a space facility of some kind on the surface of another world for at least one year would be accorded the right to the property on which the facility is located as well as a "safety zone" extending up to 1 kilometer (0.62 mile) from it. This provision would prevent people from claiming entire planets without even landing a spacecraft on them. The proposal also includes provisions for transferring property and revoking property rights if the facility is abandoned or is not used for peaceful purposes. White has presented his draft treaty and papers based on it at meetings of the International Institute for Space Law, but the proposal has not been taken up by any nation.

Although property claims on other celestial bodies have not been recognized by any nation, there is a registry for tracking those claims. The Archimedes Institute, which was established by law professor Lawrence Roberts, operates a claims registry where individuals can file claims on objects throughout the solar system. Claims filed with the Archimedes Institute have no special protection or priority over other claims because no nation has recognized such claims. However, the institute hopes that the creation of the registry will encourage the formation of new agreements that will recognize private property rights in space. SEE ALSO GOVERNANCE (VOLUME 4); LAND GRANTS (VOLUME 4); LAW (VOLUME 4); LAW OF SPACE (VOLUME 1).

*Jeff Foust*

### Bibliography

Reynolds, Glenn H., and Robert P. Merges. *Outer Space: Problems of Policy and Law.* Boulder, CO: Westview, 1994. Ward & Partners. "Sovereignty in Space." <http://www.spacelaw.com.au/content/sovereignty.htm>.

#### Internet Resources

*Space Property Rights.* Applied Space Resources. <http://www.appliedspace.com/property_rights.htm>.

White, Wayne N. "Proposal for a Multilateral Treaty Regarding Jurisdiction and Real Property Rights in Outer Space." *Space Future.* <http://www.spacefuture.com/archive/proposal_for_a_multilateral_treaty_regarding_jurisdiction_and_real_property_rights_in_outer_space.shtml>.

# Rawlings, Pat

*American Illustrator*
*1955–*

* Examples of Rawlings' art can be found in the Volume 4 articles "Lunar Bases" (page 88) and "Lunar Outposts" (page 90).

Pat Rawlings ✳ is one of the finest and best-known technical illustrators in the world. His extraordinarily realistic depictions of future spacecraft have been reproduced in hundreds of books and magazines, as well as in movies and on television, since the 1970s. Like the earlier visions of Chesley Bonestell, Rawlings's work has imparted a sense of reality to space travel. This quality has been instrumental in "selling" the reality of space travel to laypersons who otherwise might think of space travel as science fiction or fantasy.

While working for Eagle Engineering, Rawling created an internal art studio—Eagle Visuals—with a team of illustrators and model makers responsible for the majority of the artwork depicting the advanced programs of the National Aeronautics and Space Administration (NASA). Since 1989 Rawlings has worked for Science Applications International Corporation (SAIC), where he has produced artwork for nine NASA field centers and for NASA headquarters. He also has produced a series of calendars for SAIC, all of which feature his paintings. Much of the perception of the American public and that of people worldwide of the future of space exploration is due to Rawlings's visions. SEE ALSO ARTWORK (VOLUME 1); BONESTELL, CHESLEY (VOLUME 4); HUMAN MISSIONS TO MARS (VOLUME 3); LUNAR BASES (VOLUME 4); LUNAR OUTPOST (VOLUME 4); MARS BASES (VOLUME 4); MARS MISSIONS (VOLUME 4).

*Ron Miller*

**Bibliography**

Di Fate, Vincent. *Infinite Worlds.* New York: Penguin Group, 1997.

Hardy, David. *Visions of Space.* London: Paper Tiger, 1990.

# Religion

Wherever human beings travel, we bring our religions with us. "Godspeed, John Glenn," the farewell words spoken to the first American astronaut into orbit, exemplifies the characteristic human drive to carry faith into space.

Many astronauts who are religious have spoken of finding their faith strengthened by the experience of traveling in space. The ability to look back on Earth as a small blue planet, and to see the fragility of life and human existence, is an experience that brings many space travelers closer to the creator. The astronauts of the Apollo 8 mission, orbiting the Moon for the very first time in 1968, broadcast back to Earth a reading from the book of Genesis on Christmas day, in the belief that the passage discussing the creation of the world expressed their feelings of the awe and majesty of creation.

While some astronauts are agnostic or atheist, others have been highly religious. Astronauts from most of the major religions on Earth have been represented in space, including representatives of Islam, Christianity, Judaism, and Buddhism. Edwin "Buzz" Aldrin, one of the two astronauts who were the first men to land on the Moon, brought with him a small vial of consecrated wine and a tiny piece of communion wafer, in order to celebrate the holy sacrament on the surface of the Moon.

For other astronauts, the spiritual experience of space is not expressed in the terms of formal religion. After landing on the Moon with Apollo 14, Astronaut Edgar Mitchell founded the Institute of Noetic Sciences to reconcile the spiritual and humanistic values of religious traditions with scientific insights. The spiritual insight granted from spaceflight, and seeing Earth from orbit without political boundaries or petty human conflict, is profound. This insight has been tagged "the overview effect" by author Frank White.

Historically, religion and science have had a difficult relationship: in 1600, for example, Giordano Bruno was burned at the stake by the Roman Catholic Inquisition for writing that the universe is infinite and includes an indefinite number of worlds. In 1630 the scientist Galileo Galilei was tried by the church on a charge of "suspicion of heresy" for writing that Earth circled around the Sun. He was forced to recant his position, and was subjected to imprisonment. It would take over four centuries for the Roman Catholic Church to review the results of the trial and rescind the sentence.

It is now widely conceded by theologians that there is no inherent conflict between science and religion, and modern scientists have included fol-

## WHAT ARE NOETIC SCIENCES?

In the words of one of its founders, noetic science is concerned with subjective experience as opposed to materialistic science (which is essentially interested in objective experience). Noetic scientists describe the discipline as "a science of consciousness and the world of inner experience."

lowers of all religions, as well as agnostics and atheists. Some philosophers and scientists such as Frank Tipler have looked even further, and foreseen the development of human potential into God in a future "Omega point" at the final collapse of the universe, elaborating on theological concepts developed by the Jesuit priest Pierre Teilhard de Chardin.

Religion—and religious persecution—has always been a significant force to move outward. In American history, the Pilgrims were driven to settle Plymouth, Massachusetts, as a religious colony; and the settlement of Utah was incited by intolerance toward the Mormon Church in the eastern United States. Some theorists expect that the same forces may also drive space colonization, as religious intolerance has not been eliminated in the centuries since these events.

The scriptures are silent on the subject of life on other worlds. If we explore other worlds, and find other forms of intelligent life, this will bring out many questions to be addressed by religion. Do beings of other planets have souls? Are they eligible for salvation? Do they have religion, and if so, what god or gods do they worship? Questions such as these have been addressed in science fiction. Science fiction writers who have addressed the question of the religious implications of spaceflight include, among others, Arthur C. Clarke, Mary Doria Russell, James Blish, and Philip José Farmer. SEE ALSO CLARKE, ARTHUR C. (VOLUME 1); GALILEI, GALILEO (VOLUME 2).

*Geoffrey A. Landis*

The Moon, pictured here over the Metropolitan Cathedral in Mexico City, has special significance in various world religions. In the Islamic faith the Muslim lunar calendar sets the beginning and ending of Ramadan by the sighting of the crescent Moon.

**Bibliography**

Clarke, Arthur C. "The Star." In *Collected Stories of Arthur C. Clarke*. New York: Tor Books, 2001.

Paine, Thomas. *The Age of Reason*. Paris, 1794. Reissued in *Thomas Paine: Collected Writings*. New York: Library of America, 1995.

Russell, Mary Doria. *The Sparrow*. New York: Villard Books, 1996.

White, Frank. *The Overview Effect: Space Exploration and Human Evolution*. Washington, DC: American Institute of Aeronautics and Astronautics, 1987, revised 1998.

# Resource Utilization

**in situ** in the natural or original location

The purpose of resource utilization (also known as **in situ** resource utilization [ISRU]) is to reduce the mass, and thus the cost, of space missions. On Earth, explorers rarely took all the food and supplies they would need for their entire journey. Instead, they relied on the resources around them, hunting for or gathering food, chopping down trees for lumber, and so forth. By carrying with them only what they needed to get from one stop on their journey to another, they minimized the size of their expeditions and made them more adaptable to changes.

**payloads** any cargo launched aboard a rocket that is destined for space, including communications satellites or modules, supplies, equipment, and astronauts; does not include the vehicle used to move the cargo or the propellant that powers the vehicle

The same principle is applicable to exploration of the solar system. Carrying all the food, propellant, air, and other supplies needed for a human mission to the Moon or Mars would make a spacecraft very large and heavy. Given the high cost to launch **payloads**—up to $10,000 per pound—reducing the mass of a spacecraft can greatly lower the cost of a mission. The savings can be significant even for smaller robotic missions, such as proposals to land spacecraft on Mars, gather rock samples, and return them to Earth. The use of ISRU could make the difference between an affordable mission and one that is prohibitive.

**minerals** crystalline arrangements of atoms and molecules of specified proportions that make up rocks

## The Moon

**rocket** vehicle or device, especially designed to travel through space, propelled by one or more engines

**solar wind** a continuous, but varying, stream of charged particles (mostly electrons and protons) generated by the Sun; it establishes and affects the interplanetary magnetic field; it also deforms the magnetic field about Earth and sends particles streaming toward Earth at its poles

The Moon appears at first to have few resources to offer because of its barren surface and lack of an atmosphere. However, studies of lunar samples returned by the Apollo missions revealed that lunar rocks are rich in oxygen. Up to 45 percent of the mass of lunar rocks consists of oxygen locked up chemically in **minerals**. When the rocks are heated and mixed with other materials, the oxygen can be released and used as a propellant, or for breathing. The by-products of these reactions are metals such as iron and aluminum, which in powdered form could also be used as **rocket** propellant. Although there is no hydrogen contained in lunar rocks, a small amount of hydrogen has been deposited on the surface from the **solar wind**. This hydrogen could be harvested and used for propellants or combined with oxygen to make water.

There may be deposits of water ice on the Moon. Scientists theorized for years that ice could exist in the floors of craters near the lunar poles that are in permanent shadow. The ice would come from comets that collided with the Moon over the last several billion years. The existence of water ice in those craters was largely confirmed by the National Aeronautics and Space Administration's (NASA) Lunar Prospector mission in 1998, which found traces of hydrogen, and thus most likely ice, in the shadowed regions at either pole. If ice does exist there, it could be harvested and used for drink-

ing water or broken down into hydrogen and oxygen. NASA and private companies have proposed sending rovers into those craters to confirm that ice is present there and to determine how difficult it would be to harvest it.

## Mars

Mars offers even more opportunities for ISRU. The planet has a thin atmosphere composed mostly of carbon dioxide, from which oxygen can be extracted. Many scientists believe that there may be extractable deposits of water ice below the surface of Mars. Even if there are no such deposits, there are small traces of water vapor in the atmosphere.

These attributes make Mars ideal for the use of ISRU. One of the first proposals to employ ISRU on Mars was developed by Robert Zubrin, an aerospace engineer who coauthored *The Case for Mars* (1996). In the early 1990s Zubrin showed how liquid hydrogen, carried to Mars on a spacecraft, could be combined with the Martian atmosphere to form methane and oxygen, which could then be used as rocket propellant. This process, known as a Sabatier reaction, dates back to the nineteenth century and has been used

Oxygen produced on the Moon is used to refill the propellant tanks of this lunar crew's vehicle, enabling them to return directly to Earth in this artist's concept.

extensively in the chemical industry. Zubrin and his coworkers showed that a Sabatier reactor could be built easily and cheaply and generate on Mars the propellants needed to return a spacecraft to Earth.

One of the disadvantages of the Sabatier reaction is that it requires a **feedstock** of liquid hydrogen on the spacecraft that must be kept at temperatures near absolute zero. This may prove difficult on long missions to Mars, so alternatives that do not require liquid hydrogen have been studied. One concept proposed by researchers at the University of Washington uses zirconia crystals and electricity to convert carbon dioxide into carbon monoxide and oxygen, which can then be used as rocket propellant. Carbon monoxide, when combined with oxygen, is not as powerful as methane in rocket engines, but it can be made on Mars without the need for an initial supply of hydrogen.

Water is another key resource that may be found on Mars. Images of some portions of the planet suggest that there may be groundwater sources a short distance beneath the surface. A future mission could bring drilling equipment to reach these water sources and pump it to the surface. Even if subterranean water deposits are not found, there may be ways to extract small amounts of water from the atmosphere. Engineers have proposed passing Martian atmosphere through zeolite crystals. The crystals would absorb water vapor but allow carbon dioxide and other gases to pass through. The water could be extracted from the zeolite later.

## Moons, Comets, and Asteroids

The concept of ISRU can be extended to other bodies in the solar system. Comets and many asteroids are rich in water, carbon dioxide, and methane, which could be used by future missions as propellant for the trip to their next destination or home. Water ice may also exist on Phobos and Deimos, the two moons of Mars, allowing them to become refueling stations for missions to that planet. The moons of the outer planets in the solar system are also rich with various kinds of ices. Through resource utilization, it will be possible for future space explorers to "live off the land" as they travel throughout the solar system. SEE ALSO ASTEROID MINING (VOLUME 4); LIVING ON OTHER WORLDS (VOLUME 4); LUNAR BASES (VOLUME 4); LUNAR OUTPOSTS (VOLUME 4); MARS BASES (VOLUME 4); MARS DIRECT (VOLUME 4); MARS MISSIONS (VOLUME 4); NATURAL RESOURCES (VOLUME 4); POWER, METHODS OF GENERATING (VOLUME 4); SETTLEMENTS (VOLUME 4); SPACE INDUSTRIES (VOLUME 4); SPACE RESOURCES (VOLUME 4).

*Jeff Foust*

### Bibliography

Schrunk, David, Burton Sharpe, Bonnie Cooper, and Madhu Thangavelu. *The Moon: Resources, Future Development and Colonization.* New York: John Wiley & Sons, 1999.

Zubrin, Robert, with Richard Wagner. *The Case for Mars: The Plan to Settle the Red Planet and Why We Must.* New York: Free Press, 1996.

### Internet Resources

Grover, M. R., E. H. Odell, S. L. Smith-Brito, R. W. Warwick, and A. P. Bruckner. "Ares Explore: A Study of Human Mars Exploration Alternatives Using in Situ Propellant Production and Current Technology." University of Washington. <http://www.aa.washington.edu/research/ISRU/ARES/ares.htm>.

**feedstock** the raw materials introduced into an industrial process from which a finished product is made

Joosten, B. Kent, and Lisa A. Sharpe. "Enabling Lunar Exploration through Early Resource Utilization." NASA Human Spaceflight. <http://spaceflight.nasa.gov/mars/reference/lunar/lunar1.html>.

# Reusable Launch Vehicles

The last decade of the second millennium saw the emergence of the idea of sending **payloads** into space with reusable launch vehicles (RLVs). It appeared to make economic sense to reuse a launch vehicle that cost as much as a small airliner, rather than throw that vehicle away after one use. Two prototypes—the McDonnell Douglas Delta Clipper and Rotary Rocket's Roton—were built and flown at low altitude. A number of small companies emerged, each seeking to build an RLV. Although this idea has gained broad acceptance, no RLV has flown in space in recent years and none is likely to for many years.

## An Old Idea and a Proven Technology

It is a misconception that a number of technological breakthroughs are required before RLVs will be feasible. An American experimental RLV, the X-15, made its maiden flight on June 8, 1959. The X-15 was not called an RLV but a **hypersonic** airplane. It was incapable of reaching orbital speed (24,000 kilometers [15,000 miles] per hour) but flew fast enough (7,160 kilometers [4,475 miles] per hour) to reach an altitude above 100 kilometers (328,080 feet), the officially recognized boundary between Earth and space. In 199 flights the X-15 topped this altitude once, on August 22, 1963. With pilot Joe Walker at the controls, the X-15 reached 109,756 meters (360,000 feet) and became the first and only successful RLV.

The idea of the RLV can be traced back to 1928, and since that time a great many proposals have been made. The classic *The Frontiers of Space* (1969) vividly illustrates a number of RLV concepts, all of which were technically feasible at that time.

## Fated by History

If technical feasibility is not an issue, why, then, has the RLV not replaced the expendable launch vehicle (ELV)? The reasons include a complex mix of economics, politics, historical accident, and human psychology. To understand them, it is necessary to appreciate how the ELV came into being, how the market for commercial ELVs emerged, and how the operational aspects of ELVs prevent new commercial space markets from developing, and consequently, why no RLVs have been or will soon be developed.

Arthur C. Clarke's *The Promise of Space*, Chapter 14, "The Birth of Apollo" (1968), gives the most concise summary of the historical events that made the ELV imperative. In essence, the space age was a child of the Cold War. If technology had evolved in a logical manner, RLVs would have been the product. In 1957, however, the Soviet Union shocked the world by using an intercontinental ballistic missile (ICBM) to launch the world's first satellite. A series of space firsts by the Soviet Union began to make the United States look technologically and economically inferior.

This perception was a threat to national security. On May 25, 1961, President John F. Kennedy responded by making a commitment to land a

**payloads** any cargo launched aboard a rocket that is destined for space, including communications satellites or modules, supplies, equipment, and astronauts; does not include the vehicle used to move the cargo or the propellant that powers the vehicle

**hypersonic** capable of speeds over five times the speed of sound

The X-33 was expected to demonstrate the new technologies needed for a feasible reusable launch vehicle but the project was canceled in 2001.

man on the Moon and return him safely to Earth by the end of the decade. Such a feat required decisions to be made early on, the first of which was how to get there. The difficulties of making aircraft that could carry a large payload and fly fast enough to reach orbit were well known, and no such airplane had ever been built. However, hundreds of satellites and spacecraft had been launched on ICBMs, and it was correctly thought that there was no limit to the size of the payload that could be launched with a scaled-up ICBM. Ultimately, President Kennedy's goal was achieved by using the Saturn V rocket, a 2,902,991-kilogram (3,200 tons), 111-meter-tall (365 feet) ELV designed specifically to send astronauts to the Moon. On July 20, 1969, Neil Armstrong and Edwin "Buzz" Aldrin landed on the lunar surface, signaling the beginning of the end of the Cold War.

Sadly, that triumph closed the gates to space for future generations. By establishing the ELV as the "existing launch vehicle," a mode of space transportation had been established that was too expensive to permit any normal economic development of the space frontier. In the forty-five years since the Soviet Union launched the first satellite, only one commercial use has been found for space: as a location for relay stations (**geosynchronous** communication satellites [GEOSATs]) to bounce radio and television signals around the world.

**geosynchronous** remaining fixed in an orbit 35,786 kilometers (22,300 miles) above Earth's surface

Even that market would not have emerged if it had not been initiated, as a matter of national security, by the U.S. government. In 1962 Congress passed the Communications Satellite Act, which led to the formation in 1963 of the Communications Satellite Corporation (Comsat). The financing of this "risky" venture was possible only because the government backed it. The communications satellite industry grew at an astonishing rate, and was eventually was "privatized" by the Space Act of 1984. It has proved phenomenally profitable but has welded closed the gate to space that Apollo locked.

The reason for this is psychological. According to management consultant W. Edward Deming, "If you always do what you always did, you'll always get what you always got." In the case of space, doing what you always did is a matter two things: Having the government underwrite the risk of any new space venture—be it a new launch vehicle or satellite system—and reaching space by means of "launch vehicles" of any kind are things of the past. Only space projects tied to national security should be backed by the government, and since the end of the Cold War, these projects have not included commercial ventures.

The private sector has seldom had the financial courage to undertake a new kind of space venture without government guarantees. The most notable exceptions have been the global cellular telephone projects Iridium and GlobalStar. Both have been spectacular failures because they have relied on "launch" by the means used for GEOSATs. Although each GEOSAT produces revenue and requires only one launch, Iridium and GlobalStar had to place large numbers of satellites in orbit before any revenue could flow. The cost and time required to do this on single-use launch vehicles were so great that corners had to be cut in terms of the size and power of the spacecraft. The result in each case was substandard service at a price no one could afford.

## The Concept of "Launch" as the Barrier to RLVs and Space

The chief barrier to large-scale commercialization of space is the concept of the launch. The practice of making each satellite a complete, independent, stand-alone unit results in an upward cost spiral for both satellite and launch vehicle (the size of both continually increases to squeeze every ounce of revenue out of the increasingly expensive hardware) and a consequent reduction in the number of spacecraft launched each year.

An RLV must fly many times to recover its cost of development and construction. Further, it would take an extremely large and expensive RLV to carry stand-alone satellites of the GEOSAT class. An expensive RLV carrying a small number of complete stand-alone satellites each year is not economically viable.

However, there is no reason, other than those imposed by launch, that every payload cannot be a complete, stand-alone unit. On Earth one does not deliver an office building to its lot on a single truck. One brings in many trucks, each carrying small components of the building. Erecting an "office building" in space is done the same way. The International Space Station could not have been "launched" on a single rocket. It had to be taken up in modules and assembled in orbit. The significance of this is that on-orbit assembly has been demonstrated on a massive, complex scale. The assembly of smaller spacecraft on orbit should be no more difficult.

## The Prescription: Change the Way We Operate in Space

No technological breakthroughs are required for RLVs to flourish. What is required is the discarding of the very concept of the launch and adopting the same approach to space operations that is used routinely on Earth: build spaceplanes and other space transport systems and use them to carry components of space factories into orbit. After the factories are built, they should be used to produce the only thing that can be built better in space than on Earth: spacecraft. The parts for the spacecraft, along with the people to put them together and the supplies needed to keep them alive, can be delivered by space transports on a regular basis.

In this system a space transport that delivers a smaller payload but does so economically (i.e., a single-stage-to-orbit vehicle) has a decided advantage. Because it can deliver only a small load, it must fly frequently. It will therefore spread its cost of development and construction over a large number of flights, just as an airliner does.

The first spacecraft to be assembled in orbiting factories would be communications satellites, since there is an established market for them. Having put in place an orbital **infrastructure** involving people living and working in space, one then can branch out into other areas. The same habitats used as factories could be replicated, with modifications, as orbiting hotels. Because a large number of people would have already flown into space to assemble the factories, the communications satellites, and the hotels, enough experience would have been accumulated to make passenger flights safe and easy.

Once passenger travel is established, the promise of space will be realized. There are 6 billion potential payloads in the form of human beings. This far exceeds the number of spacecraft that will ever be built and represents the real market for future space transportation systems.

## Wanted: A Howard Hughes

Getting to this point will not happen soon. In light of the realities of finance and markets, the only hope for change is the emergence of an individual with the personal financial resources, technical know-how, business acumen, and vision to make it happen. What is needed is a Howard Hughes, ✷ who possessed all of these attributes and used them to advance aviation.

When such a person appears and brings about the needed changes, the opportunities will be endless. No one knows what new activities and industries will result when large numbers of people travel into space. One can be sure that things that we have never dreamed of will emerge. When people are placed in a completely new environment, they adapt both themselves and that environment in ways that cannot be predicted. This has been the history of humanity, and it will be the future of our expansion into space. SEE ALSO ACCESSING SPACE (VOLUME 1); BUSINESS FAILURES (VOLUME 1); COMMUNICATIONS SATELLITE INDUSTRY (VOLUME 1); GETTING TO SPACE CHEAPLY (VOLUME 1); HOTELS (VOLUME 4); LAUNCH VEHICLES, EXPENDABLE (VOLUME 1); LAUNCH VEHICLES, REUSABLE (VOLUME 1); SATELLITE INDUSTRY (VOLUME 1); SPACE TOURISM, EVOLUTION OF (VOLUME 4); TOURISM (VOLUME 1).

*Michael S. Kelly*

**infrastructure** the physical structures, such as roads and bridges, necessary to the functioning of a complex system

✷ In 1966 *Fortune* magazine declared aviator and financier Howard Hughes the richest man in the United States.

**Bibliography**

Bono, Philip, and Kenneth Gatland. *The Frontiers of Space.* New York: Macmillan, 1969.

Clarke, Arthur C. *The Promise of Space*, New York: Harper & Row, 1968.

McLucas, John L. *Space Commerce.* Cambridge, MA: Harvard University Press, 1991.

Thompson, Milton O. *At the Edge of Space—The X-15 Flight Program.* Washington, DC: Smithsonian Institution Press, 1991.

# Satellites, Future Designs

The nature of the satellite manufacturing industry is changing, much as the computer industry changed in the late 1970s. The satellite industry is becoming less of a scientific enterprise, wherein each spacecraft is a unique design, handcrafted and built for a very specific purpose, and more of a commodity business, in which satellites are built around a basic model and adapted to meet the customer's needs. Shopping for a modern communications satellite is more like buying a very expensive piece of industrial machinery than building a new type of airplane.

## The Spread of Satellite Technology

Still, building satellites and satellite components is a high-prestige, high-payoff industrial activity. Ambitious nations are willing to spend heavily to create a satellite manufacturing capacity for themselves. Being able to build or launch even relatively unsophisticated spacecraft is a way to assert national pride and show the world that one's country is capable of high-tech development. Argentina, Brazil, China, India, Israel, South Korea, and Taiwan all launched spacecraft in the 1990s at least partly with political and national security goals in mind. In a market in which so many nations are in competition to sell their satellites to a limited number of commercial operators, it is a classic buyers' paradise.

Orbital Sciences Corporation of the United States and Surrey Satellite Technology Limited of Britain have both helped small developing countries to build and fly their own spacecraft. The spread of satellite technology, especially Earth observation systems, is giving even the poorest nations the possibility of using spy satellites to check on their neighbors. India has developed its own series of Earth observation spacecraft, called the India Resource Satellites. Over the years, their spacecraft have gotten better and better at sending down increasingly sharp images so that now they are almost as good as the spy satellites of Western nations.

## Newer and Future Commercial Communications Satellites

Nevertheless, the cost of putting a commercially viable communications satellite into **geosynchronous orbit** (GEO), 35,880 kilometers (22,300 miles) above Earth, is still anywhere from $50 million to $70 million. For the newer and more powerful communications satellites, such as the Boeing Company's 702 model, the cost of getting up there is even higher.

The Boeing 702 model is a good example of an ultramodern communications satellite designed to operate in GEO. It will carry up to 100 **transponders** providing highly reliable communications services at what Boeing hopes will be a competitive price. With its innovative new propulsion system called XIPS, Boeing hopes the 702 will stay up longer, and with less need for complicated and expensive ground control services, than any other communications satellite on the market. The trough-shaped solar wings are a new and highly efficient design intended to act as a concentrator to increase the level of electric power generated by the gallium arsenide solar cells.

**geosynchronous orbit** a specific altitude of an equatorial orbit where the time required to circle the planet matches the time it takes the planet to rotate on its axis; an object in geostationary orbit will always remain over the same geographic location on the equator of the planet it orbits

**transponder** bandwidth-specific transmitter-receiver units

The Constellation X satellites, orbiting in close proximity to one another, will act as one large telescope. The combined efforts of these satellites will gather information on black holes and "missing matter."

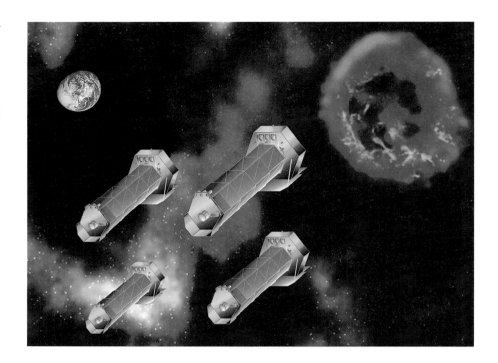

In the early twenty-first century, positions for satellites in GEO will become more and more valuable and, probably, will become the subject of expensive and lengthy international litigation. The greater the value, the more profit investors will expect from each spacecraft placed up there. One hundred transponders will not be enough to satisfy the needs of a world that demands ever more communications capability. Commercial telecommunications satellites will soon have to carry hundreds, and eventually thousands, of transponders to meet future demand. Boeing hopes that its future generations of very large commercial satellites will be far more reliable and will remain operational much longer than the current generation, whose reliability problems are well known.

## Distributed Spacecraft Systems

One way the satellite industry hopes to solve some of the reliability problems is to build satellites that will fly in formation. This is sometimes referred to as a distributed spacecraft system. The idea is to launch groups of spacecraft that will cooperate to accomplish the desired goal. Whether providing a better **multispectral** look at Earth's atmosphere, focusing on deep space, or providing less-expensive satellite phone service, future clusters of satellites will have the capability to repair the system by working around a single, broken spacecraft.

**multispectral** referring to several different parts of the electromagnetic spectrum, such as visible, infrared, and radar

Control techniques for these systems will need to be built into each satellite. The satellites will need to be able to communicate automatically among themselves—to autonomously maintain position both within the cluster and in relation to the mission's objectives. An objective could be something as simple as keeping together in orbit or as complex as traveling to Jupiter or Saturn and changing formation when they arrive there.

Old concepts and methods of spacecraft and mission design will simply not work for these future requirements. The satellite cluster, as a whole, must be able to adapt itself to new circumstances without waiting for orders from ground control. This will require new forms of artificial intelligence and a whole new field of software design. There are many difficulties to be overcome before satellite clusters become a reality, but they promise great improvements in reliability and performance.

The most interesting application for a distributed spacecraft design is the Constellation X mission being planned by the National Aeronautics and Space Administration. Its space segment will be composed of a group of X-ray telescopes based around one of the **libration points** or Lagrangian points. The mission is designed to give scientists a better look at **black holes** and to push ahead with the effort to unravel the mystery of **missing matter**.

Other applications of the concept of distributed spacecraft systems include the military's idea for a fleet of **radar** satellites that would provide real-time data of both ground and air movements as a long-term replacement for the AWACS radar surveillance and the J-Stars ground surveillance aircraft. Another military idea is to build a new class of satellites that can be refueled while in orbit, thus giving them a vastly longer operational life.

## Future Space Probes

The need for an inexpensive way to get around the solar system is driving research into "solar sails." This type of spacecraft will be propelled by the **solar wind** in a manner similar to an ordinary sailboat. It will need huge, lightweight structures to capture the energy of the solar wind. Given the right design, solar sails could be used to place research probes on the far side of the Sun, thus providing us with three-dimensional views of such spectacular events as solar **coronal mass ejections**.

More conventional deep-space missions will eventually be launched to follow up on the **Galileo mission** to Jupiter and the **Cassini mission** to Saturn. In deep space beyond the asteroid belt, solar power arrays do not work. Nuclear power systems, such as the controversial isotope thermal generator used for the Cassini mission, seem to be the only alternative. It had been thought that no more large, expensive deep-space missions would ever be launched again. Now, however, they appear to be the most effective way to reach the outer planets of our solar system.

In the near future, satellites will be even more diverse than they are today. Everything from tiny nanosats, weighing only a few ounces, to very large satellites, weighing hundreds of tons, will be launched into space. Humanity's robotic servants in space will be as diverse, and as ingeniously made, as any of the millions of other tools we have built over the ages. SEE ALSO COMMUNICATIONS, FUTURE NEEDS IN (VOLUME 4); LIGHTSAILS (VOLUME 4); SATELLITES, TYPES OF (VOLUME 1); SMALL SATELLITE TECHNOLOGY (VOLUME 1); SOLAR POWER SYSTEMS (VOLUME 4); SPACE INDUSTRIES (VOLUME 4).

*Taylor Dinerman*

### Bibliography

McCurdy, Howard E. *Faster, Better, Cheaper: Low-Cost Innovation in the U.S. Space Program.* Baltimore: John Hopkins University Press, 2001.

Sarsfield, Liam. *The Cosmos on a Shoestring: Small Spacecraft for Space and Earth Science.* Santa Monica, CA: RAND, Critical Technologies Institute, 1998.

**libration point** one of five gravitationally stable points related to two orbiting masses; three points are metastable, but L4 and L5 are stable

**black holes** objects so massive for their size that their gravitational pull prevents everything, even light, from escaping

**missing matter** the mass of the universe that cannot be accounted for but is necessary to produce a universe whose overall curvature is "flat"

**radar** a technique for detecting distant objects by emitting a pulse of radio-wavelength radiation and then recording echoes of the pulse off the distant objects

**solar wind** a continuous, but varying, stream of charged particles (mostly electrons and protons) generated by the Sun; it establishes and affects the interplanetary magnetic field; it also deforms the magnetic field about Earth and sends particles streaming toward Earth at its poles

**coronal mass ejections** large quantities of solar plasma and magnetic field launched from the Sun into space

**Galileo mission** successful robot exploration of the outer solar system; this mission used gravity assists from Venus and Earth to reach Jupiter, where it dropped a probe into the atmosphere and studied the planet for nearly seven years

**Cassini mission** a robotic spacecraft mission to the planet Saturn scheduled to arrive in July 2004 when the Huygens probe will be dropped into Titan's atmosphere while the Cassini spacecraft studies the planet

# Science Fiction

Astronautics is unique among the sciences in that it has its roots in an art form. For nearly 400 years space travel existed only in the minds of those faithful writers who kept the torch burning until engineers and scientists developed the technological ability to realize their dreams.

## Early Space Fiction

No fiction written about space travel was written until it was known that there were other worlds to go to. This did not happen until 1610, when Galileo Galilei turned a telescope toward the heavens and discovered that what hundreds of generations had assumed were five wandering stars were in fact worlds. This discovery was immediately followed by a spate of speculation about what those worlds might be like, what kind of life might exist there, and, most importantly, how human beings might be able to travel to them. Most of this speculation took the form of fiction, but until the end of the eighteenth century those flights were the stuff of outright fantasy: Neither science nor engineering knew of any method by which a human being could leave the surface of this world, let alone travel to another one.

## The Nineteenth and Twentieth Centuries

The invention of the balloon in 1783 by the Montgolfier brothers changed all that. It was clear that a balloon could never carry anyone to the Moon, but that invention was a watershed in perception. People now knew that science and technology had the potential to make spaceflight possible; surely it was just a matter of time and imagination. Scores of science fiction novels were written about travel to other worlds. Unlike previous stories, however, those written in the nineteenth century were much more inclined to take into account the actual conditions of outer space and the planets.

Paramount among all of these works were the two space novels of Jules Verne: *From the Earth to the Moon* (1865) and *Round the Moon* (1870). For the first time the problem of space travel was expressed in terms of a problem in engineering and mathematics: Verne scrupulously worked only with the science, technology, and materials available at the time when he wrote. As a result, he achieved a sense of realism that is still convincing. This realism was instrumental in inspiring an entire generation of young readers who decided to do everything they could to make Verne's dream come true. These readers included future scientists such as Hermann Oberth, Konstantin Tsiolkovsky, and Robert H. Goddard, without whose seminal work modern astronautics would have developed decades later than it did. Oberth, for example, said that he had never thought about space travel until he read *From the Earth to the Moon*. Verne's influence continued well into the twentieth century. The astronomer Robert Richardson said, "There can be no doubt that Jules Verne's *Trip to the Moon* with all its faults has exerted a powerful effect on human thought in preparing our minds for this greatest of all adventures."

Verne set a high standard for accuracy and believability that influenced the writers who followed him, and space fiction became much more realistic. Dozens of ideas that are thought of as products of modern space science were first proposed in the pages of early science fiction. The **space**

## JULES VERNE (1828–1905)

Science fiction writer Ray Bradbury said that Jules Verne embodies the whole history of humanity. Indeed, Verne lived in an era marked by and obsessed with scientific developments. His novels, filled with technological descriptions, made him one of the founders of science fiction.

**space station** large orbital outpost equipped to support a human crew and designed to remain in orbit for an extended period

An illustration from the 1872 edition of *From the Earth to the Moon* by Jules Verne. Nearly a century later, in 1969, Verne's fiction became a reality when astronaut Neil Armstrong became the first human to walk on the Moon.

**station** and the navigational satellite were invented by Edward Everett Hale in *The Brick Moon* (1869), the solar sail by G. Le Faure and Henri de Graffigny in 1889, the space suit in 1900 by George Griffith, the nuclear-powered spaceship by Garrett P. Serviss in 1910 and Arthur Train and Robert Wood in 1915, and the electromagnetic mass driver in 1930 by R. H. Romans. Even the countdown was invented by science fiction, first used in the 1929 film *Frau im Mond* (Woman in the Moon), by Fritz Lang.

## The Modern Era

After World War II the influence of science fiction on the public perception of space travel shifted from the printed page to the silver screen. Although serious fans, including many scientists, preferred the written word, which was light-years ahead of Hollywood's version of science fiction, the image most Americans had of the future of space travel in that period was shaped by what they saw in movie theaters and on television screens. This was unfortunate because, with only a few exceptions, films and television lagged decades behind the literature.

While science fiction writers were working in the present day, Hollywood science fiction was more like what had been published in the pulp magazines of the 1930s and 1940s. Films such as *Flight to Mars* (1951) and *The Terror from Beyond Space* (1958) made space travel seem silly and trivial. However, a few films made a sincere effort to combine realistic drama with real science, such as *Destination Moon* (1950), *Conquest of Space* (1955), *Forbidden Planet* (1956), and *2001: A Space Odyssey* (1968). More recently, there have been films such as *Apollo 13* (1995) and *Red Planet* (2000). On television the sole exception was *Star Trek* (1966–1969). Although taking place in the far future, that series made a genuine attempt not only to keep within the bounds of science but to convey a sense of wonder about space travel.

The link between science fiction and the history of astronautics is complex. Science fiction has served as an inspiration. It also acts as a mirror of the technology of the time in which it is written. Jules Verne, for instance, chose a giant cannon over rockets for the launch of his spacecraft, primarily because of the primitive state of rocket technology in his time (he did use rockets to maneuver his spacecraft). Similarly, in 1910 Garrett Serviss recognized that the recently discovered phenomenon of radioactivity could be a potential energy source for space travel. Science fiction also acts as a gauge of public interest in astronautics, since most authors want to tell stories that incorporate subjects of interest to their readers. SEE ALSO CLARKE, ARTHUR C. (VOLUME 1); GODDARD, ROBERT HUTCHINGS (VOLUME 1); LITERATURE (VOLUME 1); OBERTH, HERMANN (VOLUME 1); *STAR TREK* (VOLUME 4); *STAR WARS* (VOLUME 4); TSIOLKOVSKY, KONSTANTIN (VOLUME 3); VERNE, JULES (VOLUME 1).

*Ron Miller*

### Bibliography

Aldiss, Brian. *Billion Year Spree*. London: Corgi Books, 1975.

Di Fate, Vincent. *Infinite Worlds*. New York: Penguin Group, 1997.

Gunn, James. *Alternate Worlds*. New York: Prentice-Hall, 1975.

———. *The New Encyclopedia of Science Fiction*. New York: Viking Penguin, 1988.

Kyle, David A. *A Pictorial History of Science Fiction*. London: Hamlyn Publishing Group, 1976.

———. *The Illustrated Book of Science Fiction Dreams*. London: Hamlyn Publishing Group, 1977.

# Scientific Research

Successful human exploration of space depends on continued scientific research and innovative technology development. Advances in scientists' understanding of propulsion systems, power generation, resource utilization, and the physiological and psychological effects on humans of living in space are required if humans are to explore space and other planets or establish settlements on other planets.

Exploration to develop knowledge about Earth and planetary evolution in general, and the origins and conditions for life, will continue to lead us to search for life throughout the solar system and beyond. An initial **reconnaissance** of all of the planets in the solar system will ultimately be com-

**reconnaissance** a survey or preliminary exploration of a region of interest

This mirrored test stand at the Marshall Space Flight Center is used for firing solar thermal propulsion engines. Solar engines are more efficient than combustion engines that are currently in use.

pleted with a robotic mission to Pluto. Scientists are also keen to send spacecraft to Europa, one of the moons of Jupiter, to search for signs of life in a liquid ocean thought to exist below its icy crust. And the search will continue for other planetary systems beyond our own in order to answer questions such as: How typical is the solar system? How numerous are solar systems?

At present, Earth- and space-based telescopes are used to conduct the search for other planetary systems, but in the future, squadrons of miniature spacecraft may be sent on **interstellar** journeys of exploration to help answer some of life's most demanding questions: Are we alone, or is there other life out there? Are there other planets that could support humankind?

**interstellar** between the stars

153

With knowledge, innovation, and luck, the relatively low-cost Carl Sagan Memorial Station (formerly Mars Pathfinder Lander) was placed on Mars—as depicted in this rendering—and returned several images of Ares Valles.

## Propulsion Systems

All rockets in use in the early twenty-first century are propelled by some form of chemical rocket engine. Rockets with sufficient power to place a satellite in orbit use at least two stages. However, one long-term goal has been the reusable "single-stage to orbit" engine design. This would provide quick turnaround, much like a conventional aircraft, and greatly reduce the cost of getting to orbit because of reduced processing and flight preparation. An interim step may be a two-stage vehicle with boosters that fly back and land the spaceport for refurbishment after each launch.

Once a spacecraft is in orbit, other forms of propulsion are necessary. Several exotic propulsion systems have been proposed and investigated over the years. Orion was a project to design and construct a propulsion system using small atomic bombs. While this sounds impractical, many scientists think that such a propulsion system would have allowed humans to get to the Moon more quickly at a much lower cost than the Saturn V launch system. A variation of this type of propulsion is the nuclear thermal rocket. This system uses a nuclear reactor to heat a gas, which is then expelled through a nozzle, providing thrust.

The crew of a rocket ship powered by a nuclear rocket engine would need to be shielded from the reactor. One proposed solution is to place the engine at a large distance away from the crew quarters, connecting the two compartments by a long truss. In this design, distance substitutes for heavy **shielding**. ✳ Many scientists believe that if humans are to move beyond Earth orbit, some version of a nuclear rocket engine will be necessary.

Between 2002 and 2007, NASA plans to develop an improved radio-isotope power system for use in robotic planetary exploration and targets the first use of this power system for a Mars mission in 2009. During the period between 2003 and 2013, significant funding will be dedicated to the

**shielding** providing protection for humans and electronic equipment from cosmic rays, energetic particles from the Sun, and other radioactive materials

✳ This design and engine type was portrayed in the movie, *2001: A Space Odyssey.*

development of a nuclear-electric-propulsion system to enable a new class of planetary missions with multiple targets, to reduce spacecraft travel time, and to decrease mission cost.

Nuclear electric propulsion systems only use the nuclear reactor to generate electricity. The rocket engine itself is electrically powered. There are three classes of electric rocket engines: electrothermal, electrostatic, and electromagnetic. In electrothermal propulsion, the gas is raised to a high temperature and expelled through a rocket nozzle. Electrostatic propulsion systems first convert the gas to a plasma (highly ionized material) and then use electric fields to accelerate the gas to high velocity. Electromagnetic propulsion uses magnetic fields to accelerate a plasma.

Other propulsion systems include various configurations of solar sails, **ion propulsion** systems, and laser propulsion. Several systems involve the use of stationary high-powered **infrared** pulsed lasers. In one interesting system, the laser is fired at a parabolic reflector on the back of the spacecraft. This reflector focuses the laser energy, explosively heating air behind the craft and propelling it forward. In space, the reflector would be **jettisoned** and the laser would fire pulses at a block of propellant (ice would work) heating it to vapor.

## Space Power Generation

Spacecraft currently use solar power, hydrogen fuel cells, or **radioisotope thermoelectric generators** to generate electrical power and rechargeable batteries to store electrical energy. The International Space Station uses solar panels and rechargeable batteries. Solar power is converted to electrical power in large panels containing photovoltaic cells. These cells convert light directly into electricity using a **semiconductor** such as silicon or gallium arsenide. Solar panels are relatively low cost and simple. However, they are fragile, take up a lot of space, and become less effective as a spacecraft travels away from the Sun. For future missions that penetrate deeper into the solar system, and beyond, alternative power sources will be essential.

Fuel cells combine hydrogen and oxygen to make water. When hydrogen combines with oxygen, energy is released. A fuel cell converts this energy directly into electricity. Fuel cells are relatively compact and produce usable by-products, but they are complicated and expensive to produce.

Radioisotope thermoelectric generators (RTGs) convert the heat produced by the natural decay of radioactive materials to electrical power by solid-state thermoelectric converters. RTGs are lightweight, compact, robust, reliable, and relatively inexpensive. These devices allow spacecraft to operate at large distances from the Sun or where solar power systems would be impractical. They remain unmatched for power output, reliability, and durability.

## Resource Utilization

If a human colony is to be established on Earth's Moon, Mars, or elsewhere in the solar system, some means of transporting large amounts of materials to the colony site must be developed. It would be prohibitively expensive and impractical to transport materials from Earth in sufficient quantity to build a base on the Moon or Mars. However, this is not necessary, since both Earth's Moon and Mars have an abundance of raw materials that could be used for construction.

**ion propulsion** a propulsion system that uses charged particles acclerated by electric fields to provide thrust

**infrared** portion of the electromagnetic spectrum with waves slightly longer than visible light

**jettisoned** ejected, thrown overboard, or gotten rid of

**radioisotope thermoelectric generator** device using solid-state electronics and the heat produced by radioactive decay to generate electricity

**semiconductor** one of the groups of elements with properties intermediate between the metals and nonmetals

The Moon may have a substantial amount of water locked in permafrost in the bottom of deep craters near its poles where sunlight never reaches or in clays. Although it would be expensive to mine this water, it would be far cheaper than transporting water from Earth. The Moon also has surface rocks rich in light materials such as aluminum and silicon dioxide. It would require large amounts of electrical power to produce pure aluminum or glass from Moon rocks, but solar energy is abundant because of the lack of atmosphere.

The Moon may even have sufficient quantities of helium-3 to make a lunar settlement economically self-supporting. The helium-3 would be extracted from lunar soil, packaged as a compressed gas or liquid, and returned to Earth for use in **fusion** reactors. Due to the lower gravity, launching a rocket from the surface of the Moon for return to Earth is far less costly than launching a rocket from Earth.

**fusion** the act of releasing nuclear energy by combining lighter elements such as hydrogen into heavier elements

**minerals** crystalline arrangements of atoms and molecules of specified proportions that make up rocks

Mars also has significant resources available. The red color of Martian soil is due to the presence of large quantities of iron oxide. Other **minerals** and elements are also present. In addition, Mars is thought to have vast quantities of subsurface water. Asteroids have long been recognized as accessible, mineral-rich bodies in the solar system and are a ready target for resource mining. SEE ALSO ASTEROID MINING (VOLUME 4); ION PROPULSION (VOLUME 4); LIGHTSAILS (VOLUME 4); LUNAR BASES (VOLUME 4); LUNAR OUTPOSTS (VOLUME 4); MARS BASES (VOLUME 4); MARS MISSIONS (VOLUME 4); POWER, METHODS OF GENERATING (VOLUME 4); SOLAR POWER SYSTEMS (VOLUME 4).

*Elliot Richmond*

**Bibliography**

NASA Life Sciences Strategic Planning Study Committee. *Exploring the Living Universe: A Strategy for Space Life Sciences.* Washington, DC: National Aeronautics and Space Administration, 1988.

National Commission on Space. *Pioneering the Space Frontier, The Report of the National Commission on Space.* New York: Bantam Books, 1986.

Office of Technology Assessment. *Exploring the Moon and Mars: Choices for the Nation,* OTA-ISC-502, Washington, DC: U.S. Government Printing Office, 1991.

O'Neill, Gerard K. *The High Frontier: Human Colonies in Space.* New York: William Morrow and Co., 1977.

Space Science Board. *Life Beyond the Earth's Environment: The Biology of Living Organisms in Space.* Washington, DC: National Academy of Sciences, 1979.

*Space Science in the Twenty First Century: Imperatives for the Decades 1995 to 2015—Life Sciences.* Washington, DC: National Academy Press, 1988.

Wilhelms, Don E. *To a Rocky Moon: A Geologist's History of Lunar Exploration.* Tucson: University of Arizona Press, 1993.

**Internet Resources**

*Astronomy Resources from STScI.* Space Telescope Science Institute. <http://www.stsci.edu/resources/>.

NASA Human Spaceflight. <http://spaceflight.nasa.gov/history/>.

*Space Science.* National Aeronautics and Space Administration. <http://spacescience.nasa.gov/>.

# Settlements

At the beginning of the twenty-first century, people are excited by the prospect of visiting new worlds in outer space. While international space

A proposed inflatable habitat is illustrated here. This habitat could be used as a possible lunar settlement for future astronauts living and working on the Moon.

agencies continue robotic exploration of planets and asteroids in the solar system, other government agencies are planning a return to the Moon and expeditions to Mars. What is the logic of establishing a settlement on the Moon as a precondition for human settlement of Mars and beyond? Answers to this question include satisfying the need to explore, increasing scientific knowledge, enhancing understanding of life in the universe, discovering whether life existed on Mars, igniting the human spirit, making use of resources on the Moon and Mars, and ensuring the survival of humankind. Once humans have mastered the lunar environment, they will have the technical knowledge to reach Mars, Jupiter, and the stars.

## Settlement of the Moon: First Lunar Base Siting

The first step towards human settlement of the Moon is the determination of the best site for a lunar base. As a result of information gained from the Clementine mission that observed the Moon for 71 days in 1994, supported by data from Lunar Prospector (January 6, 1998–July 31, 1999), it appears that a permanently shaded region inside Shackleton crater at the Moon's south pole, 30 kilometers (18.5 miles) in diameter, contains hydrogen, likely in the form of water ice, and ammonia. Ice would not only supply water for settlers but could also be used to generate fuel for spacecraft.

**cryogenics** related to extremely low temperatures; the temperature of liquid nitrogen or lower

**infrastructure** the physical structures, such as roads and bridges, necessary to the functioning of a complex system

**regolith** upper few meters of the Moon's surface, composed of inorganic matter, such as unconsolidated rocks and fine soil

**shielding** providing protection for humans and electronic equipment from cosmic rays, energetic particles from the Sun, and other radioactive materials

**extrasolar planets** planets orbiting stars other than the Sun

**interstellar** between the stars

✳ In July 1968, Buzz Aldrin made history by becoming one of the first humans to walk the surface of the Moon.

The rim of the crater is illuminated over 80 percent of the time. Nearby there are two other places, only 10 kilometers (6.2 miles) apart, which receive illumination over 98 percent of the time. Solar energy in those areas could be used to sustain an extraction industry. In the permanently shadowed areas astronomical instruments could be operated with telescopic optics kept cold and stable using **cryogenics**. Shackleton crater could be the best site for a Moon base.

**Planet Moon: Phases for Development.** David Schrunk and his associates call the transformation of the Moon into an inhabited sister planet of Earth the "Planet Moon Project." This endeavor will draw upon every science and engineering discipline, as well as the social, economic, and political expertise of all nations. It will also provide virtually unlimited energy and material resources for humankind. Schrunk foresees an autonomous, self-governing society of over 100,000 people living on the Moon by the end of the twenty-first century. A global utility **infrastructure** would be in place to provide electrical power, communication, and transportation for the entire Moon. The global lunar electric grid network could beam substantial amounts of energy to Earth and other sites in the solar system. Manufacturing facilities would use lunar **regolith** for **shielding** against cosmic rays and as insulating material. As processing facilities gradually come into operation, various cements and building blocks, then ceramics, glasses, fibers, and metals will become available.

The Moon could also become the principal astronomical observation platform in the solar system. Very large aperture optical interferometry–based telescopes will detect **extrasolar planets**, analyze their atmospheres, and characterize their habitability, and will lay down the foundation for the human **interstellar** migration often referred to as the "Great Diaspora." The Moon will become the primary site for the construction and launch of satellites, probes, autonomous mobile robots with television cameras, and scientific instruments. Thousands of near-Earth objects will be analyzed by lunar-based telescopes and lunar-launched probes. Those objects that pose a threat will have their orbits altered by spacecraft made on the Moon. Asteroids and comets that approach the Earth-Moon system will be mined.

**Human Return to the Moon.** In the first stages of lunar development humans will return to the Moon to conduct astronomy, science, and engineering experiments and supervise ongoing construction of the lunar base. Technology to bring humans back to the Moon, possibly by 2007, already exists. Buzz Aldrin ✳ stated before Congress that "the only obstacles to that future are complacency and a lack of clear commitment" and cautioned that "if we insist that the human quest await the healing of every sore on the body politic, we condemn ourselves to stagnation."

**Building a Lunar Civilization.** Once consensus is reached that a settlement will be developed on the Moon, the next probable step will be the building of a crater lunar base. After the gathering of scientific and technical data by satellite, a domed crater serving as the site of a largely self-sufficient outpost would be developed in three phases: construction, remote systems trials, and occupied operations. Crater walls would form the base of support for a dome over the center. The circular shape of the crater would lead to a spherically efficient geometry of gracious appearance and create a circular transportation/robotic capability. Occupants would be able to look toward a central agricultural zone that receives sunlight.

Candidate power supply systems can be divided into two basic categories: solar power and nuclear power. Other potential power sources include stored energy and beamed power such as microwave or laser. Another option would be to illuminate **photovoltaic arrays** on the lunar surface from Earth, using lasers. In that case, no power-beaming equipment would have to be launched into space.

**Harnessing the Moon's Resources.** An essential requirement for cost-effective lunar base development and operation is the ability to locate, mine, process, and utilize the natural resources of the Moon. Although the Moon has essentially no atmosphere, its surface is composed of oxygen, silicon, and other elements and **minerals**. The environment features **solar radiation**, **vacuum conditions**, and low gravity that can be used for power and materials processing. The surface contains bulk soil/regolith that can provide radiation shielding. Oxygen and water from ice or extracted from clay could support life and serve as a propellant. Facilities, equipment, and solar cells could be constructed from native metals. Hydrogen is another possible source of propellant. Fusion power could come from helium.

## Beyond the Moon towards Mars

According to Mars Society founder Robert Zubrin, Mars is humanity's new frontier because it can be settled and altered, thus defining it as a New World that can create the basis for a positive future for terrestrial humanity for the next several centuries. Projections for human missions to Mars range from 2012 to 2020 and beyond. It will take many months for people to make the first trips to Mars. Advanced propulsion could shave months off the travel time, but even the most optimistic plans consider nonchemical propulsion as being somewhat down the road. Most mission scenarios show this trip happening without artificial gravity, and permanent Mars settlements remain far in the future.

**Power Generation and Storage.** The primary surface power source will be 160-kilowatt nuclear power modules that will have a lifetime of more than fifteen years and provide power to the Mars outpost for each mission. Deployment will be about 1 kilometer (0.62 mile) away from the crew habitat. As Mars receives about 44 percent as much solar radiation as Earth does, solar power is another possible power source. Power systems for pressurized long-range surface rovers would likely consist of a methane fuel cell or a **dynamic isotope power system**.

**Life on Mars: Follow the Water.** Scientists continue to debate whether the Antarctic-recovered Martian meteorite ALH84001 contains evidence of ancient life. Liquid water does not and cannot exist on the surface of Mars today, although it may have in the past. In 2003 the National Aeronautics and Space Administration (NASA) will send two rovers to Mars to hunt for signs of water in the rocks and surface soil. The European Space Agency will launch Mars Express in that year with a lander, Beagle-2, with a scientific **payload** dedicated to detecting signs of **biogenic** activity on Mars.

**photovoltaic arrays** sets of solar panels grouped together in big sheets. These arrays collect light from the Sun and use it to make electricity to power the equipment and machines

**minerals** crystalline arrangements of atoms and molecules of specified proportions that make up rocks

**solar radiation** total energy of any wavelength and all charged particles emitted by the Sun

**vacuum conditions** the almost complete lack of atmosphere found on the surface of the Moon and in space

**dynamic isotope power system** the decay of isotopes such as plutonium-238 and polonium-210 produces heat, which can be transformed into electricity by radioisotopic thermoelectric generators

**payload** any cargo launched aboard a rocket that is destined for space, including communications satellites or modules, supplies, equipment, and astronauts; does not include the vehicle used to move the cargo or the propellant that powers the vehicle

**biogenic** resulting from the actions of living organisms; or, necessary for life

**magnetosphere** the magnetic cavity that surrounds Earth or any other planet with a magnetic field. It is formed by the interaction of the solar wind with the planet's magnetic field

**SETTLEMENTS OR COLONIES? A TWENTY-FIRST-CENTURY PERSPECTIVE**

The responsibility to develop space resources completely and beneficially requires that human behavior, principles, and ethics be as advanced as the newest technologies. Reflecting the ethical aspects of space exploration, the U.S. State Department in the mid-1970s specifically prohibited the use of the term "space colony." Twenty-first-century human expansion into space must be guided by the traditional values of "liberty and justice for all." Colonialism is an inappropriate structure and value for humanity in the space age because it denies human equality. Although a new space settler or settlement (habitat, city, sphere, domicile, or residence) initially may require special status and support, progress and productive human relationships on the space frontier need to be based on equality and mutual benefit.

## Jupiter and Beyond

After the establishment of the Earth-Moon baseline infrastructure, not just Mars but Jupiter and cosmic infinity lie open for exploration. The quickest way to the stars requires familiarity with the solar system, and Jupiter's size, system complexity, and location can provide that advantage. There is no reason to limit the civil space program to Mars for the next ten to fifty years.

With more than 70 percent of solar system mass (excluding the Sun), four large Galilean satellites (Io, Europa, Callisto, and Ganymede) and more than thirty others, powerful lightning charges, a far-reaching **magnetosphere**, a ring system, and a 40,000-kilometer (24,800-mile) red spot that has been swirling at 500 kilometers (310 miles) per hour for more than three centuries, Jupiter is a near solar system within a solar system.

To understand human origins and search for extraterrestrial life, NASA and other international space agencies have developed a "follow the water" strategy for solar system exploration; Europa, along with Callisto and Ganymede, is becoming as compelling a destination as is Mars. The search for water off Earth and for life leads back to the Moon, to Jupiter and Mars, and to the stars and galaxies and beyond. SEE ALSO ALDRIN, BUZZ (VOLUME 1); ASTROBIOLOGY (VOLUME 4); COMMUNITIES IN SPACE (VOLUME 4); HUMAN MISSIONS TO MARS (VOLUME 3); LUNAR BASES (VOLUME 4); LUNAR OUTPOSTS (VOLUME 4); MARS (VOLUME 2); MARS BASES (VOLUME 4); MARS MISSIONS (VOLUME 4); MOON (VOLUME 2).

*Michael R. Cerney and Steve Durst, 2001*

**Bibliography**

Eckart, Peter, with contributions by Buzz Aldrin, Arthur C. Clarke, Harrison H. Schmitt, and John Young. *The Lunar Base Handbook: An Introduction to Lunar Base Design, Development, and Operations.* New York: McGraw-Hill, 1999.

Schrunk, David, Burton Sharpe, Bonnie Cooper, and Madhu Thangavelu. *The Moon: Resources, Future Development and Colonization.* New York: John Wiley & Sons, 1999.

Space Studies Institute. *Return to the Moon 2: Proceedings of the 2000 Lunar Development Conference.* Princeton, NJ: Space Front Press, Space Frontier Foundation, 2000.

**Internet Resources**

Hiscox, Julian A. "Biology and the Planetary Engineering of Mars." University of Alabama at Birmingham. <http://spot.colorado.edu/~marscase/cfm/articles/biorev3.html>.

Space Age Publishing Company. <http://www.spaceagepub.com>.

Zubrin, Robert. "The Significance of the Martian Frontier." Mars Society. <http://spot.colorado.edu/~marscase/cfm/articles/frontier.html>.

# Social Ethics

Human activities in space present us with novel philosophical, cultural, and ethical challenges. Moreover, space acts as a different lens through which we can explore many of our oldest and deepest social and philosophical issues. Indeed, the broad issue of whether significant resources should be devoted to space activities at all can be considered a social ethics question. Many people suggest that resources devoted to space activities detract from solving problems on Earth that desperately need more attention. Others counter that space activities can help address those problems. This broad question can have direct relevance to the motivations for space activities because the answer could determine the extent to which space will be used primarily to address Earth-based problems directly as opposed to exploratory pursuits that may or may not have direct terrestrial relevance.

If we do think significant resources should be spent on space activities, we can ask: Should those activities be aimed primarily at implementing military and political agendas, commerce, resource utilization for some or many, pure exploration for the good of humankind, none of the above, all of the above, or something else? Arguably, all of these motivations have been pursued, but should they have been? And should people continue to pursue these aims and others? The answer would appear to be yes, but what if spending too much time and money on space detracts from the well-being of humans and life on Earth? What if resource utilization causes the extinction of a very different form of life? What is more important, and why?

Many of the motivations for space activities are addressed in the 1967 United Nations Outer Space Treaty, in which Article I states that "the exploration and use of outer space, including the Moon and other celestial bodies, shall be carried out for the benefit and in the interests of all countries, irrespective of their degree of economic or scientific development, and shall be the province of all mankind." Article II specifically prohibits national appropriation by stating: "Outer space, including the Moon and other celestial bodies, is not subject to national appropriation by claim of sovereignty, by means of use or occupation, or by any other means." The 1979 United Nations Moon Treaty adds much more detail but has not been ratified by some countries, including the United States.

Arguably, two of the most challenging ethical issues presented by space exploration have to do with finding a different form of life and terraforming (changing a planet to make it suitable for Earth life), both of which relate to each other.

## A Different Form of Life

In his book *Cosmos* (1980), scientist and visionary Carl Sagan stated: "If there is life on Mars, I believe we should do nothing with Mars. Mars then belongs to the Martians, even if they are only microbes." Astrobiologist Christopher McKay has appealed to an intrinsic value of life principle, or **biocentric** view, and has suggested that Martian life-forms "have a right to continue their existence even if their extinction would benefit the biota of Earth." For some, only a noninterference policy would be acceptable, as suggested by philosopher Alan Marshall. Alternatively, McKay believes that the rights of Martian life "confer upon us the obligation to assist it in obtaining global diversity and stability."

Robert Zubrin, founder of the Mars Society, acknowledges the unique value of extraterrestrial life, but also stresses that people do not hesitate to kill terrestrial microbes in many circumstances. This is a reasonable observation, and it is also reasonable to consider that extraterrestrial life, especially of an independent origin, could be unique and valuable in a way that terrestrial microbes are not.

---

**WHAT ARE "ETHICS"?**

Ethics involves assessing what is valuable and why, informing decisions about what *should* be done. These kinds of value-based questions can be very complex and involve many points of view, which are often incompatible and contradictory. Philosophy has a long history of exploring ethical issues from many different perspectives, including "meta-ethical" points of view that explore *how* we assess what is valuable and "good." There are practical perspectives as well as ideological and metaphysical perspectives, all of which can be drawn from when thinking about what we should do in space.

**biocentric** notion that all living organisms have intrinsic value

**anthropocentrism** valuing humans above all else

Steve Gillett suggests a hybrid view that combines **anthropocentrism** as applied to terrestrial activity with biocentrism for worlds with indigenous life. This kind of pluralistic approach to ethics has commonsense appeal. J. Baird Callicott invokes weak anthropocentrism, first suggested by Bryan Norton, which suggests that things that transform and ennoble human nature have enough value to require their preservation. Callicott writes: "I can think of nothing so positively transforming of human consciousness as the discovery, study, and conservation of life somewhere off the Earth."

## Terraforming

**cosmocentric ethic** ethical position that establishes the universe as the priority in a value system or appeals to something characteristic of the universe that provides justification of value

**geocentric** a model that places Earth at the center of the universe

Martyn Fogg states that "the concept of terraforming is inspiring enough to perhaps generate a formal effort toward extending environmental ethics to the cosmic stage." Robert Haynes, Christopher McKay, and Don MacNiven are prompted by the prospect of terraforming to suggest the need for a **cosmocentric ethic**. They conclude that current ethical theories exclude the extraterrestrial environment because they are purely **geocentric**. These authors may be reflecting a deeper instinct, sensing deficiencies in existing ethical views in general. The new context, or "lens," of space exploration has rightly prompted the consideration of new and perhaps broader perspectives for ethics.

Holmes Rolston offers a view that appeals to the "formed integrity" of a "projective Universe" in which the universe creates objects of formed integrity (objects worthy of a proper name) that have intrinsic value and should be respected. However, Haynes points out that Rolston's view appears to conflict with modifying Earth even for the benefit of humans. Rolston's view would call for the preservation of extraterrestrial life and most likely oppose terraforming.

**propagate** to cause to move, to multiply, or to extend to a broader area

"Connectedness" may hold promise for a cosmocentric ethic. The interdependent connectedness of ecosystems is often cited as a foundation for justifying the value of parts of the larger whole, since the parts contribute to the maintenance of the whole. Mark Lupisella has suggested that connectedness itself may be a necessary property of the universe and that the realization of connectedness requires interaction. This view might favor realizing interaction in the form of complexity, creativity, uniqueness, diversity, and other characteristics that may further realize the dynamic interactive nature of the universe. In making choices consistent with this view, humanity might help encourage and **propagate** life and diversity on Earth and throughout the universe. Freeman Dyson writes: "Diversity is the great gift which life has brought to our planet and may one day bring to the rest of the Universe. The preservation and fostering of diversity is the great goal which I would like to see embodied in our ethical principles and in our political actions."

Ultimately, as we have been able to do in many areas of space activity, a thoughtful balance incorporating many different views is likely to be the best approach to realizing a healthy future in space for humankind. SEE ALSO COMMUNITIES IN SPACE (VOLUME 4); GOVERNANCE (VOLUME 4); LAW (VOLUME 4); LIVING IN SPACE (VOLUME 3); SETTLEMENTS (VOLUME 4); TERRAFORMING (VOLUME 4).

*Mark L. Lupisella*

## Bibliography

Callicott, J. Baird. "Moral Considerability and Extraterrestrial Life." In *Beyond Spaceship Earth: Environmental Ethics and the Solar System*, ed. E. C. Hargrove. San Francisco: Sierra Club Books, 1990.

Dyson, Freeman. *Infinite in All Directions*. New York: Harper & Row, 1988.

Fogg, Martyn. *Terraforming: Engineering Planetary Environments*. Warrendale, PA: SAE International, 1995.

Gillett, Steve. "The Ethics of Terraforming." *Amazing* (August 1992):72–74.

Haynes, Robert, and Chris McKay. "Should We Implant Life on Mars?" *Scientific American*, December 1990.

Lupisella, Mark. "Humans and Martians." *Earth Space Review* 9, no. 1 (2000):50–60.

MacNiven, Donald. "Environmental Ethics and Planetary Engineering." *Journal of the British Interplanetary Society* 48 (1995):442–443.

———. *Moral Expertise: Studies in Practical and Professional Ethics*. London: Routledge, 1990.

Marshall, Alan. "Ethics and the Extraterrestrial Environment." *Journal of Applied Philosophy* 10, no. 2 (1993):233.

Narveson, Jan. "Martians and Morals: How to Treat an Alien." In *Extraterrestrials: Science and Intelligence*, ed. Edward Regis, Jr. Cambridge: Cambridge University Press, 1985.

Norton, Bryan G. "Environmental Ethics and Weak Anthropocentrism." *Environmental Ethics* 6 (1984):131–148.

Rolston, Holmes, III. "The Preservation of Natural Value in the Solar System." In *Beyond Spaceship Earth: Environmental Ethics and the Solar System*, ed. E. C. Hargrove. San Francisco: Sierra Club Books, 1990.

Ruse, Michael. "Is Rape Wrong on Andromeda? An Introduction to Extraterrestrial Evolution, Science, and Morality." In *Extraterrestrials: Science and Intelligence*, ed. Edward Regis, Jr. Cambridge: Cambridge University Press, 1985.

Sagan, Carl. *Cosmos*. New York: Random House, 1980.

Zubrin, Robert. "The Terraforming Debate." *Mars Underground News* 3 1993.

Zubrin, Robert, with Richard Wagner. *The Case for Mars: The Plan to Settle the Red Planet and Why We Must*. New York: Free Press, 1996.

# Solar Power Systems

The first use of solar cells in space occurred on the satellite Vanguard I, which was launched on March 17, 1958. Eight tiny panels were installed symmetrically around the satellite to ensure power generation during the satellite's random tumbling. They delivered 50 to 100 milliwatts of power and provided secondary electricity for a **beacon signal generator**. Each panel had six square silicon cells, measuring 2 centimeters (0.79 inch) by 2 centimeters (0.79 inch) by 0.4 centimeters (0.16 inch), with a **photovoltaic** (PV) conversion efficiency of approximately 10 percent. The panels of solar cells were protected by a thick cover glass to avoid radiation damage from electrons and protons trapped in the **Van Allen radiation belts** that surround Earth.✶ The longevity of Vanguard I's beacon signal surpassed all expectations—lasting until May 1964. As a result, future regulations required shutting down power supplies of satellites to avoid cluttering the radio wave spectrum with unwanted signals.

The early use of solar cells was tentative, but they eventually emerged as the only viable source for satellites that were required to operate for more than a few weeks. Solar cells improved steadily and successfully met the

**beacon signal generator** a radio transmitter emitting signals for guidance or for showing location

**photovoltaic** pertaining to the direct generation of electricity from electromagnetic radiation (light)

**Van Allen radiation belts** two belts of high energy charged particles captured from the solar wind by Earth's magnetic field

✶ The radiation belts are named after American physicist James Van Allen, who discovered them.

Solar power panels flare to the sides as the Hubble Space Telescope is lifted into position by the Remote Manipulator System from the cargo bay of the space shuttle Discovery.

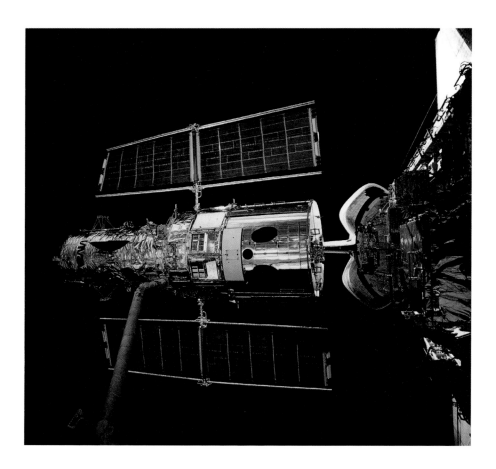

unique power requirements of space travel while other possible competitive sources were proven inadequate. Over the years, solar cells have provided electricity to thousands of space missions that operated near Earth, on the Moon, and in planetary or interplanetary missions.

## Power Requirements

Telecommunication satellites require several kilowatts of electric power, while most other satellites require several hundred watts. The long-duration human missions, Skylab, launched in 1973, and the Russian space station Mir, launched in 1986, each used 25 kilowatts from solar cells. ✳ The International Space Station has solar PV modules with a total rated generation capacity of 240 kilowatts at the beginning of life and 168 kilowatts at the end of life, with the life duration expected to be fifteen years. The space station's **solar array** has eight wings and operates at 160 volts DC. Each half-wing is 11.6 meters (38 feet) by 32.9 meters (108 feet). In each wing, there are 32,800 square silicon cells that are 8 centimeters (3.15 inches) by 8 centimeters by 0.2 centimeters (0.08 inches) thick with an average conversion efficiency of 14.2 percent. The total power of the solar array of the International Space Station is more than 2 million times larger than the first solar panels on Vanguard I.

While the demand for power by commercial communication satellites is increasing, National Aeronautics and Space Administration (NASA) missions to near-Earth targets, such as Mars or the Moon, and scientific missions to the Sun and outer planets, have been requiring decreasing amounts

✳ **Mir returned to Earth after 5,511 days in space, plunging safely into the Pacific Ocean, on March 22, 2001.**

**solar array** group of solar cells or other solar power collectors arranged to capture energy from the Sun and use it to generate electrical power

of power. The piloted missions—whether Earth orbiting, lunar, or planetary—require power systems that are an order of magnitude larger than that of the largest telecommunication power systems.

## Current Space Cells and Systems

A typical solar cell is a diode illuminated by sunlight. Diodes are prepared by forming a **pn single junction** in a **semiconductor** such as silicon. For this purpose, an n-type region in which electrons are negatively charged **majority carriers** is grown on a p-type base in which holes are positively charged majority carriers or vice versa. The early silicon cells were of p on n type. The first commercial communication satellite, Telstar I, launched in 1962, used n on p silicon cells. The cell design and performance remained fairly static during the 1960s. During the 1970s, efficiency was increased to about 14 percent by improving the cell design. The improvements were achieved by forming a heavily **doped** rear interface known as back surface field; applying **photolithography** to create finer, more closely spaced front grid fingers; and applying a texture and antireflection coating to the cell surface. Efforts were also focused on reducing costs associated with PV array components by, for example, decreasing interconnect costs and using larger cells and lighter arrays.

In the 1980s and 1990s gallium arsenide–based solar cells were developed. Gallium arsenide on germanium solar cells were developed to increase the size and to reduce the thickness of cells by increasing the mechanical strength. Multijunction cells using gallium arsenide, gallium-aluminum arsenide, and gallium-aluminum phosphide on germanium were developed to effectively use a larger portion of the solar spectrum. Typical efficiencies for gallium arsenide–based cells range from 18.5 percent for single junction diodes to 24 percent for triple junction diodes.

Gallium arsenide cells are used for critical space missions that require high power. The manufacturing costs of gallium arsenide on germanium cells are six to nine times that of silicon cells. The overall cost is reduced, however, because of the higher efficiency of the cells. More satellites can be launched on a single **rocket** because of the smaller array area. Limiting the total area of the solar array is an important factor in the viability of space power arrays because of the estimated altitude control costs, which for a ten-year **geosynchronous Earth orbit** (GEO) mission amount to $48,000 per square meter. In this regard, high-efficiency multijunction arrays are more attractive for missions requiring higher power. Megawatts of power required by larger satellite constellations will be satisfied with multijunction solar cells having still higher efficiencies of greater than 30 percent. Iridium, a constellation of sixty-six communication satellites, required a total power of 125 kilowatts and used gallium arsenide on germanium solar cells. The spectacular performance of the Pathfinder mission to Mars was made possible by the mission's gallium arsenide on germanium cells. The cells provided all the necessary power, including 280 watts for the cruise module, 177 watts for the lander, and 45 watts for the Sojourner rover.

An important consideration for satellite programs is the weight of the spacecraft. Currently, the power system typically takes up about a quarter of the total spacecraft mass budget while the solar array and support structure comprise about a third of the power system mass. Launch costs are

**pn single junction** in a transistor or other solid state device, the boundary between the two different kinds of semiconductor material

**semiconductor** one of the groups of elements with properties intermediate between the metals and nonmetals

**majority carriers** the more abundant charge carriers in semiconductors; the less abundant are called minority carriers; for n-type semiconductors, electrons are the majority carriers

**doped** semiconductor such as silicon with an addition of small amounts of an impurity such as phosphorous to generate more charge carriers (such as electrons)

**photolithography** printing that uses a photographic process to create the printing plates

**rocket** vehicle (or device) especially designed to travel through space, propelled by one or more engines

**geosynchronous Earth orbit** orbit of a satellite that revolves around the Earth without changing its position in the sky relative to the planet

estimated to be $11,000 per kilogram in **low Earth orbit** and $66,000 per kilogram in GEO. Hence, reducing spacecraft mass has a potential added benefit of lowering launch costs.

Crystalline silicon and gallium-arsenide-based solar cells, currently employed in space solar PV power arrays, are rigid and fragile. Therefore, the PV arrays employ a honeycomb core with face sheets of aluminum or alternatively very lightweight **Kevlar®** or graphite fibers. The PV array blanket is folded in an accordion style before placement in a canister. Deploying the array can pose problems. This happened in November 2000 with the large solar array on the International Space Station.

Manufacturing costs for solar arrays are an important consideration for the total spacecraft budget. The array manufacturing costs for a medium-sized 5-kilowatt satellite can exceed $2 million. Current single-crystal technology can cost more than $300 per watt at the array level and weigh more than 1 kilogram per square meter equivalent to a **specific power** of about 65 watts per kilogram.

## Future Technologies

Future missions would include very large solar power satellites as well as very small satellites. Some long-term plans envision swarms of very small, distributed, autonomous satellites called microsats or even nanosats to perform specific tasks. In all these missions, reducing the total system cost would become increasingly more important. Highly efficient gallium arsenide–based multijunction cells, concentrator systems, and thin-film cells are being developed for the future space missions. Copper-indium-gallium selenide-sulfide or amorphous hydrogenated silicon thin-film solar cells may be able to reduce both the manufacturing cost and the mass per unit power by an order of magnitude from the current levels. Moving to a thin-film technology could conservatively reduce array-manufacturing costs to less than $500,000 from the current cost of $2 million for a medium-sized 5-kilowatt satellite. For small satellites, increasing the solar array specific power from a current typical value of 65 watts per kilogram will allow for either an increase in **payload** power or payload mass, or both.

Weight benefits of higher efficiency cells are decreased and high costs become less affordable in the case of flexible thin-film blanket arrays that can be easily rolled out. Nonrigid cells also have an advantage in stability. For example, flexible amorphous hydrogenated silicon solar arrays have continued to function after being pierced by tiny **meteorites**.

## Solar Electric Propulsion

Some missions will use solar electric propulsion instead of rockets. In solar electric propulsion, electric power obtained from sunlight is used to ionize a gas and then to accelerate and emit the ions. The spacecraft is propelled in the forward direction as a reaction to the emission of ions going in the opposite direction. This technology has been successfully demonstrated in the Deep Space I mission. Because of the low initial velocities and steady acceleration, however, solar electric propulsion satellites must spend long periods in intense regions of trapped radiation belts. Studies since the year 2000 have clearly shown that copper-indium-gallium selenide-sulfide solar cells are superior to the conventional silicon and gallium arsenide solar cells in the space radiation environment. The potential for improved radiation resistance of thin-film solar cells relative to single-crystal cells, could extend the mission lifetimes substantially. Large-area amorphous silicon modules were successfully demonstrated on flexible **substrates** on the Russian space station Mir. The efficiency was relatively low but remained stable in the space environment.

Studies since 1999 have shown that thin-film cells would start to become cost-competitive in GEO and LEO missions at an efficiency of 12.6 percent. Significant technological hurdles remain, however, before thin-film technology could be implemented as the primary power source for spacecraft. A large-area fabrication process for high-efficiency cells on a lightweight substrate has not been demonstrated. Research efforts are being concentrated on the development of a large-area, high-efficiency thin-film solar cell blanket on a lightweight, space-qualified substrate that will survive severe mechanical stresses during launch, then operate for extended periods in the space environment. SEE ALSO LIVING ON OTHER WORLDS (VOLUME 4); LUNAR BASES (VOLUME 4); MARS BASES (VOLUME 4); POWER, METHODS OF GENERATING (VOLUME 4); RESOURCE UTILIZATION (VOLUME 4); SPACE RESOURCES (VOLUME 4); SPACE STATIONS OF THE FUTURE (VOLUME 4).

*Neelkanth G. Dhere*

**substrates** the surface, such as glass, metallic foil, or plastic sheet, on which a thin film of photovoltaic material is deposited

**Bibliography**

Bailey, Sheila G., and Dennis J. Flood. "Space Photovoltaics." *Progress in Photovoltaics: Research and Applications* 6 (1998):1–14.

Glaser, Peter E., et al. "First Steps to the Solar Power Satellite." *Institute of Electrical and Electronic Engineers (IEEE) Spectrum* 16, no. 5 (1979):52–58.

Iles, Peter A. "From Vanguard to Pathfinder: Forty Years of Solar Cells in Space." *Proceedings of Second World Conference and Exhibition on Photovoltaic Solar Energy Conversion, Vienna, Austria* (1998):LXVII–LXXVI.

———. "Evolution of Space Solar Cells." *Solar Energy Materials and Solar Cells* 68 (2001):1–13.

Karam, Nasser H., et al. "Development and Characterization of High-Efficiency $Ga_{0.5}In_{0.5}P/GaAs/Ge$ Dual- and Triple-Junction Solar Cells." *IEEE Transactions on Electron Devices* 46 (1999):2,116–2,125.

Kurtz, Sarah R., Daryl R. Myers, and Jerry M. Olsen. "Projected Performance of Three- and Four-Junction Devices Using GaAs and GaInP." *Proceedings of Twenty-Sixth IEEE Photovoltaic Specialists' Conference* (1997):875–878.

Landis, Geoffrey A., Sheila G. Bailey, and Michael F. Piszczor Jr. "Recent Advances in Solar Cell Technology." *Journal of Propulsion and Power* 12 (1996):835–841.

Ralph, Eugene L., and Thomas W. Woike. "Solar Cell Array System Trades: Present and Future." *Proceedings of Thirty-Seventh American Institute of Aeronautics and Astronautics Aerospace Sciences Meeting and Exhibit* (1999):1–7.

**SOLAR POWER SATELLITES**

A solar power satellite generating system was first proposed in 1969. Studies by NASA and the U.S. Department of Energy have since shown the concept to be viable. Such a system would start with geosynchronous satellites in Earth orbit that would convert sunlight into electricity and then convert the electricity into microwave energy. The satellites would then beam the microwave energy to Earth. An elliptical receiving-rectifying antenna on the ground would convert the microwave energy to direct current electricity that would be distributed along conventional lines. This type of system could provide continuous base-load power for most of the year and would require minimal storage of the electricity. Problem areas that need to be addressed include high cost, the unknown effects of microwave beams on organisms and the ionosphere, and radio-frequency allocation concerns.

# Space Elevators

The murky views which some scientists advocate as to the inevitable end of every living thing on Earth . . . should not be regarded as axiomatic. The finer part of mankind will, in all likelihood, never perish—they will migrate from sun to sun as they go out. And so there is no end to life, to intellect and the perfection of humanity. Its progress is everlasting.

Konstantin Tsiolkovsky

The perspective in this illustration of a space elevator concept is from the geostationary transfer station looking down along the length of the elevator structure towards Earth.

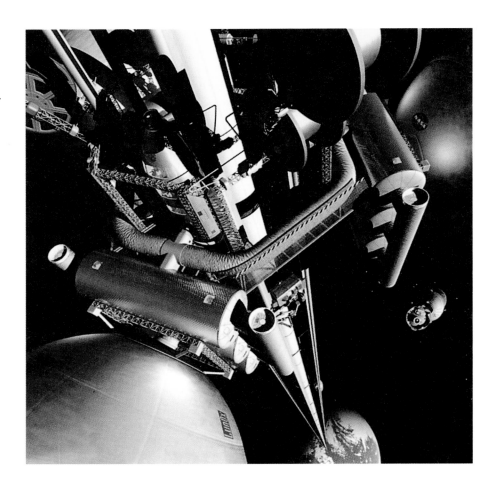

**geostationary orbit** a specific altitude of an equatorial orbit where the time required to circle the planet matches the time it takes the planet to rotate on its axis; an object in geostationary orbit will always remain over the same geographic location on the equator of the planet it orbits

**velocity** speed and direction of a moving object; a vector quantity

Tsiolkovsky made that statement as a rebuttal to the dark future predicted for humankind by Thomas Malthus, a British clergyman who believed humankind was doomed to a future of misery because of overpopulation and the inadequacy of the food supply. The year was 1895, and Tsiolkovsky, considered by many the father of the space age, went to Paris, where he saw the Eiffel Tower and had a vision of a way to make space travel affordable. His idea was an elevator that would travel up a tower that would reach into space. With easy, affordable access to space and the other planets, it would be possible for humankind to spread out across the cosmos and avoid the catastrophe predicted by Malthus.

The tower Tsiolkovsky proposed was to be 35,786 kilometers (22,300 miles) tall. It needed to be that tall in order to reach the altitude of **geostationary orbit**, where the speed of orbit matches the rotational **velocity** of Earth. Anything less than that, and the people at the top of the tower would not be in orbit and spacecraft traveling to other planets would not be able to dock there to pick them up.

With such a tower, travel to other planets would become affordable to the mass of humanity, just as the steamships and transcontinental railroad made possible mass migration of Europeans to the United States. As the man who developed the mathematics for rocket-powered spaceflight, Tsiolkovsky knew that interplanetary migration would not be affordable if only rockets were used. Thus, the idea for his tower was born. Unfortunately, it is not possible to build Tsiolkovsky's tower even with today's materials.

**LEO SPACE ELEVATOR CONCEPT**

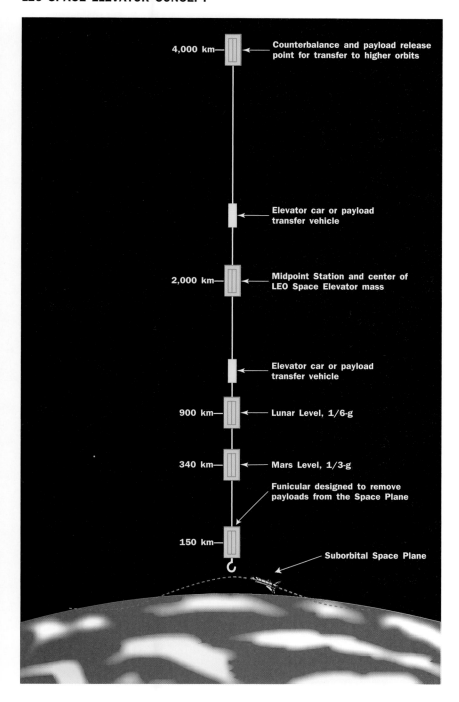

4,000 km— Counterbalance and payload release point for transfer to higher orbits

Elevator car or payload transfer vehicle

2,000 km— Midpoint Station and center of LEO Space Elevator mass

Elevator car or payload transfer vehicle

900 km— Lunar Level, 1/6-g

340 km— Mars Level, 1/3-g

Funicular designed to remove payloads from the Space Plane

150 km—

Suborbital Space Plane

## The Earth Surface to Geo Space Elevator

Tsiolkovsky's tower has been studied and refined, and it has evolved into a more practical concept that involves a cable hanging both upward and downward from geostationary orbit. With this concept, the upper half of the cable and an asteroid counterweight are needed to balance the weight of the lower half of the cable that reaches down to the surface of Earth. This upper and lower cable combination centered on geostationary orbit, called an

Earth Surface to Geo Space Elevator, was described by Arthur C. Clarke in 1978 in his book *The Foundations of Paradise*. Unfortunately, even this version of the tower is impossible to build. It was not until 1988 that an intermediate version of this concept that could be built with existing materials was conceived. It is called an Earth Orbiting Elevator.

## The Earth Orbiting Elevator

The Earth Orbiting Elevator works by starting from a much lower-altitude orbit and hanging a cable down to just above Earth's atmosphere. Since the bottom end of that cable is traveling at less than **orbital velocity** for that altitude, it is possible for a high-speed aircraft to fly to the lower end of that cable without the need for stages and drop-off propellant tanks. This is possible because the speed of orbit decreases as one moves farther away from Earth. Since the altitude where the cable starts to be built is quite a bit higher than the altitude at the bottom of the cable, the bottom of the cable ends up moving at noticeably less than orbital velocity for its altitude. This means that an aircraft flying to the bottom end of the elevator does not have to go nearly as fast as a rocket going to orbit. As a result, the aircraft needs less propellant, does not need stages, and can carry a larger **payload**. Less propellant, no staging, and more payload means significantly lower launch costs.

The upward-pointing half of the Earth Orbiting Elevator is needed to counterbalance the lower half, but unlike the Earth Surface to Geo Space Elevator, it does not need an asteroid counterweight. Also, like the earlier elevator, the length of the upper half of the Earth Orbiting Elevator cable is selected so that a spacecraft arriving at or departing from the upper end of the cable is already traveling at Earth escape velocity. This is done to minimize the amount of propellant spacecraft need to carry to travel between planets, keeping the cost of travel affordable.

## A Comparison of the Two Elevators

The differences between the two elevators can be visualized as variations of the Indian rope trick. Using this analogy, the Earth Surface to Geo Space Elevator is an Indian rope that hangs from a very high altitude cloud down to the ground and never moves. As a result, it is very easy to use. The Earth Orbiting Elevator does not reach all the way to the ground and moves across the sky as if it were a rope hanging from a low-altitude cloud on a windy day. Although it is obviously more difficult to use, the Earth Orbiting Elevator has the advantage of a significant reduction in the required cable length. The Earth Surface to Geo Space Elevator requires a cable over 47,000 kilometers (29,140 miles) long. The Earth Orbiting Elevator can be built with a cable as short as 1,500 kilometers (30 miles) but works better if one of 3,500 to 4,000 kilometers (2,170 to 2,480 miles) is used. The magnitude of the difference is obvious, and the fact that the Earth Orbiting Elevator can be built makes the choice obvious. The end result is that it is possible to build Tsiolkovsky's tower, and so the dark future predicted by Malthus is not inevitable.

## Space Elevators for the Moon and Mars

As with all transportation systems, once enough people start making the journey, there is a need for more efficient transportation systems at the

**orbital velocity** velocity at which an object needs to travel so that its flight path matches the curve of the planet it is circling; approximately 8 kilometers (5 miles) per second for low-altitude orbit around Earth

**payload** any cargo launched aboard a rocket that is destined for space, including communications satellites or modules, supplies, equipment, and astronauts; does not include the vehicle used to move the cargo or the propellant that powers the vehicle

points of arrival. As a result, space elevators have been proposed for both the Moon and Mars. In this way, Earth, the Moon, Mars, the asteroids, and even the **Earth-Moon LaGrange points** known as L4 and L5 can all be tied together by an affordable transportation system that opens up the entire inner solar system to humankind. SEE ALSO ACCESSING SPACE (VOLUME 1); CLARKE, ARTHUR C. (VOLUME 1); GETTING TO SPACE CHEAPLY (VOLUME 1); TSIOLKOVSKY, KONSTANTIN (VOLUME 3).

*Eagle Sarmont*

**Bibliography**

Clarke, Arthur C. *The Foundations of Paradise.* New York: Harcourt Brace Jovanovich, 1978.

Penzo, Paul A. "Tethers for Mars Space Operations." AAS Science & Technology Series, *The Case for Mars II* 62 (1984):445–465.

Sarmont, Eagle. "How an Earth Orbiting Tether Makes Possible an Affordable Earth-Moon Space Transportation System." SAE Technical Paper 942120.

Smitherman, David V. "Space Elevators: An Advanced Earth-Space Infrastructure for the New Millennium." NASA/CP–2000–210429, Marshall Space Flight Center.

**Internet Resources**

Sarmont, Eagle. "Affordable to the Individual Space Flight." <http://www.affordablespaceflight.com>.

# Space Industries

Traveling and living in the artificial atmosphere of a spacecraft, and guiding uncrewed satellites in their orbits around Earth and on missions to other stellar bodies call for specialized and creative technologies. While devised for specific, space-related purposes, many of these creations, or their spin-off products, find commercial markets here on Earth. As well, new industries are increasingly springing up to specifically exploit extraterrestrial materials and opportunities for commercial gain.

## From Space to the Marketplace

Space programs have been a rich source of inventions that went on to great commercial success here on Earth. The household television satellite dish, which captures television signals beamed from orbiting satellites (their commercial function itself a spinoff benefit of orbital space travel), were originally invented to correct errors in the signals from spacecraft. Medical imaging of our internal organs and modern eye examination methods arose from the technologies developed to enhance stellar images. Another feature of our everyday lives, bar coding, arose from the need for inventory control of the myriad of spacecraft parts. The ear thermometer owes its existence to the technology developed to detect **infrared** emission from newly born stars. Smoke detectors were invented to detect noxious vapors in the Skylab Earth-orbiting station launched in 1973. Computer software utilized for the design and analysis of spacecraft now enables automobile makers to virtually design an automobile prior to building a prototype. Cordless vacuum cleaners, trimmers, drills and grass shears would not exist if not for the need for self-contained power tools used by Apollo astronauts on the Moon. The joystick controller used by computer game enthusiasts and disabled people was developed for the Apollo Lunar Rover. Finally, research to squeeze a

**Earth-Moon LaGrange points** five points in space relative to Earth and the Moon where the gravitational forces on an object balance; two points, 60 degrees from the Moon in orbit, are candidate points for a permanent space settlement because of their gravitational stability

**infrared** portion of the electromagnetic spectrum with waves slightly longer than visible light

This digital data matrix (above) is an example of a "space spinoff." Originally used to identify space shuttle parts, this technology is invisible to the naked eye and is being commercialized to make barcoding tamper resistant.

**vacuum** an environment where air and all other molecules and atoms of matter have been removed

**fusion** the act of releasing nuclear energy by combining lighter elements such as hydrogen into heavier elements

function into machines of molecular dimensions has spawned an explosion of research and activity into nanotechnology. The usefulness of nanotechnology ranges from tiny but extremely powerful computers to data storage on molecular tape to molecular robots capable of operations within a human. These examples are but several of many.

This legacy continues. Some space industries directly address the needs of present-day space exploration. Such direct applications may, like the above examples, find spin-off benefits in the "real world" of tomorrow. Other industries reflect a view of space as an exploitable entrepreneurial commodity. A tangible example of space science is the Space Vacuum Epitaxy Center (SVEC) at the University of Houston. Since the late 1990s, SVEC has been researching the means by which scientific experiments could be done in the **vacuum** of space. So far, the research has yielded fifteen new technologies with commercial potential. As an example, research to construct thin films of material in space has led to the use of lasers in telecommunications and environmental testing. Another spinoff of the center's research has been an electric wire that can transport up to 100 times more current than standard copper wires.

## The Potential of Space

Space travel, to this point, mainly has been the domain of large space agencies. But, befitting its allure to our sense of adventure, space travel is a potentially huge industry. Various companies are exploring the feasibility of small, reusable spacecraft for both travel (suborbital flights could cut hours off of currently lengthy airplane trips), space tourism, and as transport vehicles for other space industries.

Another facet of space that holds commercial appeal is the energy possibilities of celestial bodies. Drilling technologies for mining operations and the use of satellites, lunar installations, or vast banks of mirrors deployed in space to collect solar power are just three examples. The use of solar panels as a power generating system arose out of the need to power orbiting satellites. Now, this technology is being refined to permit the construction of large banks of panels on the surface of the Moon, with materials mined from the lunar crust, such as silicon. The lunar panels would supply energy to a waiting Earth and could also be ferried to Mars for use in human expeditions to that planet. The Moon is also a potentially plentiful source of helium-3, an isotope that is rare on Earth. Helium-3 is a promising fuel for **fusion** reactors. Indeed, it has been estimated that lunar reserves of helium-3 could generate 10,000 times as much energy as Earth's entire remaining reserves of fossil fuel. Helium-3 also has an advantage of being nonradioactive, either before or after use. Thus, commercial interests are considering the Moon as a source of fuel for not only lunar missions but for an energy-hungry Earth. Harrison Schmitt, a former Apollo astronaut, is involved in efforts to commercialize the extraction of helium-3 from the Moon.

The prospect of mining the Moon and planets such as Mars is appealing to space agencies such as the National Aeronautics and Space Administration (NASA), because it would eliminate the need to send all materials required for a space sojourn with the departing spacecraft. This idea has created opportunities for commercial ventures. For example, there are plans for the construction of a lunar rover that would extract the material for rocket fuel on return journeys from the Moon. Similar ideas are being studied for future human missions to Mars, because local production of fuel for the return journey would greatly reduce the weight and volume of material to be carried on the outbound journey to Mars.

Another substance that potentially can be harvested from the Moon is oxygen. The Moon's crust is composed of a material known as **regolith**. Much of the regolith is enriched with oxides of silicon, from which oxygen can be extracted. In fact, upwards of 46 percent of the weight of the lunar surface may be comprised of oxygen. While much less hydrogen is present, it is there in quantities enough to produce water. In addition, evidence from the Clementine and Lunar Prospector missions to the Moon suggest that it may also be possible to extract water from more direct sources on the Moon.

**regolith** upper few meters of the Moon's surface, composed of inorganic matter, such as unconsolidated rocks and fine soil

The availability of similar reserves on Mars, and hence the commercial potential of mining the planet, is less clear. However, the 2001 Mars Odyssey probe is designed to gather information about the surface chemistry of the planet. More information will be obtained from the Reconnaissance Orbiter, scheduled for launch in 2005, and, beginning in 2007, from mobile laboratories that will be landed at chosen sites on the surface of Mars.

## Space as a Manufacturing Facility

Another lucrative niche that space offers is in manufacturing. The low or zero gravity of space enables the growth of crystals, semiconductor films, and protein assemblies that are structurally perfect. An orbiting vacuum cleaner is being devised that would sweep away orbital dust as it is towed by a spacecraft, leaving an environment in its wake that would support such high-tech manufacturing efforts.

Finally, one pressing need on the extended forays in orbit that will be the norm on the International Space Station is the need for a source of uncontaminated water. The present and future technologies that will ensure a ready supply of drinkable water, obtained from sources as varied as sweat, exhaled water vapor, and urine, will surely find a place on Earth. Particularly in desert climates, the ability to recycle water more intensively will be valuable and life saving. SEE ALSO MADE IN SPACE (VOLUME 1); MADE WITH SPACE TECHNOLOGY (VOLUME 1); NATURAL RESOURCES (VOLUME 4); SPACE RESOURCES (VOLUME 4).

*Brian Hoyle*

### Bibliography

Globus, Al, David Bailey, Jie Han, Richard Jaffe, Creon Levit, Ralph Merkle, and Deepak Srivastava. "NASA Applications of Molecular Nanotechnology." *Journal of the British Interplanetary Society* 51 (1998):145–152.

### Internet Resources

"Mars Exploration: Goal 4—Prepare for the Human Exploration of Mars." *Mars Exploration.* Jet Propulsion Laboratory. <http://mars.jpl.nasa.gov/science/human/index.html>.

# Space Resources

Future large-scale space activities will require a high degree of autonomy from Earth, with extensive reliance upon nonterrestrial sources of energy

An artist's rendition of a mining operation on the Moon. In the future, industrial operations on the Moon could increase the likelihood of lunar settlement.

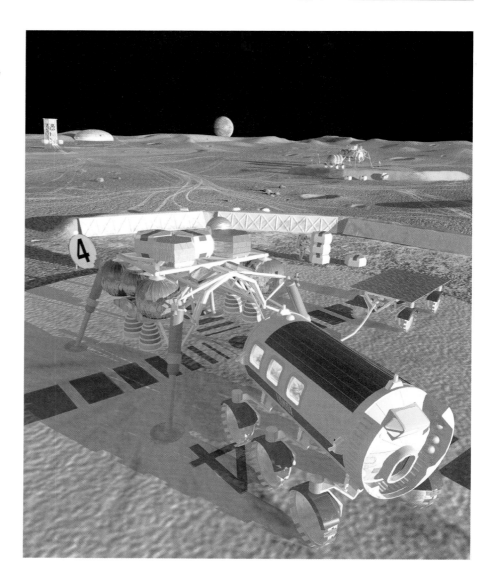

**shielding** providing protection for humans and electronic equipment from cosmic rays, energetic particles from the Sun, and other radioactive materials

**regolith** upper few meters of the Moon's surface, composed of inorganic matter, such as unconsolidated rocks and fine soil

**ilmenite** an important ore of titanium

**rutile** a red, brown, or black mineral, primarily titanium dioxide, used as a gemstone and also a commercially important ore of titanium

and materials. Ambitious missions require large masses of consumables, such as propellants and life-support fluids, which traditionally have been launched from Earth. But launch costs from Earth are so high that the greatest advantage would be realized by launching small masses of processing equipment rather than large masses of intrinsically cheap, abundant, and easily manufactured materials, such as oxygen, water, liquid hydrogen, structural metals, and radiation **shielding**. Each of the various objects in the solar system has unique potential in terms of resource extraction.

## The Moon

Operations on the Moon would benefit greatly from the use of unprocessed **regolith** for shielding. Oxygen can be extracted from the common lunar mineral **ilmenite** ($FeTiO_3$) by reduction using hydrogen, carbon, or hydrocarbons, leaving a residue of metallic iron and the refractory **rutile** ($TiO_2$). Lunar polar ice deposits may conceivably be exploited for the manufacture of liquid water, oxygen, and hydrogen, if the difficulties of mining in permanent darkness at a temperature of 100°K (−280°F) can be mastered. On a longer timescale, lunar **helium-3**, present as an embedded **solar-wind** gas in concentrations of up to $10^{-8}$ g/g, may be economically extractable for export to Earth as a clean **fusion fuel**.

## Mars

Both piloted and unpiloted missions to Mars would benefit from the universal availability of the Martian atmosphere. The principal Martian gas, carbon dioxide, can be decomposed by any of several processing techniques into carbon monoxide and oxygen for use as propellants for local transportation or for the return trip to Earth. Extraction of water from the Martian atmosphere, which would enable the use of hydrogen as a propellant, seems unreasonable because of the extreme aridity of Mars. Surface snow, ground ice, permafrost, clay **minerals**, and hydrated salts are all plausible sources of extractable water. The residual atmospheric gases after extraction of carbon dioxide principally would be nitrogen (which makes up 2.7% of the atmosphere) and argon (1.6%). Nitrogen is useful not only as a fire retardant in artificial air but also as a **feedstock** for the manufacture of ammonia, **hydrazine**, nitrogen tetroxide, and nutrients such as amino acids and organic bases.

## Near-Earth Asteroids

The **near-Earth asteroids** (NEAs) and the Martian moons Phobos and Deimos present a rich diversity of compositions, many of them rich in **volatile materials**. A substantial fraction of these bodies are energetically more accessible than Earth's Moon, in that the **velocity** increment needed to fly from low Earth orbit and soft-land on the surfaces of nearly 20 percent of the NEAs is smaller than that needed to land on the Moon. The **L-4** Lagrangian point on the orbit of Mars has captured a swarm of small asteroids, of which four are currently known.

The asteroid belt consists of bodies that seem to be well represented among the NEAs. The resources of interest in them would be the same as those in NEAs. Most extraction facilities placed on NEAs would visit the heart of the asteroid belt on each orbit around the Sun, making transfer from an NEA "gas station" to most belt asteroids easy. In a fully recycling economy, fueled by solar power, the resources in the asteroid belt would be sufficient enough to support a population of about 10 quadrillion people from now until the Sun dies of old age.

## Gas Giants

Beyond the asteroid belt lie the orbits of the four gas giant planets: Jupiter, Saturn, Uranus, and Neptune. The total number of known gas giant satellites is close to ninety and is expanding rapidly because of advances in detection technology. We may reasonably expect several hundred satellites larger than a few kilometers in diameter to be known in a few years.

Jupiter's system consists of several very close small satellites and a rudimentary ring system; four world-sized Galilean satellites named Io, Europa, Ganymede, and Callisto; and swarms of small distant satellites, with some, like the inner satellites, orbiting in the **prograde** direction, but with the outermost satellite family in **retrograde** orbits. These may well be transient moons, captured in the recent past from heliocentric orbits (orbits around

---

**helium-3** a stable isotope of helium whose nucleus contains two protons and one neutron

**solar wind** a continuous, but varying, stream of charged particles (mostly electrons and protons) generated by the Sun

**fusion fuel** fuel suitable for use in a nuclear fusion reactor

**minerals** crystalline arrangements of atoms and molecules of specified proportions that make up rocks

**feedstock** the raw materials introduced into an industrial process from which a finished product is made

**hydrazine** a dangerous and corrosive compound of nitrogen and hydrogen commonly used in high powered rockets and jet engines

**near-Earth asteroids** asteroids whose orbits cross the orbit of Earth

**volatile materials** materials that easily pass into the vapor phase when heated

**velocity** speed and direction of a moving object; a vector quantity

**L-4** the gravitationally stable Lagrange point 60 degrees ahead of the orbiting planet

**prograde** having the same general sense of motion or rotation as the rest of the solar system, that is counterclockwise as seen from above Earth's north pole

**retrograde** having the opposite general sense of motion or rotation as the rest of the solar system, clockwise as seen from above Earth's north pole

the Sun) and destined to escape again. Jupiter is also accompanied by two vast clouds of asteroids, centered on the leading and trailing Lagrange points on Jupiter's orbit. These bodies, which are spectroscopically identified as **supercarbonaceous**, are the presumed immediate source of the outermost captured satellites of Jupiter. The innermost small satellites are embedded in the inner magnetic field of Jupiter, subject to intense charged-particle radiation bombardment from Jupiter's radiation belts. The radiation environment improves with increasing distance from the planet, but the Galilean satellites (especially Io) present a daunting technical challenge to planned landing missions. All of the Galilean satellites except Io have abundant surface ice of varying degrees of purity, suitable for manufacture of propellants for return to Earth.

Saturn's system seems similar to Jupiter's, except that Saturn's extensive ring system suppresses its radiation belts. The largest Saturnian satellite, Titan, has a massive atmosphere of nitrogen, methane, and photochemical products that both invites detailed scrutiny and offers potential propellant for escape. Numerous small, distant satellites in both prograde and retrograde orbits have been discovered recently. Finding asteroids on Saturn's Lagrangian points is difficult and has not yet been accomplished.

Uranus and Neptune, with far lower escape velocities than Jupiter and Saturn, are readily accessible to entry probes. With a nuclear propulsion system, escape from their atmospheres is clearly possible. Both planets presumably contain about fifty parts per million of helium-3 gas in their atmospheres, making the extraction and retrieval of vast amounts of fusion fuel conceivable. There is enough helium-3 in the atmosphere of Uranus alone to power Earth with a population of 10 billion people at European or North American levels of energy use for at least $10^{15}$ years. The satellite system of Uranus contains several midsized moons and many small, distant satellites, most of which have been very recently discovered. Neptune's system, with the large retrograde satellite Triton, several irregular ring arcs, and a midsized distant satellite, Nereid, is dynamically interesting, suggesting violent events in its past that may have disrupted any system of small satellites that may once have been present.

## The Centaurs

The Centaurs, which cross the orbits of the gas giant planets, are analogous to the NEAs in the inner solar system. These presumably cometary bodies, which reach several hundred kilometers in size, are vulnerable to severe **perturbations** by these planets. Indeed, numerical analysis of the orbit of the Centaur Chiron suggests that it could cross Earth's path someday, possessing a **kinetic energy** about 1 million times larger than the impact energy of the asteroid that is theorized to have ended Earth's Cretaceous era (and killed off the dinosaurs). The principal resource interest of such bodies lies in their possession of abundant propellant, which could be used for self-deflection in the frightening event that such a body should be found on a path that threatens Earth.

## The Kuiper Belt

Bodies in the Kuiper belt, which lies beyond the orbit of Neptune, follow orbits that are moderately **eccentric** and moderately inclined with respect to the **ecliptic**. These bodies appear to be basically cometary in composition, although recent evidence suggests that there are two populations that are compositionally distinct. The largest-known body in the population is Pluto. Theory suggests that these bodies are about 60 percent ices by mass, with total extractable volatiles possibly reaching 70 percent.

**ecliptic** the plane of Earth's orbit

## The Oort Cloud

The Oort cloud, even more remote from human eyes and reach, consists of about 1 trillion bodies of kilometer size and larger, following orbits that are essentially random in three dimensions and lie almost exclusively outside the orbits of the planets. Typical distances from the Sun are 10,000 **astronomical units**, and typical orbital periods are on the order of 1 million years. The few Oort cloud bodies that penetrate the inner solar system are called long-period comets. The severe lack of solar energy for propulsion and processing use, and the large mean distances between nearest neighbors, makes this realm unattractive as a potential resource.

**astronomical units** one AU is the average distance between Earth and the Sun (152 million kilometers [93 million miles])

Programmatically, initial space resource use will be confined to the Moon, Mars, and NEAs. Asteroidal and lunar resources have clear application to support of large-scale space activities such as the construction of solar power satellites and lunar power stations. The transition from NEAs to the asteroid belt seems an obvious next step. Some asteroids and short-period comets in turn belong to orbital classes that offer access to the **Jovian** and Saturnian families. Scenarios involving helium-3 for use as fusion fuel lead to the consideration of Uranus as the next target. SEE ALSO ASTEROID MINING (VOLUME 4); COMET CAPTURE (VOLUME 4); NATURAL RESOURCES (VOLUME 4); RESOURCE UTILIZATION (VOLUME 4).

**Jovian** relating to the planet Jupiter

*John S. Lewis*

### Bibliography

Lewis, John S. *Mining the Sky*. Reading, MA: Helix/Addison Wesley, 1996.

Lewis, John S., Mildred Shapley Matthews, and Mary L. Guerrieri, eds. *Resources of Near-Earth Space*. Tucson: University of Arizona Press, 1993.

# Space Stations of the Future

International Space Station Alpha, which has been in operation since December 2000, is scheduled for completion in 2006. "Alpha," as it is nicknamed, is becoming the site of extensive human physiological research, life and physical science investigations, and commercial work that will continue for at least ten more years. Circling Earth once every 90 minutes, and at an altitude roughly the same as the distance from Washington, D.C. to New York City, Alpha is the latest and most evolved orbital **space station**.✳ But almost certainly there will be others. What will they be like? And how might they be used?

As the work at Alpha returns knowledge and stirs public interest, national space agencies, scientists, and business people are considering beneficial activities that could be conducted onboard future stations in orbit. Even the armed forces have considered the use of crewed space stations,

**space station** large orbital outpost equipped to support a human crew and designed to remain in orbit for an extended period

✳ **Alpha uses sunlight to generate its own power (as much as that used by ten American homes) and is constructed around air-filled modules with more room than a 747 jetliner.**

A mock-up of a potential space station work area for the future.

although no sufficient reason has yet been found to develop a capability there for the military.

In the early twenty-first century, almost all civilian interests—from basic science experiments to tourism—have found reasons to think of future facilities in space. As with other environments and territories new to human experience—such as the deep seafloor, the Antarctic continent, or even Alaska in the nineteenth century—the scope of opportunity for human activity in space is only beginning to become clear.

## Politics, People, and Purposes

The very nature of Space Station Alpha typifies a reason for human space-flight: international politics. Alpha is a cooperative program of sixteen countries. Russia was admitted to the circle in part as a gesture to apply the **rocket** industry of the former Soviet Union to peaceful purposes. China is publicly stating its intention to either join the Alpha Station partnership or build a space station of its own. If the latter happens, it may be because the feat will be touted to the world as a demonstration of China's technological and economic power, as was the case in the 1970s for America and the Soviet Union. In the future, additional nations may demonstrate their status in the same manner. But other needs will also drive nations to focus portions of their space programs on new space stations. And future orbiting facilities may be single-purpose ventures as opposed to the multipurpose Alpha.

**Science and Technology.** Proposals for scientific investigations will probably increase as new discoveries expand the interest in using the very low-gravity and high-**vacuum** environments of space. As a consequence, there will be a continuing string of future scientific space stations or laboratories. Isolation from human presence may be an important factor in the design of these lab stations. The movement of people causes vibration in the structure of space stations, and these vibrations can upset delicate experimental processes and measurements. Hence, the stations will probably be staffed

**rocket** vehicle (or device) especially designed to travel through space, propelled by one or more engines

**vacuum** an environment where air and all other molecules and atoms of matter have been removed

by robotic systems controlled from scientists' desktops on Earth. Astronaut "maintenance" crews will visit these laboratories infrequently. Also, research on virulent diseases or genetic engineering could mean that work is better done robotically in the isolation of a medical facility off the planet.

**Tourism.** In 2001 the first person to join a spaceflight for pleasure, Dennis Tito, flew to the International Space Station for six days. Primarily because Alpha was still under construction, that trip caused a furor among the partner nations other than his sponsor nation, Russia. But it also set a benchmark for popular future activities in space. More "space tourists" and nonprofessional astronauts will follow Dennis Tito. ✳

✳ South African entrepreneur Mark Shuttleworth became the second space tourist to the International Space Station in April 2002.

There may soon be vacation or sightseeing modules orbiting Earth for the use of those rich enough to buy a rocket ride into orbit. Scientist astronauts will not want to be bothered with these wealthy tourists, so a self-sustaining "orbital cabin," outfitted at first with only a picture window and the basics for human comfort, may become the foundation for "orbital resorts" further in the future. The thrill of experiencing life without gravity and viewing the ever-changing scenery as this cabin-station orbits over Earth will fuel the desire of millions to experience it firsthand.

But spaceflight for the masses is decades in the future. Until then, the vicarious experience that can be conveyed through cinema and video will have to suffice for most people. Filming and production facilities dedicated to weightlessness and space-walking action shoots may become part of a private enterprise station in orbit. This industrial park may support various nongovernment businesses in tourism, thrill-seeking, filmmaking, and theatrical productions. While research and commerce exploit orbital space in these ways, another station will function as a staging depot for expeditions to other worlds.

## Jumping Off to Other Worlds

In the near future, human expeditions to the Moon and much farther to Mars will be organized and launched from orbiting docks. Because Earth is at the bottom of a gravitational "well" that must be climbed to get anything into space, it will be useful to use Earth orbit as a kind of "ledge" near the top of that well. In terms of energy, a spacecraft is essentially halfway to any other world in the solar system once it is in orbit around Earth. Cost and risk may both be reduced by launching astronaut explorers, their vehicles, and supplies to Earth orbit, where they can be assembled and checked before propelling them completely out of Earth's gravity and outward to Mars, for instance. For that purpose, a future space station that is an orbital dock and way-station may be developed. It would be the point of departure for human or even complex robotic explorers to other planets, asteroids, or comets. This station would also be the interim stop for deep-space explorers at the end of their travels. A module or laboratory at this station will likely be the destination of the rocks, soil, and maybe even other-worldly life brought back for in-depth study. Quarantining returning explorers and their samples may be a very sensible precaution.

It is virtually certain that the twenty-first century will see increasing numbers of space stations orbiting our planet and filling diverse roles. SEE ALSO BUSINESS PARKS (VOLUME 1); HOTELS (VOLUME 4); INTERNATIONAL

SPACE STATION (VOLUMES 1 AND 3); SPACE INDUSTRIES (VOLUME 4); SPACE TOURISM, EVOLUTION OF (VOLUME 4); TOURISM (VOLUME 1).

*Charles D. Walker*

### Bibliography

Cleator, P. E. *An Introduction to Space Travel.* New York: Pitman Publishing, 1961.

National Research Council. *Evaluating the Biological Potential in Samples Returned from Planetary Satellites and Small Solar System Bodies: Framework for Decision Making.* Washington, DC: Task Group on Sample Return from Small Solar System Bodies, 1998.

# Space Tourism, Evolution of

In 1967 Barron Hilton, the chief executive officer of Hilton Hotels Corporation, stated that it was his dream to be a pioneer of space tourism. At that time, he spoke of his plans for hotels in space, including the Orbiter Hilton and the Lunar Hilton. The Orbiter Hilton would move freely around in space, orbiting Earth, whereas the Lunar Hilton would be located on the surface of the Moon. Hilton realized that he would have to wait until the time was right, but that time is now approaching.

Recently, Dennis Tito, a 60-year-old California tycoon, made his place in history as the first person to buy his way into space as a tourist, paying $20 million for the opportunity. After six weeks of intensive training with the Russian Space Agency, on April 30, 2001 Tito embarked on a week's vacation to tour the International Space Station. By the end of the week many of the people who viewed that historical event deemed his trek a success.

These efforts could spark the beginning of an age of adventure tourism, or tourism that involves an element of risk or perceived risk. Space tourism, a segment of adventure tourism, includes suborbital travel, or flights to the edge of Earth's atmosphere; trips to low Earth orbit (LEO), in which satellites orbit Earth at an altitude of 320 to 800 kilometers (200 to 500 miles); and vacations at an orbiting or lunar hotel/resort.

## Suborbital Tourism

Currently, one form of space tourism exists. From an airfield in Moscow, tourists are paying $12,000, excluding travel and lodging costs, for a "Journey to the Edge of Space." These adventurers experience a 45- to 60-minute ride to the edge of Earth's atmosphere in a MiG-25 aircraft flying at Mach 2.5, or a mile every 2 seconds, and reaching an altitude of 25 kilometers (82,000 feet). Passengers are able to view the curvature of Earth and a horizon that is 1,100 kilometers (715 miles) across. According to *Time International*, almost 4,500 adventurers have made the trip. After taking one of these flights with Space Adventures Ltd., Wally Funk, a former astronaut and pilot, said that the flight was his most thrilling experience.

The next step in suborbital travel is a 30- to 150-minute trip that will take tourists to an altitude of 100 kilometers (62 miles). After four days of training at a cost of $98,000, "extreme tourists" will be launched just short of orbit, where "space" technically begins. When the launch vehicle approaches its maximum altitude, the rocket engines will shut down and the adventurers will experience 5 minutes of uninterrupted weightlessness. Space Adventures Ltd. has accepted 144 reservations, paid in advance, for a venture that has not yet flown its maiden voyage. The companies offering these trips had plans to take people up to 100 kilometers (62 miles) in 2001. However, those plans have been delayed until technology can be developed that is safe for the civilian public. Enthusiasts expect to be hurled into space between 2003 and 2005.

The obstacle that stands in the way of suborbital spaceflight is the construction of a reusable launch vehicle (RLV) that is reliable enough to take tourists to the perimeter of space and satisfy the safety standards and regulations of the Federal Aviation Administration. This is the reason current space tourism ventures are taking place in Russia, where the government does not regulate aviation as tightly.

The challenge in creating such a vehicle is more financial than technical. The successful manufacture of an RLV that could reduce launch costs by 90 percent of the current price per pound is necessary to make routine suborbital passenger flights financially feasible.

## Orbital Tourism

**Low Earth Orbit (LEO).** The construction of a reliable RLV for suborbital travel will aid the expansion of space tourism by making available a vehicle that can be adapted for travel to LEO. This RLV, used to transport passengers into LEO, will need to have more propulsion than suborbital RLVs to achieve orbit. Another challenge will be to create enough room for approximately 50 to 100 passengers so that the venture will be economically feasible.

When a satellite is in LEO, it is traveling at 27,200 kilometers (17,000 miles) per hour and circles Earth in approximately 90 minutes. If a LEO RLV were to take travelers one or two times around Earth before landing, passengers would stay in the RLV for 1.5 to 3 hours. During this time it is likely that passengers will need to use the rest room or eat a snack, as in an airplane. Therefore, space tourism companies offering these rides will have to provide amenities that are functional in a zero-gravity environment, such as the candy and peanuts astronauts eat in space.

**International Space Station.** Currently, orbital spaceflight is available to those who are willing to pay the price. For approximately $20 million it is possible for a private voyager to fly to the International Space Station. Individuals interested in this once-in-a-lifetime experience must be willing to undergo the rigorous training program required for civilian astronauts in Russia. After medical testing to assure readiness to fly, explorers will be flown to an altitude of 24,390 meters (80,000 feet), where they will experience zero gravity at a speed of Mach 2.5. They also will discover what it is like to experience 5 Gs ✶ when they reenter Earth's atmosphere, take a space walk in the neutral-buoyancy training pool, and learn about the Soyuz spacecraft by using the cosmonaut simulator. After four to six months of training and preparation, private citizens will be given a chance to spend a week exploring the International Space Station.

**Proposed Orbital and Lunar Hotels.** The ultimate goal for space enthusiasts is the construction of the first space hotel/resort. A number of organizations

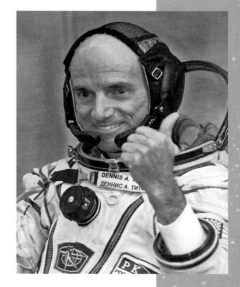

Dennis Tito, the world's first space tourist, gave a thumbs-up before boarding the Russian rocket that took him to the International Space Station in April, 2001.

✶ A person subjected to 5 Gs would feel as if she or he weighed five times as much as normal.

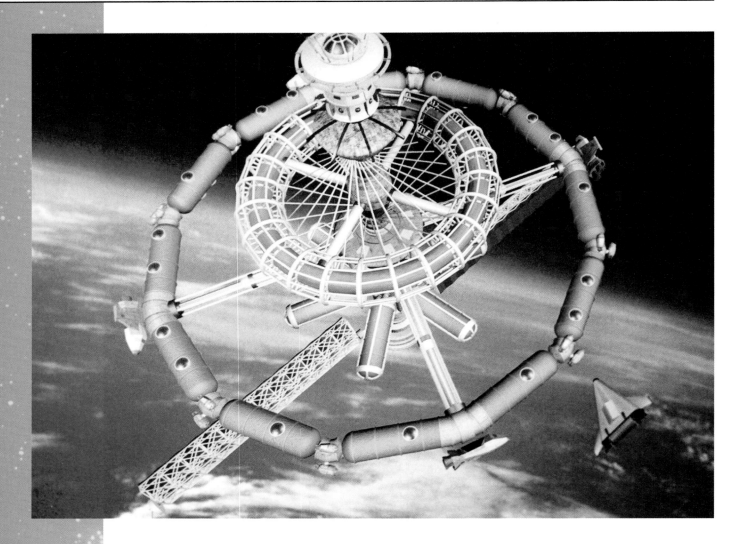

A prototype of the Space Island Group's revolving orbital hotel.

**microgravity** the condition experienced in freefall as a spacecraft orbits Earth or another body; commonly called weightlessness; only very small forces are perceived in freefall, on the order of one-millionth the force of gravity on Earth's surface

are working on space station designs for commercial purposes. It is known that an orbiting space hotel can be created. The challenge lies in the economics of the project.

There has been a significant amount of discussion among space entrepreneurs of ventures such as luxury cruise ships, orbiting hotels, and lunar hotels. The Space Tourism Society in Santa Monica, California, has plans for an "orbital yacht" featuring balloon-like rooms that would allow travelers to see Earth clearly. Passengers also would be able to enjoy activities such as dancing and sports and take a sauna while orbiting in space.

Robert Bigelow, owner of the Budget Suites of America hotel chain, has different plans. He has devoted $500 million to the research, design, and development of a space hotel by the year 2005. One Bigelow model contains two rotating modules in a **microgravity** environment similar to that of the International Space Station. One module would be used as living quarters for the passengers and crew. This section of the station would contain sleeping, cooking, showering, and rest room areas. The other module would house research laboratories. Bigelow visualizes a more spacious model than the International Space Station to create the most comfortable habitat possible for space tourists.

The Space Island Group has proposed a formation similar to a revolving bicycle wheel. The revolving motion will create an atmosphere with one-third Earth's gravity within modified shuttle fuel tanks. This amount of gravity will allow running water and a semi-normal eating, sleeping, and walking experience. For recreational purposes, passengers will be able to experience a genuine zero-gravity environment inside the station's hub. They will see cameras' views of Earth on a screen. The goal of the Space Island Group, Budget Suites, the Space Tourism Society, and many other entrepreneurial space tourism organizations is to create the ultimate tourist experience for those who can afford the voyage.

It will be interesting to watch the path space tourism takes and see how the public reacts to it. A 1997 National Aeronautics and Space Administration (NASA) study showed that one-third of Americans would be interested in taking a space voyage. Currently, many adventurers are ready to pay $60,000 to climb Mount Everest, dive to the *Titanic*, or travel to Antarctica. Although there is perceived danger in all these adventures, the companies that offer them are able to make a profit. However, there is great uncertainty about space tourism. This perception will not be altered until a greater number of extreme tourists have experienced and enjoyed a safe and reliable space adventure. The current era of space tourism can be compared to the early twentieth century, when the public saw the concept of airplane travel as absurd.

The key to the development of space tourism is its financial feasibility. Although one man has paid $20 million to visit the International Space Station, it is unlikely that many people could or would spend that kind of money. Perhaps $60,000, the equivalent of the price to climb Mount Everest, will be the "affordable ticket price" that creates a market for space tourism. As Buzz Aldrin stated, "Adventure travel will force us to improve the reliability of our launch vehicles, help to establish economic life-support systems for a large number of people, and give us experience with creating space habitats. All of these things are strong building blocks for exploration." SEE ALSO CIVILIANS IN SPACE (VOLUME 3); HOTELS (VOLUME 4); TOURISM (VOLUME 1).

*Amy Swint and Clinton L. Rappole*

## Bibliography

Carreau, Mark. "NASA Softens Stand Against Visitor's Bid." *Houston Chronicle*, April 18, 2001.

Cray, D. "100 Mile Club." *Popular Science*, November 2000, 67–70.

Ernst, Heidi. "Small Business: Entrepreneurs Looking Up Why Those in the Business of Tourism Think Outer Space Is Travel's Final Frontier." *Fortune*, October 25, 1999, 358.

Hilton, Barron. "Hotels in Space." Conference on Outer Space Tourism, Dallas, May 2, 1967.

Schonfeld, Erick. "Features/Spacebulls: Going Long One Thing Stands in the Way of a Thriving Private Space Industry: Find a Cheap Way to Get There. It Ain't for a Lack of Trying." *Fortune*, March 20, 2000, 172.

Short, Stephan. "Travel Watch: Space Tourism Can't Get off the Ground." *Time International*, December 27, 1999, 8.

Turner, F. "Worlds without Ends." *U.S. Space Program*, June 1, 1996, 36–37.

Wichman, Harvey. "The 100K Climb." *Suborbital Civilian Space Flight: Design Issues*. Claremont McKenna College. Aerospace Psychology Laboratory, pp. 1–17.

Williams, Juan. "Profile: Possibility of Space Tourism in the Foreseeable Future." *Talk of the Nation*, National Public Radio, April 30, 2001.

Wilson, J. "Postcards from the Moon." *Popular Science*, June 2000, 97–99.

**Internet Resources**

David, L. "The Tito Trek: The Benchmark for Public Space Travel." 25 April 2001. <http://www.space.com>.

# Star Trek

In the daunting arena of space exploration, there is a tendency to wonder where the path that humankind is taking will lead us. Does the future hold the promise of fantastic new technologies that will be used peacefully for the benefit of humankind? Or will those technologies end up in the hands of a society that is not mature enough to wield power responsibly? The *Star Trek* television series and movies conceived by Gene Roddenberry participate in this debate by providing an optimistic view of humans in the future. In *Star Trek*'s version of history, humankind achieved an end to war, poverty, and disease on Earth shortly after the invention of warp technology, the principle that made it possible to travel faster than light.

Throughout history, people have built bigger and better telescopes and seen farther into the universe, but despite all of these exploration attempts, humankind has not made contact with intelligent extraterrestrial life. People look into the night sky and wonder whether there are other civilizations out there. If there are, the vast distances between worlds make it seem unlikely that it will ever be possible to interact with those civilizations. Since Albert Einstein's theories suggest that it is impossible for a person to accelerate to the speed of light, it would take hundreds to thousands of years for people on a spacecraft to reach a planet in another star system by conventional means.

The warp technology of *Star Trek*, however, allows a spacecraft and its inhabitants to travel many times faster than light by moving through subspace, a theoretical parallel universe in which Einstein's theories do not apply. In a matter of hours or days it is possible to travel from one star system to another by creating a warp field that allows a spacecraft to slip into subspace. With the immense distances between civilizations no longer an issue, humans on *Star Trek* interact within a universe populated by an array of alien species.

The success of the *Star Trek* series and movies reflects genuine public interest in humankind's future in space. The writers added realism by weaving plausible scientific theories into the fabric of the *Star Trek* universe. The technologies behind the warp engine–powered starship, wormholes (theoretical bridges between two points in space), and transporters (devices that can convert matter to energy and vice versa) are all based on scientific theories. For this reason, it is natural for the audience to view these things as believable future manifestations of today's science.

Another key to *Star Trek*'s appeal is that it presents such an optimistic view of human society's future. It shows a world in which humans are no longer at war with each other. Food, resources, and transportation are avail-

## THE ORIGINS OF DR. SPOCK

In David Alexander's biography of Gene Roddenberry, he reports that the character of Dr. Spock was to have been a "red-hued Martian." Convinced, however, that space exploration would reach Mars during *Star Trek*'s run, Roddenberry changed Spock's origin to another planet, beyond the solar system: Vulcan.

able at the touch of a keypad. This hopeful portrayal shows a human civilization that has survived its technological adolescence, matured, and been enriched by alien cultures, one that thrives in a well-populated intergalactic neighborhood. SEE ALSO ANTIMATTER PROPULSION (VOLUME 4); COMMUNICATIONS, FUTURE NEEDS (VOLUME 4); FASTER-THAN-LIGHT TRAVEL (VOLUME 4); FIRST CONTACT (VOLUME 4); INTERSTELLAR TRAVEL (VOLUME 4); LASERS IN SPACE (VOLUME 4); MOVIES (VOLUME 4); RODDENBERRY, GENE (VOLUME 1); SCIENCE FICTION (VOLUME 4); TELEPORTATION (VOLUME 4); WORMHOLES (VOLUME 4).

*Jennifer Lemanski*

**Bibliography**

Berman, Rick. *Star Trek: First Contact*. Paramount Pictures, 1996.

Okuda, Michael, and Denise Okuda. *The Star Trek Encyclopedia: A Reference Guide to the Future*. New York: Pocket Books, 1997.

# Star Wars

*Star Wars: A New Hope* premiered in the spring of 1977, followed by its two sequels: *The Empire Strikes Back* in 1981 and *Return of the Jedi* in 1983. ✳ It quickly became apparent that this was a science fiction trilogy unlike any previous movies of this genre, a fact emphasized by the way the movie shattered previous box-office records and won awards, including seven of the ten Academy Awards for which it was nominated.

The movies tell the story of Luke Skywalker (actor Mark Hamill) who—together with his Jedi mentors Ben "Obi-Wan" Kenobi (Alec Guinness) and Yoda, his friends Princess Leia Organa (Carrie Fisher) and Han Solo (Harrison Ford), and his two trusty androids C-3P0 (Anthony Daniels) and R2-D2 (Kenny Baker)—battles Darth Vader (David Prowse; voice, James Earl Jones) and the evil Empire to restore peace to the Galaxy.

The most obvious difference between *Star Wars* and its predecessors was the special effects. Computer graphics were still in their infancy in 1977, and much of the technology needed to realize director George Lucas's vision had to be developed as the production of *Star Wars* progressed. The advancement of computerized special effects can be seen by comparing the initial trilogy with the "special edition" versions released in 1997—Lucas had to wait for technology to catch up with his initial vision for scenes such as the Mos Eisley spaceport in *Star Wars* and Cloud City in *The Empire Strikes Back*. Nevertheless, the special effects in the original trilogy stunned moviegoers. For the first time, spaceships were depicted as vehicles that looked as if they had been through many battles instead of appearing as shiny flying saucers. Battle scenes looked real, and moviegoers felt as if they were in the middle of the action. Aliens displayed a wide variety of appearances rather than simply looking like bulbous-headed humans with three fingers.

The *Star Wars* trilogy represented the variety of worlds that humans might encounter throughout a galaxy. Planets ranged from the desert planet of Tatooine orbiting a double star to Yoda's swamp world of Dagobah, from

✳ The prequel trilogy to *Star Wars* debuted in 1999 with *The Phantom Menace,* and the second movie, *Attack of the Clones,* was released in 2002.

Star Wars, which received seven Academy Awards, was the top-grossing film of 1977, and remains the second highest-grossing film of all time.

the ice-covered world of Hoth to the gaseous Bespin with Lando Calrissian's Cloud City. *Star Wars* presented an array of new weapons such as the light saber and a new power, the Force, which could be used for either good or evil. Some of the concepts, such as creatures living on airless asteroids and spaceships traveling at speeds greater than the speed of light, are (at least at present) definitely in the realm of science fiction. Nevertheless, there were enough scientifically reasonable concepts in the movies to make everything seem possible at some other time or place in the universe.

As a proponent of space exploration, Lucas hoped that *Star Wars* would excite the younger generation about space and its exploration. Lucas has said, "I would feel very good if someday they colonize Mars . . . and the leader of the first colony says 'I did it because I was hoping there would be a Wookiee up there.'" SEE ALSO ENTERTAINMENT (VOLUME 1); FASTER-THAN-LIGHT TRAVEL (VOLUME 4); INTERSTELLAR TRAVEL (VOLUME 4); LUCAS, GEORGE (VOLUME 1); MOVIES (VOLUME 4); SCIENCE FICTION (VOLUME 4).

*Nadine G. Barlow*

**Bibliography**

Sansweet, Stephen J. *The Star Wars Encyclopedia.* New York: Ballantine Books, 1998.

Slavicsek, Bill. *A Guide to the Star Wars Universe.* New York: Ballantine Books, 2000.

# Stine, G. Harry

**American Engineer and Writer**
**1928–1997**

Engineer, author, visionary, and hobbyist extraordinaire, G. Harry Stine is best known as the father of model rocketry for his efforts to bring science and safety to the building and launching of model rockets. Working as an engineer at the White Sands Missile Range in New Mexico when Sputnik was launched in 1957, Stine watched with dismay as enterprising hobbyists, in the grip of rocket fever, were injured or killed trying to launch their models. He consequently developed and published safety standards for model rocketeers, and founded the National Association of Rocketry in 1958. He also started the first model rocket company, Model Missiles, Inc., around this time. His *Handbook of Model Rocketry*, first published in 1965, remains the bible of rocket enthusiasts to this day.

As a visionary and advocate for inexpensive exploration and colonization of space, Stine was a proponent of single-stage-to-orbit vehicles, which are inexpensive, reusable, single-stage spacecraft that require no major refurbishing between missions. The multistage spacecraft used up until the present, like the space shuttle, **jettison** the spent fuel tanks during flight, and require expensive replacement and repair before taking off again.

**jettison** to eject, throw overboard, or get rid of

As a member of the Citizens' Advisory Council on National Space Policy, Stine contributed to the design of the McDonnell Douglas Delta Clipper Experimental craft, or DC-X, which had a successful test flight on August 18, 1993, at the White Sands Missile Range. The DC-X lifted off under rocket power, hovered at 46 meters (150 feet), then made a soft landing in its upright position with rockets thrusting. Stine predicted that such a single-stage, reusable spacecraft could reduce the cost of lifting a **payload** into space from $10,000 per pound to $1,000, making space industry and tourism an economic possibility.

**payload** any cargo launched aboard a rocket that is destined for space, including communications satellites or modules, supplies, equipment, and astronauts; does not include the vehicle used to move the cargo or the propellant that powers the vehicle

A prolific author, Stine wrote numerous nonfiction books, beginning with *Earth Satellites and the Race for Space Superiority* in 1957, and including *Halfway to Anywhere* in 1996 and *Living in Space* in 1997. From 1979 until his death in November 1997, he wrote a regular column on space issues called "The Alternate View" for *Analog Science Fiction and Fact* magazine, commenting on everything from the Moon Treaty to polluting the universe. He also wrote many science fiction novels and short stories, sometimes using the pseudonym Lee Correy. SEE ALSO LAUNCH VEHICLES, EXPENDABLE (VOLUME 1); REUSABLE LAUNCH VEHICLES (VOLUME 4); ROCKETS (VOLUME 3).

*Tim Palucka*

**Bibliography**

Stine, G. Harry. *Handbook of Model Rocketry*, 6th ed. New York: John Wiley & Sons, 1994.

# Teleportation

Humankind wanted to go to the Moon, and so the National Aeronautics and Space Administration (NASA) built a Saturn **rocket**. People wanted to live in space, and so an army of astronauts and engineers assembled a

**rocket** vehicle or device, especially designed to travel through space, propelled by one or more engines

**space station** large orbital outpost equipped to support a human crew and designed to remain in orbit for an extended period

**nuclear fusion** combining low-mass atoms to create heavier ones; the heavier atom's mass is slightly less than the sum of the mass of its constituents, with the remaining mass converted to energy

**antimatter** matter composed of antiparticles, such as positrons and antiprotons

**electrons** negatively charged subatomic particles

**protons** positively charged subatomic particles

**space station**. Now humankind wants to travel to Mars and send robots to explore other galaxies. Thus, it is necessary to design propulsion systems that go faster and farther than ever before. From solar sails, to nuclear rockets, to propulsion with hot gases, to wild ideas that rival *Star Trek*'s concept of "warp speed," scientists have embarked on an adventure that goes beyond the works of the most creative science fiction writers.

The first logical step in this process is to improve conventional rockets by packing more energy into a smaller volume. Instead of burning liquid oxygen and hydrogen, as the space shuttle's main engines do, a future rocket might burn solid hydrogen or use a very dense combustible. However, this method still requires that the vehicle carry its fuel into space.

NASA is working on a radical concept called the Lightcraft, a machine that resembles a flying saucer powered by air heated by a high-energy laser. An advanced version of the Lightcraft would be a large helium-filled balloon that would focus microwaves beamed from the ground or space. The balloon would be ringed by ion engines that would electrify the air to push the craft upward. Deep Space 1 is the first probe powered entirely by an ion engine, which runs on electrically charged gas.

A more powerful rocket would use **nuclear fusion**, the power source at the heart of the Sun. Controlled fusion—combining the nuclei of two lightweight atoms and reaping energy from the process—might achieve the speed needed to get to other planets, a speed 200 times faster than that provided by the space shuttle's main engines.

## Solar Sails and Antimatter Propulsion

Even more radical is the idea of the solar sail. Just as a sailing vessel uses the wind to push against the surface of its sail, satellites and small robotic spacecraft could use light particles from the Sun—called photons—to push a membrane made of very light carbon fibers. Because photons produce such small amounts of energy, the sail would have to be huge, up to several kilometers wide.

One of the most eccentric concepts in intergalactic propulsion is rooted in the popular belief that an **antimatter** particle coming in contact with its matter counterpart (for example, **electrons** and positrons or **protons** and antiprotons) would yield the most energy of any reaction in physics. The theory is known as antimatter annihilation. The efficiency would be thousands of times greater than that of any other method yet considered, probably taking a spacecraft to Mars in only six weeks.

Beyond the warp drives of *Star Trek*'s Enterprise but still within the realm of the possible, there are ideas for intelligent rockets that would be able to fix themselves and evolve almost like living things, achieving propulsion without rockets. Before this can happen, however, traditional space transportation will have to become like flying an airplane: routine, safe, and inexpensive. SEE ALSO ANTIMATTER PROPULSION (VOLUME 4); FASTER-THAN-LIGHT TRAVEL (VOLUME 4); ION PROPULSION (VOLUME 4); LASER PROPULSION (VOLUME 4); LIGHTSAILS (VOLUME 4); NUCLEAR PROPULSION (VOLUME 4); SCIENCE FICTION (VOLUME 4); STAR TREK (VOLUME 4); STAR WARS (VOLUME 4).

*Angela Swafford*

**Bibliography**

Friedman, Louis. *Starsailing: Solar Sails and Interstellar Travel.* New York: John Wiley & Sons, 1988.

Marchal, C. "Solar Sails and the ARSAT Satellite—Scientific Applications and Techniques." *L'Aeronautique et L'Astronautique* 127 (1987):53–57.

# Telepresence

Telepresence refers to the use of cameras and other equipment to remotely study a distant environment. This technology is primarily used to explore places that are inhospitable to humans. Scientists have used robotic vehicles on Earth to explore active volcanoes and the ocean floors. But telepresence has been used primarily to explore other worlds. Some vehicles, such as the Lunar Surveyor missions that set down on the Moon's surface in the 1960s and the Viking stations that landed on Mars in 1976, remained stationary and analyzed materials within the reach of their experiments. Other vehicles were mobile rovers, such as the Soviet Lunakhod missions that explored the Moon in 1970 and 1973 and the Sojourner rover, which was part of the Mars Pathfinder mission in 1997.

Telepresence allows scientists to learn about a hostile environment without endangering human life. In some cases, such as the exploration of Venus's surface by the Soviet Venera missions, the environment is so inhospitable that human explorers might never be sent there. In other cases, landers and rovers are used to determine if the location is safe for humans. The Lunar Surveyor missions, for example, tested a theory that the Moon's surface is covered by a thick layer of dust that would swallow up anything that landed on it. The Surveyors revealed that the Moon's surface is solid, and the Apollo lunar landings with the American astronauts proceeded without problems.

When telepresence is used on Earth, the operator is typically in near-instantaneous contact with the robot so the robot's motions can be adjusted in real-time. However, when humans are on Earth and the robot in on another world, the limited speed of the radio signals (traveling at the speed of light) means that there is a time delay between when the operator sends a command and when the robot receives it. Thus, scientists typically develop a sequence of commands to send to the robot and allow it to act autonomously until the next contact period. Rovers usually have internal "fail-safe" modes so if they get themselves into trouble (for example, trying to climb a steep slope, such as the Sojourner rover tried to do several times), they will shut down until the next sequence of commands is received from Earth. Thus, telepresence is much more complicated than simply moving a joystick and seeing how the rover responds on another world.

Scientists look forward to the day when many activities will be completely conducted by telepresence. Some of the possibilities are already apparent. Teleoperated robots are used on Earth to clean up hazardous waste sites. Some Earth-based telescopes are conducting autonomous observations, alerting the operator only when they detect something unusual. The expected increase in technological capabilities will allow future robots to conduct mining operations on asteroids or construct habitats for human

Sojourner was allowed to make some independent decisions regarding its movements, which occasionally got the little rover into trouble. Here the rover tried to climb over rocks but managed to get itself stuck. Engineers on Earth were able to transmit new signals that allowed Sojourner to find its way down.

occupation on Mars before the astronauts even leave Earth. Increased opportunities for exploration and new ways to improve the lives of humans will be available through the enhanced capabilities of future teleoperated robots. SEE ALSO ASTEROID MINING (VOLUME 4); MARS MISSIONS (VOLUME 4); NANOTECHNOLOGY (VOLUME 4); SCIENTIFIC RESEARCH (VOLUME 4).

*Nadine G. Barlow*

**Bibliography**

Sheppard, P. J., and G. R. Walker. *Telepresence.* Boston: Kluwer Academic Publishers, 1998.

Shirley, Donna. *Managing Martians.* New York: Broadway Books, 1998.

**Television** *See Entertainment (Volume 1); Movies (Volume 4); Roddenberry, Gene (Volume 1); Star Trek (Volume 4); Star Wars (Volume 4).*

# Terraforming

Terraforming is the process of altering a planet to make it more suitable for life (habitable). Usually this means making the planet suitable for most, if not all, Earth life. However, if there is dormant or hidden life on the planet, terraforming will change conditions so that this life can possibly flourish. In terraforming, there are intermediate stages where the planet has become habitable, but only to organisms that can survive in extreme environments.

Until recently, the topic of terraforming Mars was considered more the subject of science fiction novels rather than serious scientific discussion. But it is now known that we can change the climate of a planet, as we are inadvertently doing it on Earth. In addition, it is thought that billions of years ago Mars did have a climate suitable for life. The main focus of current scientific studies of terraforming is the restoration of Mars to habitable conditions.

## The Restoration of Mars

**biosphere** the interaction of living organisms on a global scale

Mars can be made suitable for life by changing its climate; there is no need to alter its distance from the Sun, its rotation rate, or the tilt of its axis. Exploration of Mars indicates that it already has enough carbon dioxide, nitrogen, and water to build a **biosphere**. The challenge is to warm the planet and release those compounds. Mars is the only one of the inner planets that can be made habitable simply by changing its climate. It is not possible to move Venus or make it spin faster or to add an atmosphere to Mercury or the Moon to make them habitable. Mars is the only practical target for near-term terraforming.

## The Habitability of Mars and Earth

In considering the possibility of restoring habitable conditions to Mars, it is important to define that term. The basic approach to this question is to look at Earth. Clearly, the present environment on Earth is habitable to microorganisms, plants, and animals. But Earth has not always been this way.

Estimates based on the size and shape of the fluvial features on Mars suggest that it has enough water to cover its entire surface with a layer 500 meters thick. This painting shows what the present Mars would look like if that much water was once again on the surface.

For most of Earth's early history, oxygen was not present and carbon dioxide levels were much higher than they are today. This early environment was habitable for microorganisms and would be habitable for most plants but not for animals and humans, which require high oxygen levels and low carbon dioxide levels. On Mars the natural habitable condition is one with high carbon dioxide and only a little oxygen.

In a habitable state, Mars would have a thick atmosphere about one to two times sea-level air pressure on Earth. This atmosphere would be composed primarily of carbon dioxide, with lower levels of nitrogen and small amounts of oxygen produced by sunlight. There may be enough oxygen to create a thin but effective ozone shield, but there will not be enough for humans and animals to breathe. This restored environment would be similar

## COMPARING EARTH, MARS, AND VENUS

| | Earth | Mars | Venus |
|---|---|---|---|
| Gravity | 1 | 0.38 | 0.91 |
| Day Length | 24h | 24h 37min 22.66sec | 117 days |
| Year | 365 days | 687 days | 225 days |
| Axis Tilt | 23°12' | 25°12' | 2°36' |
| Ave. Sunlight | 345 W/m² | 147 W/m² | 655 W/m² |
| Ave. Temperature | +15°C | −60°C | +460°C |
| Temperature Range | −60°C to +50°C | −145°C to +20°C | −460°C to +460°C |
| Pressure | 1 atm (101.3 kPa) | 1/120 atm | 95 atm |
| Atmosphere | $N_2$, $O_2$ | $CO_2$ | $CO_2$ |

to what the Martian environment might have been like 3 to 4 billion years ago, when Mars may have had a biosphere.

Currently Mars is too cold (−60°) and has an atmosphere that is too thin to allow liquid water on the surface; thus, it cannot support life. Therefore, the first step in making Mars habitable is to increase the temperature and the atmospheric pressure enough for liquid water to be stable. The most effective method is the use of super-greenhouse gases known as perfluorocarbons (PFCs). These gases have a strong warming effect even at very low concentrations, as has been seen on Earth. PFCs are not toxic to plants and animals. Unlike chlorofluorocarbons, PFCs do not contain chlorine or bromine, and thus they would not destroy the ozone layer that would form as the atmosphere thickened.

There have been other suggestions of ways to warm Mars, such as placing large orbiting mirrors, sprinkling the poles with dark dust, and crashing asteroids and comets into the surface. Unlike the use of PFCs, none of these methods are practical with today's technology.

**regolith** upper few meters of a body's surface, composed of inorganic matter, such as unconsolidated rocks and fine soil

As the temperature on Mars increases, carbon dioxide gas will be released from the **regolith** and the polar cap as it melts (the south polar cap is composed of frozen carbon dioxide and ice). This carbon dioxide will thicken the atmosphere and augment greenhouse warming. This positive feedback between thickening the atmosphere, warming the surface, and releasing carbon dioxide will continue until all the carbon dioxide is in the atmosphere. Calculations indicate that in a concentration of a few parts per million, PFCs can trigger the outgassing of carbon dioxide. At this stage, Mars would be a warm, wet world if the regolith and polar regions have the amount of carbon dioxide and water ice it is thought they have—between 100 and 1000 mbars.

If there is dormant life on Mars, it would expand rapidly into this re-created warm and wet world. The surface would once again be full of Martians. If there is no life on Mars, microorganisms and plants could be introduced from Earth.

## Ecological Changes and the Martian Biosphere

The ecological changes on Mars as it warms up will be like hiking down a mountain: from barren frozen rock at the top, through alpine tundra and arctic and alpine grasses, and eventually to trees and forests.

The first Martian pioneers from Earth will be organisms that live in the coldest, driest, most Mars-like environment in the world. These are the

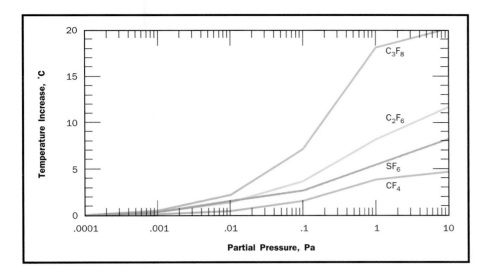

Different types of greenhouse gases can be very efficient at increasing surface temperatures.

**cryptoendolithic microbial ecosystems** found in Antarctica. In the cold, dry, ice-free regions of Antarctica, **lichens**, **algae**, and bacteria live a few millimeters below the surface of sandstone rocks, where there is a warmer, wetter environment than exists on the surface of the rock. Enough sunlight penetrates through the rock to allow photosynthesis. Similar microorganisms in a rock habitat could survive on Mars when the air temperatures reached −10°C in the daytime for a few weeks during the warmest part of the year.

With further warming and extension of the growing season, alpine plants might survive and cover vast equatorial regions. The first introduction of photosynthetic microbial ecosystems and arctic and alpine tundra will be of biological interest. However, only with the development of ecosystems based on higher plants will the ecological development of Mars become significant in terms of the production of oxygen.

Although plants will be the major biological force on Mars, as they are on Earth, small animals also could play a key role. Insects and soil invertebrates, such as earthworms, would be important in the developing ecosystems. For example, pollination by flying insects would greatly increase the diversity of plants that can be grown on Mars at every stage of the process. Unfortunately, the minimum oxygen requirements and maximum carbon dioxide tolerance of flying insects at a third of Earth gravity remains unknown.

Although life-forms from Earth might be introduced to Mars in a careful sequence, this does not imply that the resulting biosphere will develop as predicted. As life on Mars interacts with itself and the changing environment, it will follow an independent evolutionary path that will be impossible to control. This should be considered a good thing. The resulting biological system is more likely to be stable and globally adapted to the altered environment than would any preconceived ecosystems, and studying such an independent evolutionary path will contribute to scientific knowledge.

By calculating the energy required to change Mars, it is possible to estimate how long the process might take. The results indicate that to warm

**cryptoendolithic microbial ecosystems** microbial ecosystems that live inside sandstone in extreme environments such as Antarctica

**lichen** fungus that grows symbiotically with algae

**algae** simple photosynthetic organisms, often aquatic

Mars and introduce plant life would take about 100 years. It would take another 100,000 years for those plants to produce enough oxygen for humans to breathe. In the meantime humans would have to wear small oxygen masks but not pressurized space suits.

In the long term Mars will once again decay and lose its atmosphere as the carbon dioxide dissolves in water and is turned into **carbonate**. However, this will take 10 to 100 million years—long enough for a biosphere to develop.

**carbonate** a class of minerals, such as chalk and limestone, formed by carbon dioxide reacting in water

## Ethical Issues

Although terraforming a planet is technologically feasible, is it ethically correct? Perhaps the most difficult issue is the possibility that life may already be present on the planet. In terraforming Mars, the first step would be creating a thick carbon dioxide atmosphere that supports a warmer and wetter planet. These conditions closely resemble those on early Mars, when any Martian life-forms would have developed, and therefore are the conditions they are adapted to. Terraforming Mars will make the planet more favorable to any present Mars organisms rather than having the unwanted effect of destroying a different life-form.

Terraforming has as its goal the spreading of life. The process can be seen as part of evolution, in which organisms expand into every available niche either by adapting or by changing the environment. Humans can help this spread of life and contribute in a positive way to the ecological development of the solar system. SEE ALSO ASTROBIOLOGY (VOLUME 4); DOMED CITIES (VOLUME 4); ENVIRONMENTAL CHANGES (VOLUME 4); EXPLORATION PROGRAMS (VOLUME 2); LIVING ON OTHER WORLDS (VOLUME 4); MARS (VOLUME 2); MARS BASES (VOLUME 4); SCIENTIFIC RESEARCH (VOLUME 4); SOCIAL ETHICS (VOLUME 4).

*Christopher P. McKay and Margarita M. Marinova*

**Bibliography**

Clarke, Arthur C. *The Snows of Olympus.* London: Victor Gollancz, 1995.

Fogg, Martyn J. *Terraforming: Engineering Planetary Environments.* Warrendale, PA: SAE, 1995.

McKay, Christopher P. "Bringing Life to Mars." *Scientific American Presents* 10, no. 1 (1999):52–57.

McKay, Christopher P., and Margarita M. Marinova. "The Physics, Biology, and Environmental Ethics of Making Mars Habitable." *Astrobiology* 1 (2001):89–109.

McKay, Christopher P., Owen B. Toon, and James F. Kasting. "Making Mars Habitable." *Nature* 352 (1991):489–496.

# Tethers

**rockets** vehicles (or devices) especially designed to travel through space, propelled by one or more engines

**low Earth orbit** an orbit between 300 and 800 kilometers above Earth's surface

**pyrotechnics** fireworks display; the art of building fireworks

Space travel is a tremendously costly enterprise, largely because today's spacecraft use **rockets** to move around, and launching the significant amounts of fuel needed to propel those rockets is very expensive. For humankind to move beyond its current tentative foothold in **low Earth orbit** and begin frequent travel to the Moon, Mars, and other planets, the cost of traveling through space must be substantially reduced. To do this, it may be necessary to rely less on the **pyrotechnics** of rocket technologies and

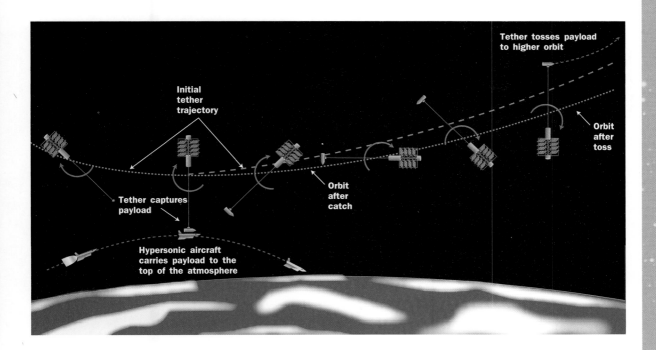

Initial tether trajectory

Tether tosses payload to higher orbit

Orbit after toss

Orbit after catch

Tether captures payload

Hypersonic aircraft carries payload to the top of the atmosphere

utilize simpler and less complex technologies. This could entail the use of long strings or wires to move **payloads** around in space without the need to burn large quantities of fuel.

A space tether can be used to move spacecraft through space through two different mechanisms. First, a high-strength string connecting two spacecraft can provide a mechanical link that enables one satellite to "throw" the other into a different orbit, much like casting a stone with a sling. Second, if the tether is made of conductive wire, currents flowing along the wire can interact with Earth's magnetic field to create propulsive forces on the tether. Both momentum-transfer and **electrodynamic** tethers can move spacecraft from one orbit to another without the use of propellant.

## Tether Experiments

A number of tether experiments have been flown in space. In the early days of the space age the Gemini 11 and 12 missions (1966) used short tethers to connect two spacecraft and rotate them around each other to study artificial gravity and other dynamics.

In the 1990s the National Aeronautics and Space Administration (NASA) conducted two series of tether experiments. One series involved a large tether flown on the space shuttle that was called the Tethered Satellite System (TSS). Unfortunately, the TSS missions encountered well-publicized problems. In the 1992 TSS-1 mission, the TSS system attempted to deploy a spherical satellite built by the Italian space agency upwards from the shuttle at the end of a 20-kilometer-long (12 miles) tether made of insulated copper wire. A few hundred meters into deployment the spool mechanism jammed, ending the experiment.

In 1996 NASA repeated the experiment. As the tether approached its full length, the rapid motion of the orbiting tether through Earth's magnetic field generated a current of over 3,500 volts along the tether. The TSS

A concept for a system in which an orbiting tether would pick a payload up from a hypersonic airplane flying at the top of the atmosphere and pull the payload into space.

**payloads** any cargo launched aboard a rocket that is destined for space, including communications satellites or modules, supplies, equipment, and astronauts; does not include the vehicle used to move the cargo or the propellant that powers the vehicle

**electrodynamic** pertaining to the interaction of moving electric charges with magnetic and electric fields

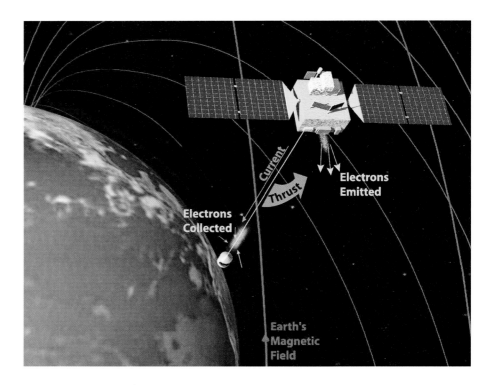

Illustration of how an electrodynamic tether can boost the orbit of a spacecraft.

**electrons** negatively charged subatomic particles

**ionosphere** a charged particle region of several layers in the upper atmosphere created by radiation interacting with upper atmospheric gases

system included devices that emitted **electrons** or ions at both ends of the tether, enabling the tether system to make electrical contact with the **ionosphere**. This allowed the induced voltage to drive a current along the tether, demonstrating that an electrodynamic tether could generate power by converting the shuttle's orbital energy into electrical energy.

A flaw in the insulation allowed an arc to jump from the tether to the deployment boom. The arc burned through the tether, causing it to part and effectively ending the electrodynamic tether part of the experiment. The break, however, showed that tethers could be used to move spacecraft to higher orbits. When the TSS tether was severed, the Italian satellite at the end of the tether was tossed 140 kilometers (87 miles) above the shuttle.

Despite the difficulties encountered in the TSS experiments, enthusiasm for tether missions remains high, largely because of the many successes of the second series of NASA tether experiments, which were based on a much smaller and less expensive system called the Small Expendable-Tether Deployer System (SEDS). Four highly successful SEDS tether experiments have been carried out as piggyback missions on upper-stage vehicles launching larger satellites. The SEDS-1 mission used a tether to drop a payload back down to Earth. The experiment showed that a spool of string could perform the same job that a rocket does. This technique could be used to drop scientific payloads from the International Space Station down to Earth. The 1993 Plasma Motor Generator mission used a modified SEDS system to deploy a 500-meter (1,640-foot) conducting wire to study electrodynamic interactions with the ionosphere. The SEDS-2 mission deployed a 20-kilometer-long (12.4 miles) tether below an upper-stage rocket and left it hanging to see how long it would survive in space. After only four days a micrometeorite or piece of space debris cut the tether, which was only about 0.8 millimeters (0.0315 inches) in diameter. This experiment showed that in order for tethers to be useful for long-duration missions in space, they must be designed to withstand cuts by micrometeorites and space debris.

## Future Uses of Tethers

One way to solve this problem was demonstrated by the Tethered Physics and Survivability experiment, which was conducted by the Naval Research Laboratory. That experiment used the SEDS system to deploy a tether constructed as a hollow braid that had ordinary knitting yarn stuffed in the middle to puff it out. Launched on June 20, 1996, the 4-kilometer-long (2.5 miles), 2.5-millimeter-diameter (0.098 inches) tether has been orbiting in space uncut for more than five years.

Another method of ensuring that tethers can survive impacts with space debris may be to fabricate them as long, spiderweb-like nets rather than as single-line cables. Tethers Unlimited is developing a flight experiment to demonstrate this and other technologies.

Tethers also may provide a cost-effective means for removing spacecraft and space trash from orbit. In late 2001 NASA planned to fly the ProSEDS experiment to demonstrate that a conducting tether can be used to lower the orbit of a spacecraft by dragging against Earth's magnetic field.

In the future, long rotating tethers may be used to toss payloads through space. Tethers Unlimited has developed a design for a Cislunar Tether Transport System that could repeatedly transport payloads to the Moon and back, and other researchers have developed designs for tether systems to take payloads to Mars and back. In addition, tethers may provide a way to lower the cost of boosting payloads into orbit. In one concept a small **hypersonic** airplane could be used to carry a payload halfway into orbit, where a rotating tether facility already in orbit could pick it up and toss it into orbit.

**hypersonic** capable of speeds over five times the speed of sound

Although a number of technical challenges have to be addressed before tethers can provide routine transport around and beyond Earth orbit, tethers have the potential to reduce the cost of space travel greatly and may play a key role in the development of space. SEE ALSO ACCESSING SPACE (VOLUME 1). GETTING TO SPACE CHEAPLY (VOLUME 1); PAYLOADS (VOLUME 3); SPACE ELEVATORS (VOLUME 4).

*Robert P. Hoyt*

### Bibliography

Cosmo, M. L., and E. C. Lorenzini. *Tethers in Space Handbook*, 3rd ed. Prepared for NASA/MSFC by Smithsonian Astrophysical Observatory, Cambridge, MA, December 1997. <http://www.harvard.edu/spgroup/handbook.html>.

Hoyt, Robert P., and C. W. Uphoff. "Cislunar Tether Transport System." *Journal of Spacecraft and Rockets* 37, no. 2 (2000):177–186.

# Time Travel

In 1898 H. G. Wells wrote his most famous novel, *The Time Machine*. In this novel, a young Victorian invented a device that allowed him to travel into the future or the past. He travels 800,000 years into the future and finds a society very different from the one he was accustomed to, inhabited by

In *Back to the Future* (1985), Marty McFly inadvertently finds himself in the 1950s, his "modern" car an oddity in a rural field.

**general relativity** a branch of science first described by Albert Einstein showing the relationship between gravity and acceleration

**black holes** objects so massive for their size that their gravitational pull prevents everything, even light, from escaping

**event horizon** the imaginary spherical shell surrounding a black hole that marks the boundary where no light or any other information can escape

the Eloi and the Morlocks. The Eloi appear to live an idyllic life, but the time traveler discovers that there is a horrible price they must pay.

Writers such as Wells used fiction to comment on their own society. However, serious paradoxes raised by time travel have led many to contend that it is impossible. For example, what if a time traveler accidentally killed his own father, long before he was born? Isaac Newton thought of time as an arrow, traveling in a straight line at constant speed. But Albert Einstein theorized that time was much more variable. To Einstein, time could slow down and speed up in strong gravitational fields or when an object was traveling at high speed. The faster we travel through space, the slower we travel through time, at least to a stationary observer. Einstein's equations of **general relativity** allow several varieties of time travel. For example, in a rotating universe, moving against the direction of rotation would be moving backwards in time. Our expanding universe does not have this property.

A more interesting time travel possibility is presented by rapidly rotating, massive **black holes**. Such a black hole does not have an **event horizon**, but appears to be a ring. Moving through the center of the ring might lead to a different place and time—a wormhole through space. Nevertheless, no physical process currently known by scientists can produce a black hole with enough rotational speed for this to happen. Even if it did occur, such an object might be unstable and it might collapse if anything did pass through its center.

Stephen Hawking once suggested that time travel must be impossible, because if it were possible, we should have had visitors from the future. Since we have never seen a tourist from the future, time travel must be impossible. However, others have suggested that this argument breaks down if tourists from the future are simply not interested in us, or that time travel might be possible but impractical because of the enormous amounts of energy required.

If time travel is possible after all, how do we deal with the paradoxes? One way is to postulate the existence of alternate realities. Quantum mechanics teaches us that a given system can exist in two different states, and we do not know which one until we examine the system. So, if we were to travel back in time and prevent, say, the assassination of U.S. President John F. Kennedy, we would have created a parallel universe. We would have changed the past for someone else, but not us. SEE ALSO BLACK HOLES (VOLUME 2); EINSTEIN, ALBERT (VOLUME 2); KENNEDY, JOHN F. (VOLUME 3); SCIENCE FICTION (VOLUME 4); WORMHOLES (VOLUME 4).

*Elliot Richmond*

### Bibliography

Adler, Bill, ed. *Time Machines: The Greatest Time Travel Stories Ever Written*. New York: Carroll & Graf Publishing, 1998.

Gardner, Martin. *Time Travel and Other Mathematical Bewilderments*. New York: W. H. Freeman, 1988.

Hawking, Stephen. *A Brief History of Time*. Toronto: Bantam Books, 1988.

Herbert, Nick. *Quantum Reality: Beyond the New Physics*. New York: Anchor Books Doubleday, 1987.

Parker, Barry R. *Cosmic Time Travel: A Scientific Odyssey*. New York: Plenum Press, 1991.

### Internet Resources

"Sagan on Time Travel." *Nova Online*. PBS. <http://www.pbs.org/wgbh/nova/time/sagan.html>.

"The Physics of Time Travel." Explorations in Science with Dr. Michio Kaku. <http://www.mkaku.org/time_travel.htm>.

# Traffic Control

In the early twenty-first century, there are approximately 5000 commercial and private airplanes in the air at any one moment. The task of the U.S. Air Traffic Control System is to ensure the safe operation of these commercial and private aircraft. Air traffic controllers coordinate the movements of these planes, keep them at safe distances from each other, direct them during take-off and landing from airports, reroute them around bad weather, and ensure that air traffic flows smoothly. Other nations around the world maintain and operate similar air traffic control systems.

As space travel becomes a more common activity, it may become essential to institute a similar traffic control system for spacecraft. However, a more urgent problem is presented by the number of individual objects that are in orbit around Earth. The Space Surveillance Network (SSN) is currently tracking around 7,000 artificial objects circling Earth. The risk of collision with an object in space increases rapidly as the number of objects increases. A bit of space debris as small as a paint chip can do severe damage if it collides with a satellite because the relative **velocity** between the two objects can be as high as 25,000 kilometers per hour. The National Aeronautics and Space Administration (NASA) has calculated that the probability of a collision between a space station–sized satellite and a piece of orbital debris is 46 percent over the lifetime of the spacecraft unless avoidance techniques are used.

A space traffic control system would therefore have two separate missions. The current role of tracking and cataloging functioning and

**velocity** speed and direction of a moving object; a vector quantity

In 1999, NASA's "Future Flight Central" opened at Ames Research Center. It is a full-scale virtual airport control tower designed to test ways to monitor potential traffic problems.

**transponders** bandwidth-specific transmitter-receiver units

**radar** a technique for detecting distant objects by emitting a pulse of radio-wavelength radiation and then recording echoes of the pulse off the distant objects

**payloads** any cargo launched aboard a rocket that is destined for space, including communications satellites or modules, supplies, equipment, and astronauts; does not include the vehicle used to move the cargo or the propellant that powers the vehicle

nonfunctioning orbital objects currently performed by SSN would need to be transferred to the new space traffic control system. This mission would also include a system for predicting and warning satellite operators of potential collisions between different spacecraft or between spacecraft and debris.

The future role of the space traffic control system would also include the monitoring of all space traffic and determination of the best orbits for the insertion of new satellites into Earth orbit. Moreover, it would guide and monitor the greatly increased numbers of both cargo- and passenger-carrying space vehicles anticipated in future decades. Such a system would require full utilization of both current and advanced technology. New satellites and spacecraft would carry **transponders** similar to the devices carried by modern aircraft. These would transmit identifying information back to the space traffic control **radar** system. Older satellites without transponders and nonfunctioning space debris would be tracked by more sophisticated equipment.

In order for the new system to function efficiently, it must have complete access to all of the information currently maintained in the SSN and the North American Aerospace Defense Command databases. Of greater importance, however, will be making the program international. Currently, each nation provides its own air traffic control system and aircraft flying over international boundaries are "handed off" from one system to another as the aircraft crosses the boundary. While the United States has taken the lead in monitoring and tracking space debris and functioning satellites, other countries must fully participate in any space traffic control system. It must be a truly international effort, supported by firm treaties between the nations with launch capabilities. At present, the United States, the Russian Federation, the European Space Agency, China, and Japan are all capable of launching **payloads** into any Earth orbits. These countries must all cooperate in the design and implementation of a space traffic control system. SEE ALSO NAVIGATION (VOLUME 3); SPACE DEBRIS (VOLUME 2); TRACKING OF SPACECRAFT (VOLUME 3).

*Elliot Richmond*

**Bibliography**

"Addressing Challenges of the New Millennium." *6ᵗʰ International Space Cooperation Workshop Report.* AIAA:7–14, March 2001.

Johnson, Nicholas L. "The Earth Satellite Population: Official Growth and Constituents." In *Preservation of Near-Earth Space for Future Generations*, ed. John A. Simpson. New York: Cambridge University Press, 1994.

Kessler, Donald J. "The Current and Future Environment: An Overall Assessment," in *Preservation of Near-Earth Space for Future Generations*, ed. John A. Simpson. New York: Cambridge University Press, 1994.

Nieder, Raymond L. "Implication of Orbital Debris for Space Station Design," AIAA 90–1331, 1990.

U.S. Congress, Office of Technology Assessment. *Orbiting Debris: A Space Environmental Problem* (Background Paper), OTA-BP-ISC-72. Washington, DC: U.S. Government Printing Office, 1990.

# TransHab

TransHab (short for "Transit Habitat") is the first space inflatable module designed by the National Aeronautics and Space Administration (NASA). It was conceived as a technology capable of supporting a crew of six on an extended space journey, such as a six-month trip to Mars. During its development in 1997–2001 at NASA's Johnson Space Center in Houston, Texas, TransHab was considered for use on International Space Station "Alpha" as a habitation module for two reasons: first, because of its superior ability to support crew needs, and second, to test it for possible use on a human mission to Mars.

## History

TransHab was first conceived in 1997 by a team of engineers and architects at the Johnson Space Center. A space human factors group was asked to join the design team in developing the best size and layout for the spacecraft. Based in part on psychological, social, and operational lessons learned from earlier American and Russian missions, the team recommended a three-level internal layout with crew quarters isolated at the center; mechanical systems grouped together in a separate "room"; and exercise and hygiene situated on a different level from the public functions of kitchen, dining and conferencing. The total volume is over 342 cubic meters.

All spacecraft flown up until now have been of an exoskeletal type—that is, its hard outer shell acts both as a pressure container and as its main channel for structural loading. This includes the rest of Alpha, which is currently under construction in low Earth orbit at about 250 miles above the Earth.

By contrast, TransHab is the first endoskeletal space habitat, consisting of a dual system: a light, reconfigurable central structure and a deployable pressure shell. The shell is so resilient because it is made of several layers,

TransHab represents a major breakthrough in that it solves the "problem" of inflatables and at the same time invents a whole new way of building for space and Earth.

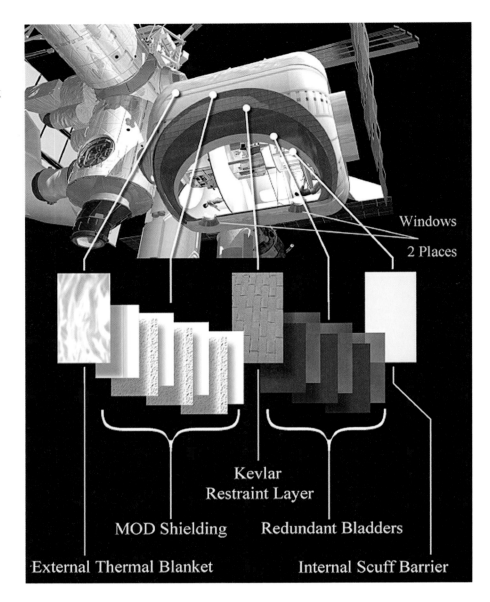

Windows
2 Places

Kevlar
Restraint Layer

MOD Shielding    Redundant Bladders

External Thermal Blanket    Internal Scuff Barrier

each with its own specific purpose. Principal among these is the restraint layer, which is interwoven to distribute tremendous loads evenly and efficiently around its torus, much in the same way as the reeds in a round basket are woven to spread weight and give the basket strength. Each strap is made of Kevlar®, an aramid-fiber material, which has a very high strength-to-weight ratio and great impact resistance, and is often used today in the making of bulletproof vests. Woven together into the vehicle's main shell, these straps when inflated form a system that is capable of withstanding up to 4 atmospheres of pressure differential (over 54 psi) between interior and exterior.

Inside the restraint layer, multiple bladders of heavy, flexible plastic are mounted to hold in the air. Although only one bladder is necessary to do the job, the requirements for safety in spacecraft design are so high that TransHab's designers put in three bladder layers to protect the vehicle in case one of them failed. On the outside of the restraint layer, a shield of impact-resistant layers separated by open-cell foam is mounted to defend TransHab against the tiny meteor-like particles that are often encountered in space, traveling at velocities up to 7 kilometers per second. The outermost layer of the shell is made of a glass fiber cloth that resists abrasion by the charged particles in Earth's **ionosphere**.

## Why Was TransHab Considered for the International Space Station?

TransHab is designed around human requirements, not just engineering solutions to the challenges of spaceflight. It is roomy and offers enough stowage space to take care of a crew for over six months, and it houses all the crew activities from sleeping to exercise. This reduces clutter and activity elsewhere on the International Space Station, enhancing the environment for the scientific experiments that are the station's primary purpose.

## For the Human Exploration of Mars

TransHab could also play an important part of the human exploration of Mars or other bodies in the solar system. Without an inflatable module such as TransHab, the cost of getting a crew safely to a remote destination such as Mars could be much higher, and if the alternative is a constricted, conventional spacecraft, the crew would be much more likely to experience stress before the most challenging part of their mission begins on Mars. This makes TransHab a central part of NASA's Mars Design Reference Mission (DRM), as the crew habitat for the journey between planets. At the beginning of the DRM, TransHab is launched in a space shuttle bay, deflated, and packaged tight; once in orbit it can be unfolded, inflated, and deployed. At that time, elements that served structural functions during launch are reconfigured to serve as walls, partitions, and furnishings.

All of this is possible because it is specifically designed for use in a **microgravity** environment, so its pieces are lighter than other modules. Once ready to go, TransHab would be attached to the propulsion and guidance systems that take it and its crew on the six-month trip to the Red Planet. When they reach Mars, the crew would "park" TransHab in orbit and take a transfer ship to the surface, where their surface habitat is already in place and waiting for them. At the end of their 425-day scientific expedition on Mars, the crew would then launch back up to orbit and reboard TransHab for the journey home. SEE ALSO HABITATS (VOLUME 3); HUMAN MISSIONS TO MARS (VOLUME 3); INTERNATIONAL SPACE STATION (VOLUMES 1 AND 3); LONG-DURATION SPACEFLIGHT (VOLUME 3); MARS MISSIONS (VOLUME 4); HUMAN FACTORS (VOLUME 3).

*Constance M. Adams*

**ionosphere** a charged particle region of several layers in the upper atmosphere created by radiation interacting with upper atmospheric gases

**microgravity** the condition experienced in freefall as a spacecraft orbits Earth or another body; commonly called weightlessness; only very small forces are perceived in freefall, on the order of one-millionth the force of gravity on Earth's surface

### Bibliography

Adams, Constance. "Four Legs in the Morning: Issues in Crew Quarter Design for Long-Duration Space Facilities." *Proceedings of the 28th International Conference on Environmental Science (ICES).* Warrendale, PA: Society of Automotive Engineers, 1998.

————. "Defin(design)ing the Human Domain: the Process of Architectural Integration of Long-Duration Space Facilities." *Proceedings of the 28th International Conference on Environmental Science (ICES).* Warrendale, PA: Society of Automotive Engineers, 1998.

Adams, Constance, and Matthew McCurdy. "Habitability as a Tier-One Criterion in Advanced Space Design—Part One: Habitability." *Proceedings of the 29th International Conference on Environmental Science (ICES)*. Warrendale, PA: Society of Automotive Engineers, 1999.

———— "Habitability as a Tier-One Criterion in Advanced Space Mission Design: Part Two—Evaluation of Current Elements." *Proceedings of Space 2000: The Seventh International Conference and Exposition on Engineering, Construction, Operations and Business in Space*. Reston, VA: American Society of Civil Engineers, 2000.

Connors, Mary, et al. *Living Aloft*. Washington, DC: National Aeronautics and Space Administration, 1985.

Hill, James. "The New Millennium: Adams/Kennedy." *Texas Architect*, January 2000.

Kennedy, Kriss, and Constance Adams. "ISS TransHab: A Space Inflatable Habitation Module." *Proceedings of Space 2000: The Seventh International Conference and Exposition on Engineering, Construction, Operations and Business in Space.* Reston VA: American Society of Civil Engineers, 2000.

**Internet Resources**

Rapaport, Nina. "Space Inflator." *Metropolis* July 1999. <http://www.metropolismag.com/new/content/arch/jy99spac.htm>.

Williams, Florence. "Design 2002: Putting a Room of One's Own in Orbit" *The New York Times*. December 30, 1999. <http://archives.nytimes.com/>.

# Utopia

"Utopia" is a term that English statesman and author Thomas More coined in the early sixteenth century in his novel of the same name. It is derived from two Greek words: *Eutopia* (meaning "good place") and *Outopia* (meaning "no place"). Utopia is therefore a good place that does not exist. A space utopia, one could claim, is a good place that can exist only in space.

The word "utopia" conjures up the vision of an ideal society, where people are physically and morally free, where they work not because of need but out of pleasure, where love knows no laws, and where everyone is an artist. A space utopia is the same paradise set elsewhere and served with a generous dose of science fiction.

Space utopias resonate mostly in the United States, because of its history as an immigrant nation with an open frontier; its tolerance for small, like-minded, isolated communities; its preference for the individual as opposed to the government; and its faith in technology to solve human problems.

A good example of space utopia is the human-made space habitat first described by Princeton University physicist Gerard K. O'Neill in his book *The High Frontier* (1977). Situated at L-5, an equilibrium point between Earth and the Moon, and made of lunar material, this hypothetical habitat is entirely controlled by its creators, including the gravity, terrain, landscape, and weather. Energy is obtained from the Sun, while air, water, and materials are constantly recycled. The few thousand inhabitants in these settlements lead happy and productive lives, dedicated to learning, service, production, commerce, science, and exploration. Their society combines control over the environment, the beauty of self-made nature, the shared plenty of a consumer economy, and the intimacy of village life. There is little crime and no racial, ethnic, religious, or economic strife. Government is democratic and limited, imposing few legal, fiscal, or moral restraints on its citizens, thereby enabling them to pursue their individual happiness.

The likelihood of the successful existence of space utopias is diminished as the inherent difficulties of utopias on Earth are compounded by the rigors of the space environment. Social and biological scientists, humanists, and theologians argue that a large-scale utopian society is against human nature, if for no other reason than it ignores the human drive for power. Social scientists argue that the demise of small-scale utopian communities is caused by their inability to sufficiently isolate themselves from the rest of society and to survive the transition to new group leadership. Faced with fading communities, American Mennonites emigrated to the jungles of Central America, and few cults in the United States have survived their charismatic leaders. While many utopian cults transformed into established religions and institutions with bureaucratic organization independent of their founders, there are examples of those that could not and, instead, have found violent death (People's Temple followers, led by the Reverend Jim Jones, in Guyana, 1978; Branch Davidians, led by David Koresh, in Texas, 1993; and Heaven's Gate followers, led by Marshall Applewhite, in California, 1997).

The harsh and unforgiving environment of space precludes the existence of human groups without strict authority structures, at least within our solar system. The International Space Station operates under a rigorous chain of command sanctioned by international law. Space utopian societies may have to wait for routine travel between solar systems and the availability of uninhabited Earthlike planets. SEE ALSO COMMUNITIES IN SPACE (VOLUME 4); O'NEILL, GERARD K. (VOLUME 4); O'NEILL COLONIES (VOLUME 4); SETTLEMENTS (VOLUME 4); SOCIAL ETHICS (VOLUME 4).

*Michael Fulda*

### Bibliography

Finney, Ben R., and Eric M. Jones, ed. *Interstellar Migration and the Human Experience.* Berkeley: University of California Press, 1985.

Harrison, Albert A. *Spacefaring: The Human Dimension.* Berkeley: University of California Press, 2001.

# Vehicles

Space vehicles encompass different categories of spacecraft, including **satellites**, **rockets**, space **capsules**, **space stations**, and colonies. In general, satellites are considered any object launched by a rocket for the purpose of orbiting Earth or another celestial body. A rocket, on the other hand, is a vehicle or device, especially designed to travel through space, propelled by one or more engines.

## A Brief History of Space Vehicles

The Soviet Union launched the first successful satellite, Sputnik 1 in October 1957. America's first satellite, Explorer 1, followed Sputnik by three months, in January 1958. Soon after satellites orbited the Earth, space capsules were launched containing closed compartments designed to hold and

**satellites** any objects launched by a rocket for the purpose of orbiting the Earth or another celestial body

**rockets** vehicles (or devices) especially designed to travel through space, propelled by one or more engines

**capsule** a closed compartment designed to hold and protect humans, instruments, and/or equipment, as in a spacecraft

**space stations** large orbiting outposts equipped to support human crews and designed to remain in orbit around Earth for an extended period

protect humans and/or equipment. Less than three years after Sputnik 1, both the United States and Soviet Union put capsules into space with humans aboard. In 1961 cosmonaut Yuri Gagarin became the first person in space aboard a Vostok space capsule. A month later, American astronaut Alan Shepard in the Mercury capsule Freedom 7 made a 14.8-minute suborbital flight, becoming the first U.S. astronaut in space.

While the American space program focused first on the Apollo missions to the Moon and then turned to development of the space shuttle (the first reusable launch vehicle) and low Earth orbit operations, the Soviet Union established a series of space stations in Earth orbit. Space stations are large spacecraft equipped to support a crew and remain in orbit for an extended period of time to serve as a base for launching exploratory expeditions, conducting scientific research, repairing satellites, and performing other space-related activities. The Soviets' first space station, Salyut 1, was launched in 1971. Later, the Soviet Union and Russia orbited the Mir space station. America's first space station, and the only one that it deployed during the first four decades of human spaceflight, was the 100-ton Skylab launched in 1973. Today, the United States, Russia and other international partners are constructing the International Space Station, Alpha.

## The Future of Space Vehicles

A major imperative for the future is to reduce the cost of getting to orbit. To this end significant funds have already been invested in technology development towards a single-stage-to-orbit reusable space vehicle to replace the shuttle. Problems with the X-33 scaled prototype led to a recognition that development of such a vehicle is still years away. The U.S. government has committed to a series of shuttle upgrades to keep the fleet flying and to improve safety and capability. A likely intermediate stage is development of a two-stage-to-orbit reusable vehicle, possibly building on shuttle components with fly-back boosters. (The shuttle discards its solid rocket boosters minutes after launch. The casings are reclaimed from the sea and towed back to land to be reused. A booster that could fly back to the space center runway on automatic pilot after fulfilling its role in boosting the spacecraft launch would be a significant advance.)

**payloads** any cargo launched aboard a rocket that is destined for space, including communications satellites or modules, supplies, equipment, and astronauts; does not include the vehicle used to move the cargo or the propellant that powers the vehicle

**antimatter** matter composed of antiparticles, such as positrons and antiprotons

**libration points** one of five gravitationally stable points related to two orbiting masses; three points are metastable, but L4 and L5 are stable

Looking to the far horizon, space elevators, launch systems driven by a massive catapult system (the so-called slingatron), or sophisticated magnets, could revolutionize the way **payloads** are launched to space. New forms of nuclear propulsion, plasma propulsion, **antimatter** systems, vastly improved solar sail techniques, faster-than-light travel, or the exploitation of zero point energy for transportation through space could move humankind into a new space age that leaves traditional chemical propulsion behind.

The establishment of permanent space colonies has fascinated people for decades. Permanent settlements have been proposed for the Moon and Mars, as well as stable positions in space equidistant from both Earth and Moon called the Lagrangian **libration points**. Space visionaries advocated a space colony at L5 early in the space age. More recently NASA scientists have considered placing a space station at L2. In the future, space transportation vehicles serving humans and space habitats will become more spacious and more conducive to long journeys or permanent habitation.

Eventually, space settlers, like the immigrants who came to America, might consider their settlement "home" and become increasingly self-sufficient by growing their own food and using solar energy to generate electricity and manufacture goods. SEE ALSO CAPSULES (VOLUME 3); GETTING TO SPACE CHEAPLY (VOLUME 1); LAUNCH VEHICLES, EXPENDABLE (VOLUME 1); LUNAR BASES (VOLUME 4); MARS BASES (VOLUME 4); REUSABLE LAUNCH VEHICLES (VOLUME 4); SATELLITES, TYPES OF (VOLUME 4); SETTLEMENTS (VOLUME 4); SPACE ELEVATORS (VOLUME 4); SPACE SHUTTLE (VOLUME 3); SPACE STATIONS OF THE FUTURE (VOLUME 4).

*Pat Dasch and John F. Kross*

### Bibliography

Hacker, Barton C., and James M. Grimwood. *On the Shoulders of Titans: A History of Project Gemini.* Washington, DC: NASA Historical Series (NASA SP-4203), 1977.

Lewis, Richard S. *Appointment on the Moon.* New York: The Viking Press, 1968.

Millis, Marc G. "Breaking through to the Stars." *Ad Astra* 9, no. 1 (January–February 1997):36–41.

Puthoff, H. E. "Space Propulsion: Can Empty Space Itself Provide a Solution?" *Ad Astra* 9, no. 1 (January–February 1977):42–46.

Yenne, Bill. *The Encyclopedia of US Spacecraft.* New York: Exeter Books, 1988.

### Internet Resources

*Colonization of Space.* NASA Ames Research Center. <http://lifesci3.arc.nasa.gov/SpaceSettlement/75SummerStudy/Table_of_Contents1.html>.

# Wormholes

Space-time wormholes are hypothetical objects in German-born Jewish physicist Albert Einstein's general theory of relativity, where intense gravitational fields warp space and time to provide shortcuts from one part of our universe to another (or worse, perhaps, a route from our universe to some other universe). Physicists have not found solid experimental evidence that wormholes exist, but there are reasonably convincing theoretical arguments that strongly suggest that wormholes should be part of the theory of **quantum gravity**.

As theoretical objects, wormholes were invented and named in the late 1950s by American physicist John Archibald Wheeler, an early pioneer in the quest for quantum gravity. Since then they have become a standard tool in science fiction (such as in the television series *Star Trek* and *Farscape* and the novel *Einstein's Bridge*), but they have also attracted a lot of serious scientific attention. Although physicists cannot conduct any experiments yet, wormholes can be used in "thought experiments" to see how solid and reliable certain theories are.

Science fiction stories make wormhole travel look relatively straightforward, if not exactly easy. The physicists' conception is more conservative and less encouraging: Naturally occurring wormholes, if they exist at all, are likely to be extremely small, about 10 septillion ($10^{25}$) times smaller than a typical atom. They are expected to be part of a quantum-mechanical "space-time foam" that is expected to arise at extremely short distances. Wormholes of this size are not useful for human travel, or even for sending signals.

**quantum gravity** an attempt to replace the inherently incompatible theories of quantum physics and Einstein gravity with some deeper theory that would have features of both, but be identical to neither

Wormholes theoretically provide passageways between two points in our own universe, or between universes.

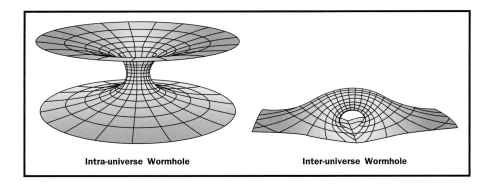

**Intra-universe Wormhole**　　　**Inter-universe Wormhole**

**black hole** object so massive for its size that its gravitational pull prevents everything, even light, from escaping

**vacuum** a space where air and all other molecules and atoms of matter have been removed

**space-time** in relativity, the four-dimensional space through which objects move and in which events happen

**quantum physics** branch of physics that uses quantum mechanics to explain physical systems

Creating a large wormhole, or artificially enlarging a small naturally occurring wormhole, would require the manipulation of large quantities of matter—planet loads of mass. A wormhole 1 meter (about 1 yard) across would require the manipulation of objects with the mass of the planet Jupiter and the squeezing of them into a region about a meter wide. Worse, because the gravitational field of a wormhole is in some sense repulsive (one would not want a **black hole** to form), one would need to manipulate large quantities of what is called "exotic matter," which is basically negative energy matter with less energy than the energy of an equal volume of **vacuum**.

Needless to say, we do not currently have the technology needed to do this, nor is there any realistic hope of acquiring such technology in the foreseeable future. We cannot even manipulate positive masses the size of Jupiter, nor have we ever found large quantities of negative mass lying around anywhere. So realistically, the prospects for space travel using wormholes is close to zero. This will not stop physicists from investigating the subject, but one should try to not be overly enthusiastic about the chances.

Because wormholes connect distant places, and the laws of **space-time** physics seem to treat space and time on an almost equal footing, it has also been suggested that wormholes should be able connect distant times: If you find a wormhole, it would seem at first glance to be relatively easy to turn it into a time machine. Now this does scare the physics community; allowing time travel into physics is, to say the least, awkward. There is an idea called "chronology protection," formulated by English physicist Stephen Hawking, to the effect that **quantum physics** may "keep the universe safe for historians" by automatically destroying any wormhole that gets too close to forming a time machine. As Hawking put it: "there is considerable evidence in favour of [chronology protection] based on the fact that we have not been invaded by hordes of tourists from the future." SEE ALSO COSMOLOGY (VOLUME 2); EINSTEIN, ALBERT (VOLUME 2); ZERO-POINT ENERGY (VOLUME 4).

*Matt Visser*

**Bibliography**

Morris, Michael S., and Kip S. Thorne. "Wormholes in Spacetime and Their Use for Interstellar Travel: A Tool for Teaching General Relativity." *American Journal of Physics* 56 (1988):395–412.

Thorne, Kip S. *Black Holes and Time Warps: Einstein's Outrageous Legacy*. New York: Norton, 1994.

Visser, Matt. *Lorentzian Wormholes: From Einstein to Hawking*. Reading, MA: American Institute of Physics Press, 1996.

# Zero-Point Energy

**Quantum physics** predicts the existence of an underlying sea of zero-point energy at every spot in the universe. This is different from the **cosmic microwave background** and is also referred to as the electromagnetic **quantum vacuum**, since it is the lowest energy state of otherwise empty space. This energy is so enormous that most physicists believe that even though zero-point energy seems to be an inescapable consequence of elementary quantum theory, it cannot be physically real. However, a minority of physicists accept it as real energy that we cannot directly sense because it is the same everywhere, even inside our bodies and measuring devices. From this perspective, the ordinary world of matter and energy is like a foam atop the quantum vacuum sea. It does not matter to a ship how deep the ocean is below it. If zero-point energy is real, there is the possibility that it can be tapped as a source of energy or be harnessed to generate a propulsive force for space travel.

## New Propulsion for Space Travel

The propeller or the jet engine of an aircraft pushes air backwards to propel the aircraft forward. A ship or boat propeller does the same thing with water. On Earth there is always air or water available to push against. But a rocket in space has nothing to push against, and so it needs to carry propellant to eject in place of air or water. As the propellant shoots out the back, the rocket reacts by moving forward. The fundamental problem is that a deep-space rocket would have to start out with all the propellant it would ever need. This quickly results in the need to carry more and more propellant just to propel the propellant. The breakthrough needed for deep-space travel is to overcome the need to carry propellant at all. How can one generate a propulsive force without carrying and ejecting propellant?

One possibility may involve a type of Casimir force. The Casimir force is an attraction between parallel metallic plates that has now been well measured. It can be attributed to a minutely tiny imbalance in the zero-point energy between the plates and the zero-point energy outside the plates. This is not currently useful for propulsion since it just pulls the plates together. If, however, some asymmetric variation of the Casimir force could be found, one could use it to sail through space as if propelled by a kind of quantum fluctuation wind. This is pure speculation at present.

The other requirement for space travel is energy. A thought experiment published by physicist Robert Forward in 1984 demonstrated how the Casimir force could in principle be used to extract energy from the quantum vacuum. Theoretical studies in the early 1990s verified that this was not contradictory to the laws of thermodynamics (because the zero-point energy is different from a thermal reservoir of heat). Unfortunately, the Forward process cannot be cycled to yield a continuous extraction of energy. A

**quantum physics** branch of physics that uses quantum mechanics to explain physical systems

**cosmic microwave background** ubiquitous, diffuse, uniform, thermal radiation created during the earliest hot phases of the universe

**quantum vacuum** consistent with the Heisenberg uncertainty principle, vacuum is not empty but is filled with zero-point energy and particle-antiparticle pairs constantly being created and then mutually annhilating each other

Casimir engine would be one whose cylinders could fire only once, after which the engine becomes useless.

## The Heisenberg Uncertainty Principle

The basis of zero-point energy is the Heisenberg uncertainty principle, one of the fundamental laws of quantum physics. According to this principle, the more precisely one measures the position of a moving particle, such as an electron, the less exact the best possible measurement of its momentum (mass times velocity) will be, and vice versa. The least possible uncertainty of position times momentum is specified by Planck's constant, h. A parallel uncertainty exists between measurements involving time and energy. This minimum uncertainty is not due to any correctable flaws in measurement but rather reflects an intrinsic quantum fuzziness in the very nature of energy and matter.

A useful calculational tool in physics is the ideal harmonic oscillator: a hypothetical mass on a perfect spring moving back and forth. The Heisenberg uncertainty principle dictates that such an ideal harmonic oscillator—one small enough to be subject to quantum laws—can never come entirely to rest, because that would be a state of exactly zero energy, which is forbidden. In this case the average minimum energy is one-half h times the frequency, hf/2.

## The Origin of Zero-Point Energy

The zero-point energy is electromagnetic in nature and is like ordinary radio waves, light, **X rays**, gamma rays, and so forth. Classically, electromagnetic radiation can be pictured as waves flowing through space at the speed of light. The waves are not waves of anything substantive but are ripples in a state of a theoretically defined field. However, these waves do carry energy, and each wave has a specific direction, frequency, and **polarization state**. This is called a "propagating mode of the electromagnetic field."

Each mode is subject to the Heisenberg uncertainty principle. This means that each mode is equivalent to a harmonic oscillator. From this analogy, every mode of the field must have hf/2 as its average minimum energy. This is a tiny amount of energy, but the number of modes is enormous and indeed increases as the square of the frequency. The product of the tiny energy per mode times the huge spatial density of modes yields a very high theoretical zero-point energy density per cubic centimeter.

From this line of reasoning, quantum physics predicts that all of space must be filled with electromagnetic zero-point fluctuations (also called the zero-point field), creating a universal sea of zero-point energy. The density of this energy depends critically on where in frequency the zero-point fluctuations cease. Since space itself is thought to break up into a kind of **quantum foam** at a tiny distance scale called the Planck scale ($10^{-33}$ centimeters), it is argued that the zero-point fluctuations must cease at a corresponding Planck frequency ($10^{43}$ hertz). If this is the case, the zero-point energy density would be 110 orders of magnitude greater than the radiant energy at the center of the Sun.

## Inertia, Gravitation, and Zero-Point Energy

Theoretical work from the 1990s suggests a tantalizing connection between inertia and zero-point energy. When a passenger in an airplane feels pushed

**X rays** high-energy radiation just beyond the ultraviolet portion of the spectrum

**polarization state** degree to which a beam of electromagnetic radiation has all of the vibrations in the same plane or direction

**quantum foam** notion that there is a smallest distance scale at which space itself is not a continuous medium, but breaks up into a seething foam of wormholes and tiny black holes far smaller than a proton

against his seat as the airplane accelerates down the runway, or when a driver feels pushed to the left when her car makes a sharp turn to the right, what is doing the pushing? Since the time of English physicist and mathematician Isaac Newton (1642–1727), this pushing feeling has been attributed to an innate property of matter called inertia. In 1994 a process was discovered whereby the zero-point fluctuations could be the source of the push one feels when changing speed or direction, both being forms of acceleration. The zero-point fluctuations could be the underlying cause of inertia. If that is the case, then people are actually sensing the zero-point energy with every move they make. The zero-point energy would be the origin of inertia, hence the cause of mass.

The principle of equivalence would require an analogous connection for gravitation. German-born American physicist Albert Einstein's general theory of relativity successfully accounts for the motions of freely falling objects on geodesics (the shortest distance between two points in curved **space-time**), but it does not provide a mechanism for generating a reaction force for objects when they are forced to deviate from geodesic tracks. A theoretical study sponsored by the National Aeronautics and Space Administration has demonstrated that an object undergoing acceleration or one held fixed in a gravitational field would both experience the same kind of asymmetric pattern in the zero-point radiation field, the asymmetry yielding the inertia reaction force or weight, respectively. The weight one measures on a scale would be due to zero-point energy.

**space-time** in relativity, the four-dimensional space through which objects move and in which events happen

The possibility that electromagnetic zero-point energy may be involved in the production of inertial and gravitational forces opens the possibility that both inertia and gravitation might someday be controlled and manipulated. Imagine being accelerated from zero to light speed in a fraction of a second without experiencing any devastating **G forces**. Such a science fiction–like possibility could someday become real and have a profound impact on propulsion and space travel. SEE ALSO ACCESSING SPACE (VOLUME 1); POWER, METHODS OF GENERATING (VOLUME 4).

**G force** the force an astronaut or pilot experiences when undergoing large accelerations

*Bernard Haisch*

**Bibliography**

Haisch, Bernard, Alfonso Rueda, and H. E. Puthoff. "Inertia as a Zero-Point-Field Lorentz Force." *Physical Review A* 49 (1994):678–694.

Rueda, Alfonso, and Bernard Haisch. "Contribution to Inertial Mass by Reaction of the Vacuum to Accelerated Motion." *Foundations of Physics* 28 (1998):1,057–1,108.

———. "Inertia Mass as Reaction of the Vacuum to Accelerated Motion." *Physics Letters A* 240, no. 3 (1998):115–126.

# Zubrin, Robert

**American Aerospace Engineer**
**1952–**

Robert Maynard Zubrin is an aerospace engineer credited for revolutionizing plans for the human exploration of Mars. After an early career as a teacher, Zubrin went to graduate school in the mid-1980s, earning a doctorate in nuclear engineering from the University of Washington.

As an engineer for the aerospace firm Martin Marietta (now Lockheed Martin) starting in the late 1980s, Zubrin worked on projects ranging from a nuclear rocket engine to a spaceplane. His best-known work at the company, however, was the development of "Mars Direct," a new architecture for human missions to Mars that would rely on the resources available on Mars to reduce their cost. Mars Direct attracted the attention of the National Aeronautics and Space Administration, which incorporated aspects of the proposal into its Mars mission plans.

Zubrin also coauthored a popular book about Mars Direct, *The Case for Mars* (1996). Zubrin used the success of the book as a springboard in 1998 for creating the Mars Society, a membership organization that promotes the human exploration of Mars. Zubrin serves as president of the society, which has supported a number of research projects designed to further technology needed for future Mars missions. Zubrin also founded Pioneer Astronautics, a small aerospace firm in Colorado he created after leaving Lockheed Martin in 1996. SEE ALSO HUMAN MISSIONS TO MARS (VOLUME 3); MARS (VOLUME 2); MARS BASES (VOLUME 4); MARS DIRECT (VOLUME 4).

*Jeff Foust*

**Bibliography**

Zubrin, Robert. *Entering Space: Creating a Spacefaring Civilization*. New York: Jeremy P. Tarcher/Putnam, 1999.

———. *First Landing*. New York: Ace Books, 2001.

Zubrin, Robert, with Richard Wagner. *The Case for Mars: The Plan to Settle the Red Planet and Why We Must*. New York: Free Press, 1996.

**Internet Resources**

"Dr. Robert Zubrin." *Pioneer Astronautics*. <http://www.pioneerastro.com/Team/rzubrin.html>.

# Photo and Illustration Credits

## Volume 1

AP/Wide World Photos, Inc.: **2, 5, 25, 26, 41, 56, 77, 82, 84, 113, 115, 117, 143, 148, 151, 153, 156, 161, 180, 208, 211;** Associated Press: **7;** NASA: **13, 21, 28, 30, 32, 34, 38, 43, 54, 67, 71, 79, 80, 90, 94, 96, 101, 102, 107, 121, 123, 158, 169, 178, 182, 193, 195, 200, 203, 207;** MSFC–NASA: **15;** Photograph by Kipp Teague. NASA: **16;** Illustration by Bonestell Space Art. © Bonestell Space Art: **18, 19;** Reuters/Mike Theiler/Archive Photos: **20;** © Roger Ressmeyer/Corbis: **46, 144, 199;** The Kobal Collection: **49, 73;** AP Photo/ Lenin Kumarasiri: **53;** © Bettmann/CORBIS: **58, 64;** © CORBIS: **60, 98;** © Reuters NewMedia Inc./CORBIS: **63;** © AFP/Corbis: **86, 165, 185;** Courtesy NASA/JPL/Caltech: **92;** International Space University: **106;** European Space Agency/Photo Researchers, Inc.: **109;** Photograph by David Parker. ESA/National Audubon Society Collection/ Photo Researchers, Inc.: **119;** © Joseph Sohm, ChromoSohm Inc./Corbis: **126;** Archive Photos, Inc.: **129, 134;** Illustration by Pat Rawlings. NASA: **136, 190;** Photograph © Dr. Dennis Morrison and Dr. Benjamin Mosier. Instrumentation Technology Associates, Inc.: **139;** © Dr. Allen Edmunsen. Instrumentation Technology Associates, Inc.: **140;** ©NASA/Roger Ressmeyer/Corbis: **157;** The Dwight D. Eisenhower Library: **162;** Landsat 7 Science Team/USDA Agricultural Research Service/NASA: **172;** Richard T. Nowitz/Corbis: **186;** Courtesy of Walter A. Lyons: **189;** UPI/Corbis-Bettmann: **206;** The Library of Congress: **213.**

## Volume 2

NASA and The Hubble Heritage Team (STScl/AURA): **2, 51, 53, 206;** NASA/ JHUAPL: **4, 5;** AP/Wide World Photos/ Johns Hopkins University/NASA: **6;** © Roger Ressmeyer/Corbis: **8, 21, 24, 122, 147, 170, 171, 174;** NASA: **11, 29, 33, 37, 54, 65, 69, 72, 91, 96, 99, 100, 102, 107, 113, 117, 127, 128, 130, 135, 143, 149, 155, 157, 162, 165, 166, 178, 183, 191, 195, 196, 200, 203, 204, 209, 217;** NASA/STScl: **15;** © Royal Observatory, Edinburgh/Science Photo Library, National Audubon Society Collection/Photo Researchers, Inc.: **17;** Illustration by Don Davis. NASA: **26;** The Library of Congress: **28, 30, 68;** Photograph by Robert E. Wallace. U.S. Geological Survey: **36;** The Bettmann Archive/Corbis-Bettmann: **39;** Photograph by Kipp Teague. NASA: **41;** Courtesy of NASA/JPL/Caltech: **43, 44, 79, 88, 94, 110, 111, 116, 136, 150, 161, 176, 181, 215;** © AFP/Corbis: **49, 58, 60;** © Corbis: **57, 185;** © Bettmann/Corbis: **75, 81, 84, 119;** Courtesy of NASA/JPL/ University of Arizona: **77;** Courtesy of NASA/JPL: **78, 144, 167, 175, 212;** AP/Wide World Photos: **85, 139, 164, 173, 208;** David Crisp and the WFPC2 Science Team (JPL/Caltech): **93;** Courtesy of Robert G. Strom and the Lunar and Planetary Lab: **102;** © Rick Kujawa: **105;** © Richard and Dorothy Norton, Science Graphics: **106;** © Reiters NewMedia Inc./Corbis: **108;**

Stephen and Donna O'Meara/Photo Researchers, Inc.: **120**; Photograph by Seth Shostak. Photo Researchers, Inc.: **133**; © Sandy Felsenthal/Corbis: **140**; MSFC–NASA: **169**; National Oceanic and Atmospheric Administration/Department of Commerce: **184**; Spectrum Astro, Inc., 2000: **189**; Photo Researchers, Inc.: **199**; Courtesy of SOHO/EIT Consortium: **202**; Kenneth Seidelmann, U.S. Naval Observatory, and NASA: **211**.

## Volume 3

© Bettmann/Corbis: **2, 83**; NASA: **4, 6, 10, 14, 16, 17, 18, 20, 25, 26, 35, 38, 41, 43, 45, 48, 51, 53, 55, 57, 59, 60, 64, 65, 66, 70, 72, 74, 76, 78, 80, 85, 90, 94, 97, 101, 103, 107, 108, 111, 113, 120, 123, 126, 128, 131, 133, 134, 139, 140, 142, 144, 148, 150, 152, 158, 160, 161, 169, 172, 176, 178, 181, 184, 185, 188, 192, 193, 196, 200, 202, 207, 209, 211, 214, 219, 223, 225, 226, 233, 235**; Courtesy of Brad Joliff: **13**; © Metropolitan Tucson Convention & Visitors Bureau: **22**; AP/Wide World Photos: **28, 32, 155, 164, 203, 217**; MSFC–NASA: **49, 106, 118, 130, 154, 163, 175**; © NASA/Roger Ressmeyer/Corbis: **61**; Archive Photos, Inc.: **65, 137, 171**; Courtesy of NASA/JPL/Caltech: **73**; Illustration by Pat Rawlings. NASA: **88**; Hulton Getty Collection/Archive Photos: **116**; © Roger Ressmeyer/Corbis: **167, 222**; Photo

Researchers, Inc.: **189**; The Library of Congress: **216**; Getty Images: **228**.

## Volume 4

NASA: **2, 8, 10, 14, 19, 22, 26, 35, 46, 54, 59, 67, 72, 82, 88, 90, 93, 99, 104, 112, 113, 119, 120, 122, 130, 144, 148, 153, 157, 164, 172, 189, 200, 202**; Denise Watt/NASA: **4**; Courtesy of NASA/JPL/Caltech: **5, 62, 100, 116**; © Corbis: **7, 126**; © Ted Streshinsky/Corbis: **17**; Photo courtesy of NASA/Viking Orbiter : **9**; Royal Observatory, Edinburgh/Science Photo Library/Photo Researchers, Inc.: **23**; © Paul A. Souders/Corbis: **25**; AP/Wide World Photos: **32, 155, 181, 182, 186**; © Charles O'Rear/Corbis: **39, 139**; Photograph by Detlev Van Ravenswaay. Picture Press/Corbis–Bettmann: **41**; Kobal Collection/Lucasfilm/20th Century Fox: **43**; Kobal Collection/Universal: **44**; Courtesy of NASA/JPL: **65, 94**; MSFC–NASA: **69, 80**; © Reuters NewMedia Inc./Corbis: **74**; © Bettmann/Corbis: **78, 151**; © AFP/Corbis: **102**; Agence France Presse/Corbis–Bettmann: **107**; Archive Photos, Inc.: **109, 135**; Dennis Davidson/NASA: **86**; Paramount Pictures/Archive Photos: **110**; John Frassanito and Associates/NASA: **141**; Illustration by Pat Rawlings. NASA: **168, 174**; Painting by Michael Carroll: **191**; Tethers Unlimited, Inc.: **195, 196**; Kobal Collection/Amblin/Universal: **198**.

# Glossary

**ablation** removal of the outer layers of an object by erosion, melting, or vaporization

**abort-to-orbit** emergency procedure planned for the space shuttle and other spacecraft if the spacecraft reaches a lower than planned orbit

**accretion** the growth of a star or planet through the accumulation of material from a companion star or the surrounding interstellar matter

**adaptive optics** the use of computers to adjust the shape of a telescope's optical system to compensate for gravity or temperature variations

**aeroballistic** describes the combined aerodynamics and ballistics of an object, such as a spacecraft, in flight

**aerobraking** the technique of using a planet's atmosphere to slow down an incoming spacecraft; its use requires the spacecraft to have a heat shield, because the friction that slows the craft is turned into intense heat

**aerodynamic heating** heating of the exterior skin of a spacecraft, aircraft, or other object moving at high speed through the atmosphere

**Agena** a multipurpose rocket designed to perform ascent, precision orbit injection, and missions from low Earth orbit to interplanetary space; also served as a docking target for the Gemini spacecraft

**algae** simple photosynthetic organisms, often aquatic

**alpha proton X-ray** analytical instrument that bombards a sample with alpha particles (consisting of two protons and two neutrons); the X rays are generated through the interaction of the alpha particles and the sample

**altimeter** an instrument designed to measure altitude above sea level

**amplitude** the height of a wave or other oscillation; the range or extent of a process or phenomenon

**angular momentum** the angular equivalent of linear momentum; the product of angular velocity and moment of inertia (moment of inertia = mass $\times$ radius$^2$)

**angular velocity** the rotational speed of an object, usually measured in radians per second

**anisotropy** a quantity that is different when measured in different directions or along different axes

**annular** ring-like

**anomalies** phenomena that are different from what is expected

**anorthosite** a light-colored rock composed mainly of the mineral feldspar (an aluminum silicate); commonly occurs in the crusts of Earth and the Moon

**anthropocentrism** valuing humans above all else

**antimatter** matter composed of antiparticles, such as positrons and antiprotons

**antipodal** at the opposite pole; two points on a planet that are diametrically opposite

**aperture** an opening, door, or hatch

**aphelion** the point in an object's orbit that is farthest from the Sun

**Apollo** American program to land men on the Moon; Apollo 11, 12, 14, 15, 16, and 17 delivered twelve men to the lunar surface between 1969 and 1972 and returned them safely back to Earth

**asthenosphere** the weaker portion of a planet's interior just below the rocky crust

**astrometry** the measurement of the positions of stars on the sky

**astronomical unit** the average distance between Earth and the Sun (152 million kilometers [93 million miles])

**atmospheric probe** a separate piece of a spacecraft that is launched from it and separately enters the atmosphere of a planet on a one-way trip, making measurements until it hits a surface, burns up, or otherwise ends its mission

**atmospheric refraction** the bending of sunlight or other light caused by the varying optical density of the atmosphere

**atomic nucleus** the protons and neutrons that make up the core of an atom

**atrophy** condition that involves withering, shrinking, or wasting away

**auroras** atmospheric phenomena consisting of glowing bands or sheets of light in the sky caused by high-speed charged particles striking atoms in Earth's upper atmosphere

**avionics** electronic equipment designed for use on aircraft, spacecraft, and missiles

**azimuth** horizontal angular distance from true north measured clockwise from true north (e.g., if North = 0 degrees; East = 90 degrees; South = 180 degrees; West = 270 degrees)

**ballast** heavy substance used to increase the stability of a vehicle

**ballistic** the path of an object in unpowered flight; the path of a spacecraft after the engines have shut down

**basalt** a dark, volcanic rock with abundant iron and magnesium and relatively low silica common on all of the terrestrial planets

**base load** the minimum amount of energy needed for a power grid

**beacon signal generator** a radio transmitter emitting signals for guidance or for showing location

**berth space** the human accommodations needed by a space station, cargo ship, or other vessel

**Big Bang** name given by astronomers to the event marking the beginning of the universe when all matter and energy came into being

**biocentric** notion that all living organisms have intrinsic value

**biogenic** resulting from the actions of living organisms; or, necessary for life

**bioregenerative** referring to a life support system in which biological processes are used; physiochemical and/or nonregenerative processes may also be used

**biosignatures** the unique traces left in the geological record by living organisms

**biosphere** the interaction of living organisms on a global scale

**bipolar outflow** jets of material (gas and dust) flowing away from a central object (e.g., a protostar) in opposite directions

**bitumen** a thick, almost solid form of hydrocarbons, often mixed with other minerals

**black holes** objects so massive for their size that their gravitational pull prevents everything, even light, from escaping

**bone mineral density** the mass of minerals, mostly calcium, in a given volume of bone

**breccia** mixed rock composed of fragments of different rock types; formed by the shock and heat of meteorite impacts

**bright rays** lines of lighter material visible on the surface of a body and caused by relatively recent impacts

**brown dwarf** star-like object less massive than 0.08 times the mass of the Sun, which cannot undergo thermonuclear process to generate its own luminosity

**calderas** the bowl-shaped crater at the top of a volcano caused by the collapse of the central part of the volcano

**Callisto** one of the four large moons of Jupiter; named for one of the Greek nymphs

**Caloris basin** the largest (1,300 kilometers [806 miles] in diameter) well-preserved impact basin on Mercury viewed by Mariner 10

**capsule** a closed compartment designed to hold and protect humans, instruments, and/or equipment, as in a spacecraft

**carbon-fiber composites** combinations of carbon fibers with other materials such as resins or ceramics; carbon fiber composites are strong and light-weight

**carbonaceous meteorites** the rarest kind of meteorites, they contain a high percentage of carbon and carbon-rich compounds

**carbonate** a class of minerals, such as chalk and limestone, formed by carbon dioxide reacting in water

**cartographic** relating to the making of maps

**Cassini mission** a robotic spacecraft mission to the planet Saturn scheduled to arrive in July 2004 when the Huygens probe will be dropped into Titan's atmosphere while the Cassini spacecraft studies the planet

**catalyst** a chemical compound that accelerates a chemical reaction without itself being used up; any process that acts to accelerate change in a system

**catalyze** to change by the use of a catalyst

**cell culture** a means of growing mammalian (including human) cells in the research laboratory under defined experimental conditions

**cellular array** the three-dimensional placement of cells within a tissue

**centrifugal** directed away from the center through spinning

**centrifuge** a device that uses centrifugal force caused by spinning to simulate gravity

**Cepheid variables** a class of variable stars whose luminosity is related to their period. Their periods can range from a few hours to about 100 days and the longer the period, the brighter the star

**Čerenkov light** light emitted by a charged particle moving through a medium, such as air or water, at a velocity greater than the phase velocity of light in that medium; usually a faint, eerie, bluish, optical glow

**chassis** frame on which a vehicle is constructed

**chondrite meteorites** a type of meteorite that contains spherical clumps of loosely consolidated minerals

**cinder field** an area dominated by volcanic rock, especially the cinders ejected from explosive volcanoes

**circadian rhythm** activities and bodily functions that recur every twenty-four hours, such as sleeping and eating

**Clarke orbit** geostationary orbit; named after science fiction writer Arthur C. Clarke, who first realized the usefulness of this type of orbit for communication and weather satellites

**coagulate** to cause to come together into a coherent mass

**comet matrix material** the substances that form the nucleus of a comet; dust grains embedded in frozen methane, ammonia, carbon dioxide, and water

**cometary outgassing** vaporization of the frozen gases that form a comet nucleus as the comet approaches the Sun and warms

**communications infrastructure** the physical structures that support a network of telephone, Internet, mobile phones, and other communication systems

**convection** the movement of heated fluid caused by a variation in density; hot fluid rises while cool fluid sinks

**convection currents** mechanism by which thermal energy moves because its density differs from that of surrounding material. Convection current is the movement pattern of thermal energy transferring within a medium

**convective processes** processes that are driven by the movement of heated fluids resulting from a variation in density

**coronal holes** large, dark holes seen when the Sun is viewed in X-ray or ultraviolet wavelengths; solar wind emanates from the coronal holes

**coronal mass ejections** large quantities of solar plasma and magnetic field launched from the Sun into space

**cosmic microwave background** ubiquitous, diffuse, uniform, thermal radiation created during the earliest hot phases of the universe

**cosmic radiation** high energy particles that enter Earth's atmosphere from outer space causing cascades of mesons and other particles

**cosmocentric ethic** an ethical position that establishes the universe as the priority in a value system or appeals to something characteristic of the universe that provides justification of value

**cover glass** a sheet of glass used to cover the solid state device in a solar cell

**crash-landers** or hard-lander; a spacecraft that collides with the planet, making no—or little—attempt to slow down; after collision, the spacecraft ceases to function because of the (intentional) catastrophic failure

**crawler transporter** large, tracked vehicles used to move the assembled Apollo/Saturn from the VAB to the launch pad

**cryogenic** related to extremely low temperatures; the temperature of liquid nitrogen or lower

**cryptocometary** another name for carbonaceous asteroids—asteroids that contain a high percentage of carbon compounds mixed with frozen gases

**cryptoendolithic microbial** microbial ecosystems that live inside sandstone in extreme environments such as Antarctica

**crystal lattice** the arrangement of atoms inside a crystal

**crystallography** the study of the internal structure of crystals

**dark matter** matter that interacts with ordinary matter by gravity but does not emit electromagnetic radiation; its composition is unknown

**density-separation jigs** a form of gravity separation of materials with different densities that uses a pulsating fluid

**desiccation** the process of drying up

**detruents** microorganisms that act as decomposers in a controlled environmental life support system

**diffuse** spread out; not concentrated

**DNA** deoxyribonucleic acid; the molecule used by all living things on Earth to transmit genetic information

**docking system** mechanical and electronic devices that work jointly to bring together and physically link two spacecraft in space

**doped** semiconductor such as silicon with an addition of small amounts of an impurity such as phosphorous to generate more charge carriers (such as electrons)

**dormant comet** a comet whose volatile gases have all been vaporized, leaving behind only the heavy materials

**downlink** the radio dish and receiver through which a satellite or spacecraft transmits information back to Earth

**drag** a force that opposes the motion of an aircraft or spacecraft through the atmosphere

**dunites** rock type composed almost entirely of the mineral olivine, crystallized from magma beneath the Moon's surface

**dynamic isotope power** the decay of isotopes such as plutonium-238, and polonium-210 produces heat, which can be transformed into electricity by radioisotopic thermoelectric generators

**Earth-Moon LaGrange** five points in space relative to Earth and the Moon where the gravitational forces on an object balance; two points, 60 degrees from the Moon in orbit, are candidate points for a permanent space settlement due to their gravitational stability

**eccentric** the term that describes how oval the orbit of a planet is

**ecliptic** the plane of Earth's orbit

**EH condrites** a rare form of meteorite containing a high concentration of the mineral enstatite (a type of pyroxene) and over 30 percent iron

**ejecta** the pieces of material thrown off by a star when it explodes; or, material thrown out of an impact crater during its formation

**ejector ramjet** engine design that uses a small rocket mounted in front of the ramjet to provide a flow of heated air, allowing the ramjet to provide thrust when stationary

**electrodynamic** pertaining to the interaction of moving electric charges with magnetic and electric fields

**electrolytes** a substance that when dissolved in water creates an electrically conducting solution

**electromagnetic spectrum** the entire range of wavelengths of electromagnetic radiation

**electron** a negatively charged subatomic particle

**electron volts** units of energy equal to the energy gained by an electron when it passes through a potential difference of 1 volt in a vacuum

**electrostatic separation** separation of substances by the use of electrically charged plates

**elliptical** having an oval shape

**encapsulation** enclosing within a capsule

**endocrine** system in the body that creates and secretes substances called hormones into the blood

**equatorial orbit** an orbit parallel to a body's geographic equator

**equilibruim point** the point where forces are in balance

**Europa** one of the large satellites of Jupiter

**eV** an electron volt is the energy gained by an electron when moved across a potential of one volt. Ordinary molecules, such as air, have an energy of about $3 \times 10^{-2}$ eV

**event horizon** the imaginary spherical shell surrounding a black hole that marks the boundary where no light or any other information can escape

**excavation** a hole formed by mining or digging

**expendable launch vehicles** launch vehicles, such as a rocket, not intended to be reused

**extrasolar planets** planets orbiting stars other than the Sun

**extravehicular activity** a space walk conducted outside a spacecraft cabin, with the crew member protected from the environment by a pressurized space suit

**extremophiles** microorganisms that can survive in extreme environments such as high salinity or near boiling water

**extruded** forced through an opening

**failsafe** a system designed to be failure resistant through robust construction and redundant functions

**fairing** a structure designed to provide low aerodynamic drag for an aircraft or spacecraft in flight

**fault** a fracture in rock in the upper crust of a planet along which there has been movement

**feedstock** the raw materials introduced into an industrial process from which a finished product is made

**feldspathic** rock containing a high proportion of the mineral feldspar

**fiber-optic cable** a thin strand of ultrapure glass that carries information in the form of light, with the light turned on and off rapidly to represent the information sent

**fission** act of splitting a heavy atomic nucleus into two lighter ones, releasing tremendous energy

**flares** intense, sudden releases of energy

**flybys** flight path that takes the spacecraft close enough to a planet to obtain good observations; the spacecraft then continues on a path away from the planet but may make multiple passes

**fracture** any break in rock, from small "joints" that divide rocks into planar blocks (such as that seen in road cuts) to vast breaks in the crusts of unspecified movement

**freefall** the motion of a body acted on by no forces other than gravity, usually in orbit around Earth or another celestial body

**free radical** a molecule with a high degree of chemical reactivity due to the presence of an unpaired electron

**frequencies** the number of oscillations or vibrations per second of an electromagnetic wave or any wave

**fuel cells** cells that react a fuel (such as hydrogen) and an oxidizer (such as oxygen) together; the chemical energy of the initial reactants is released by the fuel cell in the form of electricity

**fusion** the act of releasing nuclear energy by combining lighter elements such as hydrogen into heavier elements

**fusion fuel** fuel suitable for use in a nuclear fusion reactor

**G force** the force an astronaut or pilot experiences when undergoing large accelerations

**galaxy** a system of as many as hundreds of billions of stars that have a common gravitational attraction

**Galilean satellite** one of the four large moons of Jupiter first discovered by Galileo

**Galileo mission** succesful robot exploration of the outer solar system; this mission used gravity assists from Venus and Earth to reach Jupiter, where it dropped a probe into the atmosphere and studied the planet for nearly seven years

**gamma rays** a form of radiation with a shorter wavelength and more energy than X rays

**Ganymede** one of the four large moons of Jupiter; the largest moon in the solar system

**Gemini** the second series of American-piloted spacecraft, crewed by two astronauts; the Gemini missions were rehearsals of the spaceflight techniques needed to go to the Moon

**general relativity** a branch of science first described by Albert Einstein showing the relationship between gravity and acceleration

**geocentric** a model that places Earth at the center of the universe

**geodetic survey** determination of the exact position of points on Earth's surface and measurement of the size and shape of Earth and of Earth's gravitational and magnetic fields

**geomagnetic field** Earth's magnetic field; under the influence of solar wind, the magnetic field is compressed in the Sunward direction and stretched out in the downwind direction, creating the magnetosphere, a complex, teardrop-shaped cavity around Earth

**geospatial** relating to measurement of Earth's surface as well as positions on its surface

**geostationary** remaining above a fixed point above Earth's equator

**geostationary orbit** a specific altitude of an equatorial orbit where the time required to circle the planet matches the time it takes the planet to rotate on its axis. An object in geostationary orbit will always remain over the same geographic location on the equator of the planet it orbits

**geosynchronous** remaining fixed in an orbit 35,786 kilometers (22,300 miles) above Earth's surface

**geosynchronous orbit** a specific altitude of an equatorial orbit where the time required to circle the planet matches the time it takes the planet to rotate on its axis. An object in geostationary orbit will always remain over the same geographic location on the equator of the planet it orbits

**gimbal motors** motors that direct the nozzle of a rocket engine to provide steering

**global change** a change, such as average ocean temperature, affecting the entire planet

**global positioning systems** a system of satellites and receivers that provide direct determination of the geographical location of the receiver

**globular clusters** roughly spherical collections of hundreds of thousands of old stars found in galactic haloes

**grand unified theory** (GUT) states that, at a high enough energy level (about $10^{25}$ eV), the electromagnetic force, strong force, and weak force all merge into a single force

**gravitational assist** the technique of flying by a planet to use its energy to "catapult" a spacecraft on its way—this saves fuel and thus mass and cost of a mission; gravitational assists typically make the total mission duration longer, but they also make things possible that otherwise would not be possible

**gravitational contraction** the collapse of a cloud of gas and dust due to the mutual gravitational attraction of the parts of the cloud; a possible source of excess heat radiated by some Jovian planets

**gravitational lenses** two or more images of a distant object formed by the bending of light around an intervening massive object

**gravity assist** using the gravity of a planet during a close encounter to add energy to the motion of a spacecraft

**gravity gradient** the difference in the acceleration of gravity at different points on Earth and at different distances from Earth

**gravity waves** waves that propagate through space and are caused by the movement of large massive bodies, such as black holes and exploding stars

**greenhouse effect** process by which short wavelength energy (e.g., visible light) penetrates an object's atmosphere and is absorbed by the surface, which reradiates this energy as longer wavelength infrared (thermal) energy; this energy is blocked from escaping to space by molecules (e.g., $H_2O$ and $CO_2$) in the atmosphere; and as a result, the surface warms

**gyroscope** a spinning disk mounted so that its axis can turn freely and maintain a constant orientation in space

**hard-lander** spacecraft that collides with the planet or satellite, making no attempt to slow its descent; also called crash-landers

**heliosphere** the volume of space extending outward from the Sun that is dominated by solar wind; it ends where the solar wind transitions into the interstellar medium, somewhere between 40 and 100 astronomical units from the Sun

**helium-3** a stable isotope of helium whose nucleus contains two protons and one neutron

**hertz** unit of frequency equal to one cycle per second

**high-power klystron tubes** a type of electron tube used to generate high frequency electromagnetic waves

**hilly and lineated terrain** the broken-up surface of Mercury at the antipode of the Caloris impact basin

**hydrazine** a dangerous and corrosive compound of nitrogen and hydrogen commonly used in high powered rockets and jet engines

**hydroponics** growing plants using water and nutrients in solution instead of soil as the root medium

**hydrothermal** relating to high temperature water

**hyperbaric chamber** compartment where air pressure can be carefully controlled; used to gradually acclimate divers, astronauts, and others to changes in pressure and air composition

**hypergolic** fuels and oxidizers that ignite on contact with each other and need no ignition source

**hypersonic** capable of speeds over five times the speed of sound

**hyperspectral** imaging technique in remote sensing that uses at least sixteen contiguous bands of high spectral resolution over a region of the electromagnetic spectrum; used in NASA spacecraft Lewis' payload

**ilmenite** an important ore of titanium

**Imbrium Basin impact** largest and latest of the giant impact events that formed the mare-filled basins on the lunar near side

**impact craters** bowl-shaped depressions on the surfaces of planets or satellites that result from the impact of space debris moving at high speeds

**impact winter** the period following a large asteroidal or cometary impact when the Sun is dimmed by stratospheric dust and the climate becomes cold worldwide

**impact-melt** molten material produced by the shock and heat transfer from an impacting asteroid or meteorite

**in situ** in the natural or original location

**incandescence** glowing due to high temperature

**indurated rocks** rocks that have been hardened by natural processes

**information age** the era of our time when many businesses and persons are involved in creating, transmitting, sharing, using, and selling information, particularly through the use of computers

**infrared** portion of the electromagnetic spectrum with waves slightly longer than visible light

**infrared radiation** radiation whose wavelength is slightly longer than the wavelength of light

**infrastructure** the physical structures, such as roads and bridges, necessary to the functioning of a complex system

**intercrater plains** the oldest plains on Mercury that occur in the highlands and that formed during the period of heavy meteoroid bombardment

**interferometers** devices that use two or more telescopes to observe the same object at the same time in the same wavelength to increase angular resolution

**interplanetary trajectories** the solar orbits followed by spacecraft moving from one planet in the solar system to another

**interstellar** between the stars

**interstellar medium** the gas and dust found in the space between the stars

**ion propulsion** a propulsion system that uses charged particles accelerated by electric fields to provide thrust

**ionization** removing one or more electrons from an atom or molecule

**ionosphere** a charged particle region of several layers in the upper atmosphere created by radiation interacting with upper atmospheric gases

**isotopic ratios** the naturally occurring ratios between different isotopes of an element

**jettison** to eject, throw overboard, or get rid of

**Jovian** relating to the planet Jupiter

**Kevlar®** a tough aramid fiber resistant to penetration

**kinetic energy** the energy an object has due to its motion

**KREEP** acronym for material rich in potassium (K), rare earth elements (REE), and phosphorus (P)

**L-4** the gravitationally stable Lagrange point 60 degrees ahead of the orbiting planet

**L-5** the gravitationally stable Lagrange point 60 degrees behind the orbiting planet

**Lagrangian point** one of five gravitationally stable points related to two orbiting masses; three points are metastable, but L4 and L5 are stable

**laser-pulsing** firing periodic pulses from a powerful laser at a surface and measuring the length of time for return in order to determine topography

**libration point** one of five gravitationally stable points related to two orbiting masses; three points are metastable, but L4 and L5 are stable

**lichen** fungus that grows symbiotically with algae

**light year** the distance that light in a vacuum would travel in one year, or about 9.5 trillion kilometers (5.9 trillion miles)

**lithosphere** the rocky outer crust of a body

**littoral** the region along a coast or beach between high and low tides

**lobate scarps** a long sinuous cliff

**low Earth orbit** an orbit between 300 and 800 kilometers above Earth's surface

**lunar maria** the large, dark, lava-filled impact basins on the Moon thought by early astronomers to resemble seas

**Lunar Orbiter** a series of five unmanned missions in 1966 and 1967 that photographed much of the Moon at medium to high resolution from orbit

**macromolecules** large molecules such as proteins or DNA containing thousands or millions of individual atoms

**magnetohydrodynamic waves** a low frequency oscillation in a plasma in the presence of a magnetic field

**magnetometer** an instrument used to measure the strength and direction of a magnetic field

**magnetosphere** the magnetic cavity that surrounds Earth or any other planet with a magnetic field. It is formed by the interaction of the solar wind with the planet's magnetic field

**majority carriers** the more abundant charge carriers in semiconductors; the less abundant are called minority carriers; for n-type semiconductors, electrons are the majority carriers

**malady** a disorder or disease of the body

**many-bodied problem** in celestial mechanics, the problem of finding solutions to the equations for more than two orbiting bodies

**mare** dark-colored plains of solidified lava that mainly fill the large impact basins and other low-lying regions on the Moon

**Mercury** the first American piloted spacecraft, which carried a single astronaut into space; six Mercury missions took place between 1961 and 1963

**mesons** any of a family of subatomic particle that have masses between electrons and protons and that respond to the strong nuclear force; produced in the upper atmosphere by cosmic rays

**meteor** the physical manifestation of a meteoroid interacting with Earth's atmosphere; this includes visible light and radio frequency generation, and an ionized trail from which radar signals can be reflected. Also called a "shooting star"

**meteorites** any part of a meteoroid that survives passage through Earth's atmosphere

**meteoroid** a piece of interplanetary material smaller than an asteroid or comet

**meteorology** the study of atmospheric phenomena or weather

**meteorology satellites** satellites designed to take measurements of the atmosphere for determining weather and climate change

**microgravity** the condition experienced in freefall as a spacecraft orbits Earth or another body; commonly called weightlessness; only very small forces are perceived in freefall, on the order of one-millionth the force of gravity on Earth's surface

**micrometeoroid flux** the total mass of micrometeoroids falling into an atmosphere or on a surface per unit of time

**micrometeoroid** any meteoroid ranging in size from a speck of dust to a pebble

**microwave link** a connection between two radio towers that each transmit and receive microwave (radio) signals as a method of carrying information (similar to radio communications)

**minerals** crystalline arrangements of atoms and molecules of specified proportions that make up rocks

**missing matter** the mass of the universe that cannot be accounted for but is necessary to produce a universe whose overall curvature is "flat"

**monolithic** massive, solid, and uniform; an asteroid that is formed of one kind of material fused or melted into a single mass

**multi-bandgap photovoltaic** photovoltaic cells designed to respond to several different wavelengths of electromagnetic radiation

**multispectral** referring to several different parts of the electromagnetic spectrum, such as visible, infrared, and radar

**muons** the decay product of the mesons produced by cosmic rays; muons are about 100 times more massive than electrons but are still considered leptons that do not respond to the strong nuclear force

**near-Earth asteroids** asteroids whose orbits cross the orbit of Earth; collisions between Earth and near Earth asteroids happen a few times every million years

**nebulae** clouds of interstellar gas and/or dust

**neutron** a subatomic particle with no electrical charge

**neutron star** the dense core of matter composed almost entirely of neutrons that remain after a supernova explosion has ended the life of a massive star

**New Millennium** a NASA program to identify, develop and validate key instrument and spacecraft technologies that can lower cost and increase performance of science missions in the twenty-first century

**Next Generation Space Telescope** the telescope scheduled to be launched in 2009 that will replace the Hubble Space Telescope

**nuclear black holes** black holes that are in the centers of galaxies; they range in mass from a thousand to a billion times the mass of the Sun

**nuclear fusion** the combining of low-mass atoms to create heavier ones; the heavier atom's mass is slightly less than the sum of the mass of its constituents, with the remaining mass converted to energy

**nucleon** a proton or a neutron; one of the two particles found in a nucleus

**occultations** a phenomena that occurs when one astronomical object passes in front of another

**optical interferometry** a branch of optical physics that uses the wavelength of visible light to measure very small changes within the environment

**optical-interferometry based** the use of two or more telescopes observing the same object at the same time at the same visible wavelength to increase angular resolution

**optical radar** a method of determining the speed of moving bodies by sending a pulse of light and measuring how long it takes for the reflected light to return to the sender

**orbit** the circular or elliptical path of an object around a much larger object, governed by the gravitational field of the larger object

**orbital dynamics** the mathematical study of the nature of the forces governing the movement of one object in the gravitational field of another object

**orbital velocity** velocity at which an object needs to travel so that its flight path matches the curve of the planet it is circling; approximately 8 kilometers (5 miles) per second for low-altitude orbit around Earth

**orbiter** spacecraft that uses engines and/or aerobraking, and is captured into circling a planet indefinitely

**orthogonal** composed of right angles or relating to right angles

**oscillation** energy that varies between alternate extremes with a definable period

**osteoporosis** the loss of bone density; can occur after extended stays in space

**oxidizer** a substance mixed with fuel to provide the oxygen needed for combustion

**paleolake** depression that shows geologic evidence of having contained a lake at some previous time

**Paleozoic** relating to the first appearance of animal life on Earth

**parabolic trajectory** trajectory followed by an object with velocity equal to escape velocity

**parking orbit** placing a spacecraft temporarily into Earth orbit, with the engines shut down, until it has been checked out or is in the correct location for the main burn that sends it away from Earth

**payload** any cargo launched aboard a rocket that is destined for space, including communications satellites or modules, supplies, equipment, and astronauts; does not include the vehicle used to move the cargo or the propellant that powers the vehicle

**payload bay** the area in the shuttle or other spacecraft designed to carry cargo

**payload fairing** structure surrounding a payload; it is designed to reduce drag

**payload operations** experiments or procedures involving cargo or "payload" carried into orbit

**payload specialists** scientists or engineers selected by a company or a government employer for their expertise in conducting a specific experiment or commercial venture on a space shuttle mission

**perihelion** the point in an object's orbit that is closest to the Sun

**period of heavy meteoroid** the earliest period in solar system history (more than 3.8 billion years ago) when the rate of meteoroid impact was very high compared to the present

**perturbations** term used in orbital mechanics to refer to changes in orbits due to "perturbing" forces, such as gravity

**phased array** a radar antenna design that allows rapid scanning of an area without the need to move the antenna; a computer controls the phase of each dipole in the antenna array

**phased-array antennas** radar antenna designs that allow rapid scanning of an area without the need to move the antenna; a computer controls the phase of each dipole in the antenna array

**photolithography** printing that uses a photographic process to create the printing plates

**photometer** instrument to measure intensity of light

**photosynthesis** a process performed by plants and algae whereby light is transformed into energy and sugars

**photovoltaic** pertaining to the direct generation of electricity from electromagnetic radiation (light)

**photovoltaic arrays** sets of solar panels grouped together in big sheets; these arrays collect light from the Sun and use it to make electricity to power the equipment and machines

**photovoltaic cells** cells consisting of a thin wafer of a semiconductor material that incorporates a p-n junction, which converts incident light into electrical power; a number of photovoltaic cells connected in series makes a solar array

**plagioclase** most common mineral of the light-colored lunar highlands

**planetesimals** objects in the early solar system that were the size of large asteroids or small moons, large enough to begin to gravitationally influence each other

**pn single junction** in a transistor or other solid state device, the boundary between the two different kinds of semiconductor material

**point of presence** an access point to the Internet with a unique Internet Protocol (IP) address; Internet service providers (ISP) like AOL generally have multiple POPs on the Internet

**polar orbits** orbits that carry a satellite over the poles of a planet

**polarization state** degree to which a beam of electromagnetic radiation has all of the vibrations in the same plane or direction

**porous** allowing the passage of a fluid or gas through holes or passages in the substance

**power law energy spectrum** spectrum in which the distribution of energies appears to follow a power law

**primary** the body (planet) about which a satellite orbits

**primordial swamp** warm, wet conditions postulated to have occurred early in Earth's history as life was beginning to develop

**procurement** the process of obtaining

**progenitor star** the star that existed before a dramatic change, such as a supernova, occurred

**prograde** having the same general sense of motion or rotation as the rest of the solar system, that is, counterclockwise as seen from above Earth's north pole

**prominences** inactive "clouds" of solar material held above the solar surface by magnetic fields

**propagate** to cause to move, to multiply, or to extend to a broader area

**proton** a positively charged subatomic particle

**pseudoscience** a system of theories that assumes the form of science but fails to give reproducible results under conditions of controlled experiments

**pyroclastic** pertaining to clastic (broken) rock material expelled from a volcanic vent

**pyrotechnics** fireworks display; the art of building fireworks

**quantum foam** the notion that there is a smallest distance scale at which space itself is not a continuous medium, but breaks up into a seething foam of wormholes and tiny black holes far smaller than a proton

**quantum gravity** an attempt to replace the inherently incompatible theories of quantum physics and Einstein gravity with some deeper theory that would have features of both, but be identical to neither

**quantum physics** branch of physics that uses quantum mechanics to explain physical systems

**quantum vacuum** consistent with the Heisenberg uncertainty principle, vacuum is not empty but is filled with zero-point energy and particle-antiparticle pairs constantly being created and then mutually annihilating each other

**quasars** luminous objects that appear star-like but are highly redshifted and radiate more energy than an entire ordinary galaxy; likely powered by black holes in the centers of distant galaxies

**quiescent** inactive

**radar** a technique for detecting distant objects by emitting a pulse of radio-wavelength radiation and then recording echoes of the pulse off the distant objects

**radar altimetry** using radar signals bounced off the surface of a planet to map its variations in elevation

**radar images** images made with radar illumination instead of visible light that show differences in radar brightness of the surface material or differences in brightness associated with surface slopes

**radiation belts** two wide bands of charged particles trapped in a planet's magnetic field

**radio lobes** active galaxies show two regions of radio emission above and below the plane of the galaxy, and are thought to originate from powerful jets being emitted from the accretion disk surrounding the massive black hole at the center of active galaxies

**radiogenic isotope techniques** use of the ratio between various isotopes produced by radioactive decay to determine age or place of origin of an object in geology, archaeology, and other areas

**radioisotope** a naturally or artificially produced radioactive isotope of an element

**radioisotope thermoelectric** device using solid state electronics and the heat produced by radioactive decay to generate electricity

**range safety destruct systems** system of procedures and equipment designed to safely abort a mission when a spacecraft malfunctions, and destroy the rocket in such a way as to create no risk of injury or property damage

**Ranger** series of spacecraft sent to the Moon to investigate lunar landing sites; designed to hard-land on the lunar surface after sending back television pictures of the lunar surface; Rangers 7, 8, and 9 (1964–1965) returned data

**rarefaction** decreased pressure and density in a material caused by the passage of a sound wave

**reconnaissance** a survey or preliminary exploration of a region of interest

**reflex motion** the orbital motion of one body, such as a star, in reaction to the gravitational tug of a second orbiting body, such as a planet

**regolith** upper few meters of a body's surface, composed of inorganic matter, such as unconsolidated rocks and fine soil

**relative zero velocity** two objects having the same speed and direction of movement, usually so that spacecraft can rendezvous

**relativistic time dilation** effect predicted by the theory of relativity that causes clocks on objects in strong gravitational fields or moving near the speed of light to run slower when viewed by a stationary observer

**remote manipulator system** a system, such as the external Canada2 arm on the International Space Station, designed to be operated from a remote location inside the space station

**remote sensing** the act of observing from orbit what may be seen or sensed below on Earth

**retrograde** having the opposite general sense of motion or rotation as the rest of the solar system, clockwise as seen from above Earth's north pole

**reusable launch vehicles** launch vehicles, such as the space shuttle, designed to be recovered and reused many times

**reusables** launches that can be used many times before discarding

**rift valley** a linear depression in the surface, several hundred to thousand kilometers long, along which part of the surface has been stretched, faulted, and dropped down along many normal faults

**rille** lava channels in regions of maria, typically beginning at a volcanic vent and extending downslope into a smooth mare surface

**rocket** vehicle or device that is especially designed to travel through space, and is propelled by one or more engines

**"rocky" planets** nickname given to inner or solid-surface planets of the solar system, including Mercury, Venus, Mars, and Earth

**rover** vehicle used to move about on a surface

**rutile** a red, brown, or black mineral, primarily titanium dioxide, used as a gemstone and also a commercially important ore of titanium

**satellite** any object launched by a rocket for the purpose of orbiting the Earth or another celestial body

**scoria** fragments of lava resembling cinders

**secondary crater** crater formed by the impact of blocks of rock blasted out of the initial crater formed by an asteroid or large meteorite

**sedentary lifestyle** a lifestyle characterized by little movement or exercise

**sedimentation** process of depositing sediments, which result in a thick accumulation of rock debris eroded from high areas and deposited in low areas

**semiconductor** one of the groups of elements with properties intermediate between the metals and nonmetals

**semimajor axis** one half of the major axis of an ellipse, equal to the average distance of a planet from the Sun

**shepherding** small satellites exerting their gravitational influence to cause or maintain structure in the rings of the outer planets

**shield volcanoes** volcanoes that form broad, low-relief cones, characterized by lava that flows freely

**shielding** providing protection for humans and electronic equipment from cosmic rays, energetic particles from the Sun, and other radioactive materials

**sine wave** a wave whose amplitude smoothly varies with time; a wave form that can be mathematically described by a sine function

**smooth plains** the youngest plains on Mercury with a relatively low impact crater abundance

**soft-landers** spacecraft that uses braking by engines or other techniques (e.g., parachutes, airbags) such that its landing is gentle enough that the spacecraft and its instruments are not damaged, and observations at the surface can be made

**solar arrays** groups of solar cells or other solar power collectors arranged to capture energy from the Sun and use it to generate electrical power

**solar corona** the thin outer atmosphere of the Sun that gradually transitions into the solar wind

**solar flares** explosions on the Sun that release bursts of electromagnetic radiation, such as light, ultraviolet waves, and X rays, along with high speed protons and other particles

**solar nebula** the cloud of gas and dust out of which the solar system formed

**solar prominence** cool material with temperatures typical of the solar photosphere or chromosphere suspended in the corona above the visible surface layers

**solar radiation** total energy of any wavelength and all charged particles emitted by the Sun

**solar wind** a continuous, but varying, stream of charged particles (mostly electrons and protons) generated by the Sun; it establishes and affects the interplanetary magnetic field; it also deforms the magnetic field about Earth and sends particles streaming toward Earth at its poles

**sounding rocket** a vehicle designed to fly straight up and then parachute back to Earth, usually designed to take measurements of the upper atmosphere

**space station** large orbital outpost equipped to support a human crew and designed to remain in orbit for an extended period; to date, only Earth-orbiting space stations have been launched

**space-time** in relativity, the four-dimensional space through which objects move and in which events happen

**spacecraft bus** the primary structure and subsystems of a spacecraft

**spacewalking** moving around outside a spaceship or space station, also known as extravehicular activity

**special theory of relativity** the fundamental idea of Einstein's theories, which demonstrated that measurements of certain physical quantities such as mass, length, and time depended on the relative motion of the object and observer

**specific power** amount of electric power generated by a solar cell per unit mass; for example watts per kilogram

**spectra** representations of the brightness of objects as a function of the wavelength of the emitted radiation

**spectral lines** the unique pattern of radiation at discrete wavelengths that many materials produce

**spectrograph** an instrument that can permanently record a spectra

**spectrographic studies** studies of the nature of matter and composition of substances by examining the light they emit

**spectrometers** an instrument with a scale for measuring the wavelength of light

**spherules** tiny glass spheres found in and among lunar rocks

**spot beam technology** narrow, pencil-like satellite beam that focuses highly radiated energy on a limited area of Earth's surface (about 100 to 500 miles in diameter) using steerable or directed antennas

**stratigraphy** the study of rock layers known as strata, especially the age and distribution of various kinds of sedimentary rocks

**stratosphere** a middle portion of a planet's atmosphere above the tropopause (the highest place where convection and "weather" occurs)

**subduction** the process by which one edge of a crustal plate is forced to move under another plate

**sublimate** to pass directly from a solid phase to a gas phase

**suborbital trajectory** the trajectory of a rocket or ballistic missile that has insufficient energy to reach orbit

**subsolar point** the point on a planet that receives direct rays from the Sun

**substrate** the surface, such as glass, metallic foil, or plastic sheet, on which a thin film of photovoltaic material is deposited

**sunspots** dark, cooler areas on the solar surface consisting of transient, concentrated magnetic fields

**supercarbonaceous** term given to P- and D-type meteorites that are richer in carbon than any other meteorites and are thought to come from the primitive asteroids in the outer part of the asteroid belt

**supernova** an explosion ending the life of a massive star

**supernovae ejecta** the mix of gas enriched by heavy metals that is launched into space by a supernova explosion

**superstring theory** the best candidate for a "theory of everything" unifying quantum mechanics and gravity, proposes that all particles are oscillations in tiny loops of matter only $10^{-35}$ meters long and moving in a space of ten dimensions

**superstrings** supersymmetric strings are tiny, one dimensional objects that are about $10^{-33}$ cm long, in a 10-dimensional spacetime. Their different vibration modes and shapes account for the elementary particles we see in our 4-dimensional spacetime

**Surveyor** a series of spacecraft designed to soft-land robotic laboratories to analyze and photograph the lunar surface; Surveyors 1, 3, and 5–7 landed between May 1966 and January 1968

**synchrotron radiation** the radiation from electrons moving at almost the speed of light inside giant magnetic accelerators of particles, called synchrotrons, either on Earth or in space

**synthesis** the act of combining different things so as to form new and different products or ideas

**technology transfer** the acquisition by one country or firm of the capability to develop a particular technology through its interactions with the existing technological capability of another country or firm, rather than through its own research efforts

**tectonism** process of deformation in a planetary surface as a result of geological forces acting on the crust; includes faulting, folding, uplift, and downwarping of the surface and crust

**telescience** the act of operation and monitoring of research equipment located in space by a scientist or engineer from their offices or laboratories on Earth

**terrestrial planet** a small rocky planet with high density orbiting close to the Sun; Mercury, Venus, Earth, and Mars

**thermodynamically** referring to the behavior of energy

**thermostabilized** designed to maintain a constant temperature

**thrust fault** a fault where the block on one side of the fault plane has been thrust up and over the opposite block by horizontal compressive forces

**toxicological** related to the study of the nature and effects on humans of poisons and the treatment of victims of poisoning

**trajectories** paths followed through space by missiles and spacecraft moving under the influence of gravity

**transonic barrier** the aerodynamic behavior of an aircraft moving near the speed of sound changes dramatically and, for early pioneers of transonic flight, dangerously, leading some to hypothesize there was a "sound barrier" where drag became infinite

**transpiration** process whereby water evaporates from the surface of leaves, allowing the plant to lose heat and to draw water up through the roots

**transponder** bandwidth-specific transmitter-receiver units

**troctolite** rock type composed of the minerals plagioclase and olivine, crystallized from magma

**tunnelborer** a mining machine designed to dig a tunnel using rotating cutting disks

**Tycho event** the impact of a large meteoroid into the lunar surface as recently as 100 million years ago, leaving a distinct set of bright rays across the lunar surface including a ray through the Apollo 17 landing site

**ultramafic lavas** dark, heavy lavas with a high percentage of magnesium and iron; usually found as boulders mixed in other lava rocks

**ultraviolet** the portion of the electromagnetic spectrum just beyond (having shorter wavelengths than) violet

**ultraviolet radiation** electromagnetic radiation with a shorter wavelength and higher energy than light

**uncompressed density** the lower density a planet would have if it did not have the force of gravity compressing it

**Universal time** current time in Greenwich, England, which is recognized as the standard time that Earth's time zones are based

**vacuum** an environment where air and all other molecules and atoms of matter have been removed

**vacuum conditions** the almost complete lack of atmosphere found on the surface of the Moon and in space

**Van Allen radiation belts** two belts of high energy charged particles captured from the solar wind by Earth's magnetic field

**variable star** a star whose light output varies over time

**vector sum** sum of two vector quantities taking both size and direction into consideration

**velocity** speed and direction of a moving object; a vector quantity

**virtual-reality simulations** a simulation used in training by pilots and astronauts to safely reproduce various conditions that can occur on board a real aircraft or spacecraft

**visible spectrum** the part of the electromagnetic spectrum with wavelengths between 400 nanometers and 700 nanometers; the part of the electromagnetic spectrum to which human eyes are sensitive

**volatile** ices (e.g., $H_2O$ and $CO_2$) that are solids inside a comet nucleus but turn into gases when heated by sunlight

**volatile materials** materials that easily pass into the vapor phase when heated

**wavelength** the distance from crest to crest on a wave at an instant in time

**X ray** form of high-energy radiation just beyond the ultraviolet portion of the spectrum

**X-ray diffraction analysis** a method to determine the three-dimensional structure of molecules

# Cumulative Index